science & technology in the arts

A TOUR THROUGH THE REALM OF SCIENCE/ART

Stewart Kranz

Edited by Margaret Holton
Interviews edited by Elizabeth S. Fowler, Jr.
Designed by Lorraine Hohman, Myron S. Hall 3rd, Jean King

VNR VAN NOSTRAND REINHOLD COMPANY
NEW YORK CINCINNATI TORONTO LONDON MELBOURNE

Van Nostrand Reinhold Company Regional Offices:
New York Cincinnati Chicago Millbrae Dallas

Van Nostrand Reinhold Company International Offices:
London Toronto Melbourne

BOOKS BY STEWART KRANZ

Science & Technology in the Arts 1974

The Compleat Videocassette User's Guide 1973
(coauthor John Barwick)

The Fourth "R" 1970
(coauthor Joseph Deley)

The Design Continuum 1966
(coauthor Robert Fisher)

FORTHCOMING BOOKS BY STEWART KRANZ
(coauthor Robert Fisher)

Two-dimensional Design: Slide Set and Student Book
Three-dimensional Design: Slide Set and Student Book

Litton Educational Publishing, Inc., 1974
Library of Congress Catalog Card Number 78-167830
ISBN Number 0-442-24532-7

All rights reserved. No part of this work may be reproduced or used in any
form or by any means—graphic, electronic, or mechanical, including
photocopying, recording, taping, or information storage and retrieval systems—without written permission of the publisher. Manufactured in Japan.

The author and Van Nostrand Reinhold Company have taken all possible
care to trace ownership of every work of art reproduced in this book and
to make full acknowledgment for its use. Every effort has been made to
give accurate and faithful attribution to all scientific material and apparatus,
sketches, drawings, diagrams, photographs; to environments, public or
private, to artistic events, public or private, reviewed in this book in whole
or in part. Every effort has been made to assure proper credit to artists,
performers, museums, galleries, photographers, and other persons or
groups contributing material for use in this book. The author has made
every effort to report accurately the interviews granted him, which were
openly taped at the time with full knowledge of those interviewed and
permission for inclusion in this book. If errors have accidentally occurred,
they will be corrected in subsequent editions, providing notification is
sent to the publisher.

Type set by V & M Typographical, Inc.
Printed and bound by Toppan Printing Ltd. Tokyo, Japan

Published in 1974 by Van Nostrand Reinhold Company
A Division of Litton Educational Publishing, Inc.
450 West 33rd Street, New York, N.Y. 10001
Published simultaneously in Canada by
Van Nostrand Reinhold Limited
16 15 14 13 12 11 10 9 8 7 6 5 4 3 2 1

Library of Congress Cataloging in Publication Data

Kranz, Stewart.
  Science and technology in the arts.

  Bibliography: p.
  1. Science and the arts. 2. Technology and the
arts. I. Title.
NX180.S3K72 709'.04 78-167830
ISBN 0-442-24532-7

Mildred Maynard, M. D. 1921–1968

To my late dear friend Mildred Maynard, a distinguished psychiatrist, who was also associated with the Special Reading Service of the Board of Education, New York City. She held a B.A. degree from Hunter College, a medical degree from Howard University College of Medicine, and was a fellow at the Post-Graduate Center for Mental Health in New York City.

contents

COLOR ILLUSTRATIONS

A detailed listing appears at the back of the book, page 323.

ABBREVIATIONS USED IN THIS BOOK

CALCOMP — California Computer Products, Inc.
CBS — Columbia Broadcasting System
COMSTAT — A publicly-held communications-satellite corporation
CRT — Cathode ray tube
E.A.T. — Experiments in Art & Technology
EVR — Electronic Video Recording
IBM — International Business Machines
IDI — Input-directed image
I/O — Input-output
L.E.M. (LM) — Lunar Excursion Module
LLRV — Lunar Landing Research Vehicle
LSD — A psychochemical hallucinogenic drug: *lysergic acid diethylamide*
MA BELL — The Bell Telephone Company
MOMA (MAMMA) — Museum of Modern Art, New York City
N.A.S.A. — National Aeronautics & Space Agency
PPM — Photograph Per Month
RCA — Radio Corporation of America
STA — Science+Technology+Art
STAR — Street Transvestite Action Revolution
TELSA — A special Czechoslovakian electron microscope
USCO — [The] "US" Company (intermedia artists cooperative)
W.P.A. — Works Progress Admnistration

Photographs not otherwise credited were taken by the author.

acknowledgments

The author wishes to express his thanks to the following scientists, engineers, and artists who kindly consented to interviews for this book:

Abel, Ray • Videotape and film producer
Anderson, R. Wayne • High-speed and Time-lapse photographer
Anuskiewicz, Richard • American painter, optical artist

Badal, Claudio • E.A.T. Staff (1968–9)
Berr, Al • Manager, Opera Today, Inc.
Birren, Faber • Color consultant, author
Bragg, Dr. David G. • Radiology
Bystricky, Dr. Vojtech • Professor of Electronic Micrography

Callahan, Michael • Multimedia systems engineer
Cassen, Jackie • Kinetic light artist
Coker, Cecil • Expert in synthetic speech research
Collins, Michael • Director Smithsonian Space Museum. Former astronaut
Collins, Patricia • Artistic Director, Opera Today, Inc.
Compton, Boyd • Administrator, Undergraduate Intermedia Program
Conant, Theodore R. • Distinguished educator and filmmaker

Daly, Thomas C. • Supervising film editor, National Film Board of Canada
D'Avino, Carmen • Film animation innovator
Dessart, George • Film producer and educator
Dorfsman, Louis • Vice President, Advertising and Design, CBS/Broadcast Group
Douglas, J. Creighton • Chief, Audio-Visual/Expositions, Information Canada

Edgerton, Susan • E.A.T. staff member (1968–9)

Fisher, Robert • Lumia sculptor, educator
Flynn, Ralph • E.A.T. staff member (1968–9)
Frankenthaler, Helen • American Abstract Expressionist painter
Friedlander, Gordon D. • Formerly Assistant Curator, Burndy Library of Science. Now with the Institute of Electrical and Electronics Engineers, Inc.

Gabor, Dr. Dennis • Inventor of Holography. Pulitzer prize winner
Gardener, Herb • Videotape engineer, chroma key switching
Geldzahler, Henry • Curator of Twentieth Century Art, Metropolitan Museum of Art, New York City
Gilbert, Dr. John V. • Multimedia Opera composer, educator
Ginsberg, Arthur • Videotape artist
Globus, Stephen • Curator, Museum of the Media, New York City
Globus, Richard • Curator, Museum of the Media, New York City
Globus, Ron • Curator, Museum of the Media, New York City
Goldmark, Dr. Peter Carl • Inventor: Electronic video recording (EVR), long-playing record, field sequential camera
Gottlieb, Adolph • American abstract painter
Graham, Beardsley • Communications consultant, founder of COMSTAT Satellite Communications Corporation

Hammid, Alexander • Cinematographer, editor with Francis Thompson
Harlow, Dr. William M. • Filmmaker, time-lapse photographer, educator

Jones, Dr. Tom Douglas • Lumia artist and teacher
Julesz, Dr. Bela • Perceptual and sensory research scientist

Kaplan, Herbert • Music Director, Opera Today
Kepes, Gyorgy • Director, Institute of Advanced Visual Research, MIT; artist, filmmaker
Kersta, Dr. Lawrence G. • Speech recognition expert, Author
Kingsley, Gershon • Electronic composer (Moog Synthesizer)
Klüver, Dr. Billy • Laser scientist, founder of Experiments in Art and Technology (E.A.T.)
Kress, Robert • Designer of Lunar Module Simulator for Grumman Aircraft Company

LaRue, Dr. Jan • Musicologist, computer-analyzed musical scores, educator
LaRussa, Joseph • Designer: Mercury, Gemini, Apollo Visual Simulators for NASA; Chief Engineer, Farrand Optical Company
Levine, Les • American environmental artist
Lichtenstein, Roy • American Pop painter
Lin, Dr. Lawrence H. • Holography scientist
Litwin, Dr. George H. • Psychologist. Director, Intermedia Systems Corporation, Cambridge, Massachusetts
London, Mel • Filmmaker
Lourie, Dr. Janice R. • Computer design expert, multimedia artist
Lye, Len • Dean of American kinetic sculptors, film animator, educator

Machover, Carl • Computer design expert, graphic input expert. Information Displays, Inc., New York City
MacNeill, Ian • Program Director, National Film Board of Canada
Martin, Anthony • Intermedia artist, systems designer, educator
Mathews, Dr. Max • Director of Behavioral Research Laboratory, Bell Laboratories, Murray Hill, New Jersey

Nagrin, Daniel • Choreographer, dancer, intermedia artist
Nelson, Theodor H. • Computer systems designer, creator of computer graphics programs
Nikolais, Alwin • Choreographer, electronic composer, educator
Noll, Dr. A. Michael • Mathematician, computer-generated still- and motion-picture graphics and art

Oster, Dr. Gerald • Chemist, optical artist, author, and educator

Pasquella, Donald • Intermedia photographer
Pike, Major S. S. • Skywriting pioneer
Poole, Peter • Director of E.A.T. Brooklyn Museum Competition and Exhibition

Radok, Emil • Creator of the Diapolyekran multimedia exhibit, Czech Pavilion, Expo '67
Reilly, John • Videotape artist, Global Village
Rondum, Erik M. • Designer of cinerama camera systems, filmmaker
Rothstein, Arthur • Photographer. Director of Photography, former Look magazine

Salzman, Eric • Electronic music composer, author, critic, and educator
Schoener, Allon • Intermedia designer—Harlem On My Mind
Schwartz, Tony • Sound designer and theorist
Segal, George • American environmental sculptor
Sidenius, Christian • Lumia systems designer and performer
Stanton, Dr. Frank • Retired head of CBS. Now head of the American National Red Cross.
Stern, Gerd • Founder of USCO Artists Cooperative, Creative Director, Intermedia Systems
Stern, Rudi • Intermedia artist, Global Village
Stine, Commander Leon L., Jr. • Director of Simulation Systems, U.S. Naval Training Center, Groton, Connecticut
Stoodley, Dr. Gerald R. • Engineer-designer, computer-generated graphics, Grumman Aircraft Corporation
Subotnick, Morton • Composer of electronic music, Buchla Synthesizer, educator
Summers, Elaine • Cinema dance composer, filmmaker, educator

Thompson, Francis E. • Filmmaker, Camera system innovator, producer

Unger, H. Albert • Designer, photographer, educator

VanDerBeek, Stan • Filmmaker, multimedia designer, animator, educator
Varian, Elayne • Director and Curator, The Contemporary Wing, Finch College Museum of Art
Vasulka, Woody • Videotape artist
Von Micsky, Dr. Lajos I. • Chief of the Ultrasonic Division of Radiology, St. Luke's Hospital, New York City

Whatmore, Marvin C. • President Cowles Communications, New York
Whitman, Robert • Environmental artist, designer, filmmaker
*Wilfred, Thomas • Inventor of Lumia, artist, performer, educator
Wise, Howard • Art patron. Former New York City gallery owner
Wistrand, John • Industrial designer

*As seen through the eyes of Christian Sidenius and Jackie Cassen.

The author also wishes to express his thanks and appreciation to all the many other contributors to this book, in particular:

Artists
West Abrashkin, Chryssa, Francois Dallegret, John Goodyear, Robert Harvey, Alice Hay, John Healey, John Hoppe, Allan Kaprow, Gyula Kosice, Stanley Landsman, Richard Lindner, Preston McClanahan, Bruno Munari, Peter Myer, Claes Oldenburg, Nam June Paik, Abraham Palatnik, Steve Paxton, Robert Rauschenberg, Earl Reiback, Larry Rivers, James Rosenquist, Lucas Samaras, Carolee Schneemann, Nicolas Schöffer, Jesus Soto, Thomas Tadlok, USCO Group, George Vander Sluis.

Photographers
George Beker, David Berlin, John Brockman & Associates, Geoffrey Clements and Sam Falk of the New York Times Magazine, Michael Fredericks, Jr. (see below), Al Fiese, Sherwin Greenberg, McGranahan & May, Inc., Hella Hammid, Ken Kay, Robert R. McElroy, Dr. George Markstein, Cornell· Aeronautical Laboratories, Buffalo, New York, Herbert Migdoll, Peter Moore, Bob Moreland, Tom Rummler, Susan Schiff-Faludi, Studio Ives Hervochon, Paris, Ken Thompson Group, Inc.

I owe Michael Fredericks, Jr. a particular debt of gratitude. Mike took all the marvelous color shots of Helen Frankenthaler, Roy Lichtenstein, George Segal, and their paintings and sculptures. He also did the shots of the James Rosenquist environmental painting when it was displayed at the Metropolitan Museum of Art. His photographs of Woodstock and related material in chapter 1 help to set the philosophical framework for this book. Today he is a successful freelance photographer, but it still gives me pleasure to remember him as a student of mine at the Ardsley High School, Ardsley, New York, too many years past.

Galleries and Museums
American Museum of Natural History, New York City; Albright-Knox Art Gallery, Buffalo, New York; Art Institute of Chicago; Cordier & Ekstrom Gallery, New York City; Finch College Museum of Art; Janis Sidney Gallery, New York City; The Jewish Museum, New York City; the Metropolitan Museum of Art (see below); Museum of Contemporary Art, Chicago; Museum of Modern Art, New York City; Museum of Contemporary Crafts, New York City; Nelson Gallery of Art, Kansas City, Missouri; Pace Gallery, New York City; The Waddell Gallery, Inc., New York City; Walters Art Gallery, Baltimore, Maryland; The Howard Wise Gallery, New York City.

Although Howard Wise retired recently, his influence and his gallery are probably more responsible for the development of a real collaboration between artist, scientists, and engineer than any other single sponsorship in America. He often held

shows in his gallery that involved enormous installation costs—more to give new talent a platform than to realize any immediate profit. He has been most kind to the author in allowing him to photograph many exhibits and by arranging appointments with a number of the artists included in this book. His intelligence, dignity, and style assured many contemporary artists a special opportunity.

The author wishes to express his great gratitude to Mr. Harry S. Parker III, chairman of the Education Department of the Metropolitan Museum of Art, for his gracious permission to use the large collection of color photographs of works by artists Richard Anuskiewicz, Adolph Gottlieb, Helen Frankenthaler, James Rosenquist, and George Segal for reproduction in this book. The photographs are the work of Michael Fredericks Jr. They were produced for the Metropolitan Museum of Art Education Department under a grant from the Geigy Chemical Company.

Special Contributors
Architectural League Exhibit, New York City; Armco Steel Corporation, Ashland, Kentucky; Dr. Lloyd M. Beidler, Professor of Biophysics, Florida State University, Tallahassee, Florida; Bell Laboratories; Dr. Laurence Rosler, Bell Laboratories; Calcomp—California Computer Products, Inc., Anaheim, California; Canadian Pacific; CBS Laboratories; Eastman Kodak Company; Farrand Optical Company, Inc., New York City; Dr. Akira Fukami, Engineering Research Institute, University of Tokyo; Grumman Aerospace and Aircraft Engineering Corporation; General Electric Company; IBM Data Processing Division; Mark Systems, Inc., Santa Clara, California; Milwaukee Art Center, Milwaukee, Wisconsin; National Film Board of Canada, Montreal; NASA, Houston, Texas; *Options* Exhibit, Milwaukee Art Center; Arthur Paul, Vice President and Art Director of *Playboy* Magazine; Hugh Hefner, Publisher, *Playboy* Magazine (see below); U.S.A. Aberdeen Research and Development Center, Aberdeen Proving Grounds, Aberdeen, Maryland; Ben Whitney, Marketing Coordinator, Intermedia; WCBS-TV "Repertoire Workshop"; Carl Zeiss, Inc., New York City.

I want to express personal gratitude to Mr. Hugh Hefner for allowing me a unique privilege in reproducing color and black-and-white photographs from a series of paintings and sculptures commissioned by Playboy Magazine. Although Mr. Hefner is better known for his contribution to the history of erotica, his most significant contribution, in my opinion, has been to bring issues for social reform into a mass magazine. The generation he has influenced so profoundly are the protagonists for radical change in the form and content of the arts as reviewed in this book.

Producer Merrill Brockway
Architect Buckminster Fuller
Josef Svoboda

It is a particular regret to the author that he was unable to interview Josef Svoboda personally. Svoboda is one of the most important artists in the world today working in this medium. We have had correspondence and he was kind enough to provide me with numerous photographs and diagrams of his work for inclusion in this book.

Sources of quotations
California Computer Products, Inc., Anaheim, California; John Canaday, New York Times; Directions 1: *Options,* 1968. Milwaukee Art Center Exhibition; Exhibition Program of the Magic Theatre, Nelson Gallery of Art, Kansas City, Missouri; Herbert Gardener, *How We Did It;* Billy Klüver, "Theater and Engineering—an Experiment, 2. Notes by an Engineer," *Art Forum,* Feb. 1967; Norman McLaren, "Notes on 'Le Merle' "; Professor Leslie Mezei, University of Toronto; A. Michael Noll, Stereographic Projections by Digital Computer, *Computer-generated Three-dimensional Movies, and Computers and the Visual Arts;* Gerald Oster, "Optical Art," *Applied Optics,* Nov. 1965; Presentation by Dr. Peter Carl Goldmark, MIT, Oct. 17, 1967; Remarks by Frank Stanton to the North Carolina State Art Society, Nov. 29, 1967; *Textile World,* Jan. 1967 (McGraw-Hill); Arthur Rothstein, "Visual Photographics"—address of the 16th Annual Conference, Research and Engineering Council of the Graphic Arts Industry, Pittsburgh, Pa., May 16–18, 1966; Robert Reinhold, *New York Times,* Feb. 18, 1972; Allon Schoener, Electronic Museum Theatre; *The Walls Come Tumbling Down*—WCBS-TV; Thomas Wilfred, *The Journal of Esthetics and Art Criticism,* March 1948.

Manuscript Preparation
I am indebted to Elizabeth S. Fowler for the extensive help she gave me during the considerable time this book was under preparation. Mrs. Fowler transcribed most of the interviews from the tapes and gave skillfull assistance in the deleting of extraneous material. Her contribution to this book cannot be fully measured in this brief acknowledgment.

Typing
My thanks go to Mrs. Bonnie Drinkard for her major share in the big job of typing the final manuscript and to Mrs. Suzanne Divens for her help, to Mrs. Jane Webb, Mrs. Mary C. Kreycir, and Mrs. Judy Fisher for the retyping of pages with corrections and changes.
My special appreciation goes to Stephanie Remillard, who organized all the permissions material and aided with other important organizational problems.

THE PUBLISHER

In my estimation Jean Koefoed, Vice President and Publisher of Trade Books at Van Nostrand Reinhold Company, has no peer in his field. An open-minded creative man, Mr. Koefoed manages to combine the excitement of new publishing concepts with sound fiscal policy—keeping his authors up on their toes and down to earth.
I must also mention my long and rewarding association with Margaret Holton, my editor at VNR. She has suffered with my prose for many years. I am quite sure that my work as an author has been deeply influenced by her remarkable professional grasp of both form and content.
My very sincere appreciation goes to Lorraine Hohman, VNR Art Director, for her unflagging enthusiasm and attention to the development of the basic design concept of this book. In this, Mrs. Hohman was joined by my old friend the late Myron Hall 3rd and Jean King, both of Visuality Design Services, who worked out the final realization. Mr. Hall had a hand in the designing of all my books for VNR; his blend of high skills and impeccable taste in book design will be missed.
And finally, warm thanks to James Leone, VNR Production Manager, for his invaluable contribution. Mr. Leone gave generous time to supervising the crafting of this complicated volume, both here and in Japan.

foreword

If we consider the implications of recent social criticism such as Alvin Toffler's *Future Shock* or films such as Stanley Krubrick's *2001* or *Clockwork Orange,* we can hardly take a sanguine posture in evaluating the implications of the transience of contemporary life. Recently my friend Peter Dow invited me to attend a planning session at the Educational Development Center in Cambridge. A psychologist, a professor of the History of Science at Harvard, and a professor of engineering at MIT were trading disciplines. In the course of the discussion a scientist at the meeting spoke with some real chagrin about his frustration when confronted by the frenetic change in scientific development today. He spoke of the relatively recent development of the jet propulsion engine and he noted rather ironically that this invention may hold its place in the sun as a propulsion system for only another decade or so before it, too, will become obsolete, as rockets or other forms of power come into use, whereas Thomas Watt's steam engine held the mechanical propulsion center stage for well over a hundred years.

In his work, alluded to above, Toffler, states, "It can even be argued that our artists are employing homeopathic magic, behaving like primitives who, awed by a force they do not comprehend, attempt to exert control over it by simplemindedly imitating it. But whatever one's attitude toward contemporary art, transience remains an implacable fact, a social and historical tendency so central to our times that it cannot be ignored. And it is clear that artists are reacting to it." (*Future Shock,* Alvin Toffler, Bantam Books, NYC, 1970, page 175.) Toffler goes on to point out that the Impressionist revival lasted for almost 35 years while the Op and Pop movement held critical and public interest for less than five years.

Today the definition of "the art experience" is undergoing a formidable transformation. Scientists with passing or real interest in aesthetic expression are moving into areas undreamed of for the respectable professional even ten years ago. At the same time, experienced engineers, traditionally a strongly conservative group, are sprouting beards, and even donning beads during their evening and weekend excursions into the disdained world of the art sub-culture. By way of contrast, the contemporary artist may come from a computer study center, an industrial design class, or a neon-sign factory. The method, the medium, and the goals have shifted so radically that the contemporary observer of the art scene is left somewhat breathless.

One basic function of this book is to explore the parameters of this unprecedented and profoundly interesting movement in contemporary art.

Interviews with the personalities introduced in each chapter appear after the author's general discourse. The interviews are focused on the basic theme of the book; they are not intended as definitive statements by the protagonists. Broadly, the author conceived of the illustrative material as reflective of the environment, personality, or activity revealed in the interview. He did not presume to reflect the entire scope of an artist's creative work, nor show the full range of a scientist's, artist's, or engineer's professional life. To a large degree the reader should approach the interview and photo-essay sections as impressions absorbed during the author's visits to the studio or laboratory of each remarkable person presented here.

Stewart Kranz

1 introduction

Sociological Significance of the Collaboration Between Artist and Scientist: Science + Art, Intermedia, Multimedia, and Spectator-Activated Art

The decade of the sixties was a reckless time; certainly not the stuff of history. We murdered Jack and Bobby Kennedy—who were white—and we also took Martin Luther King and Malcolm X—they were black.

A whole generation, born of the anxiety of World War II, grew up and saw the whole show, and they turned away. Paul Goodman, who was old enough and should have been the Enemy, saw them growing up and called it absurd. No one can say for sure, but the new generation of young Americans seemed to call the house down. Suddenly, Mom, Apple Pie, and the R.O.T.C. were dirty words. And so were LBJ., Tricky Dick, Vietnam. And the CIA. Ché Guevera, the Black Panthers, Muhammad Ali, and Charles Reich became the symbols of a subtle but pernicious contempt for a newly defined Establishment.

Perhaps the whole decade was summed up from August 15 through August 17, 1969, on Max Yasgur's 600-acre farm in Bethel, New York. All day it rained, and all night it was cold, and yet half a million young American boys and girls from the comfortable middle class made the scene. Their suspicious elders secretly expected a new Sodom and Gomorrah, complete with multiple couplings and wild trips ending with rape and murder. To almost everyone's surprise, the entire event was filled with a good cheer and a remarkable show of fraternal empathy. In spite of an almost total lack of proper food, sanitary facilities, or even a place to sleep, this enormous crowd of "unsupervised" youths conducted itself at the altar of rock and folk music in a manner that stood as a mute rebuke to the generation of their parents. Although no one, at this point in time, can assess the full meaning of the huge gathering, one interpretation holds that Bethel had occurred to a very large extent through disenchantment, because the youth of the sixties seemed unable to accept what they felt was an unjust and cruel war abroad combined with profound racial hatred at home. The Bethel meeting, in this premise, was a great coming-together to share a common sorrow and to share the loneliness that goes with alienation from a world created by their misguided parents. Little did we all know that Kent State and Jackson State would follow so swiftly.

If a significant reorientation of an entire generation has taken place—and only time will tell—one can see change as well in the currents of the arts. It has been traditional for the artist to rebel, to outrage, and to march to the roll of a distant drummer; however, in the decade of the sixties, a remarkable reorientation in the function, the means, and, to a large extent, the goals of the artist became quite apparent. In a phrase, the emphasis shifted from the end

1-1B

1-1C

Addendum. On July 29, 1973, a significant sociological phenomenon occurred at Watkins Glen, N. Y., the site of a fifteen-hour "Summer Jam" of rock music. Although over six hundred thousand fans poured into Watkins Glen, creating the largest rock festival ever held in the United States, the excesses of the Woodstock Festival at Bethel were absent. Nudity and hard drugs were minimal, more milk than beer was sold, and there were no major incidents. The vast crowd was very orderly, even serene, and streamed out at 4 a.m. in a mood of delight and elation. "We're professionals now," explained Rock Impressario Bill Graham. In four short years, Woodstock had matured.

1-2. Study in black and white.
(Photograph by
Michael Fredericks, Jr.)

1-3. War in the sixties: the loss of innocence.
(Photograph by Michael Fredericks, Jr.)

to the means. The idea of "Art as Object" was rejected; the significant part of the aesthetic experience became the moment when the spectator came in contact with the work of "art." With this new art, spectator involvement took on the characteristics of a partnership between artist and participant—a partnership devoted to the ideal that pleasure, whimsey, insight, and even disgust, were ends in themselves. The Neo-Classical monolithic palaces of culture (the museums nurtured by the proud possessors) were rejected in favor of the loft on the Bowery, Judson Memorial Church, a house along the beach at Carmel, or downstairs at the Fillmore Palace, East or West. If the whole thing offended John Canaday and Emily Genauer, so much the better. The new art was a happening, an event, an intermedia dance, an environmental experience, and, most of all, a coming together of the new family who knew how to love its own. It was also a bit of a sham, but only the insiders were supposed to know that.

Just as the science/artists of the sixties embraced the great god of technology, General Ned Ludd, lying in his Nottingham grave, must have once more recalled with bitter irony his own futile attempt to destroy his implacable antagonists. Now, as Ludd would clearly see, not only have the fruits of technology triumphed completely over the artisans of the textile trade, but their sophisticated stepchildren (the computer-graphic systems, the Moog synthesizers, the lasers, the kinetic light systems, the multimedia programmers, the cinemagraphic paraphernalia, the videotape recorders, and the cathode-ray tubes) have been enthusiastically adopted by the creative artists themselves. It has been 159 years since the General and his followers stormed the textile factories and destroyed the dreaded progeny of the Industrial Revolution; and yet, the battle has raged unabated to this day.

With the incredible explosion of scientific and technical knowledge since the end of World War II, a new and more sinister connotation has been attributed to the proliferation of the tools of technology. As the means for technological aggrandizement have flourished, the human prerogatives to control its inexorable growth have seemed to diminish alarmingly. One index to the profundity of this concern is seen in the rise in the study of the history of science in American universities during the sixties. Robert Reinhold, in a *New York Times* article (February 18, 1970), reported that in 1950 there were only five professional historians of science in North America. In a short decade or so, this number has risen to over 125 scholars, and advanced degrees are offered in over twenty-five major universities. Reinhold notes, "According to many of its practitioners, the field's rising star is closely linked to a growing tension, even revulsion, among student and public over consequences of science and technology and a heightened public awareness that science is the central motor force of twentieth-century civilization."

How, then, can the thoughtful protagonists of the arts respond to the growing movement of science-art, one in which both the means and the ends are inexorably inter-

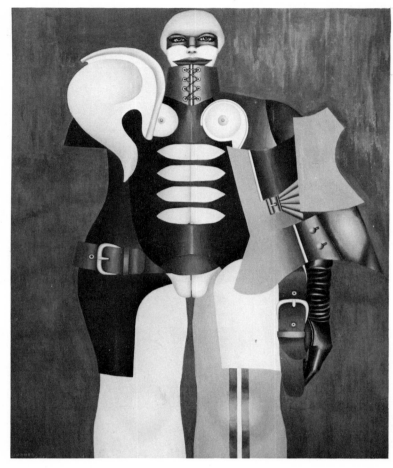

1-4. Painting by Richard Lindner, *Angel in Me*. 1966. Oil on canvas, 60" x 40". (Courtesy Cordier & Ekstrom Gallery, New York City; photographer, Geoffrey Clements.)

twined with the most advanced tools of a suspicious technology? One interpretation holds that this development is simply a disaster. It is as if science and technology, like a latter-day Cortez, have landed with dazzling but apocryphal force in the land of naïve humanists. Subliminally, the humanists know that their traditional worship of the individual and his peculiar capacities is based on a profound understanding of man's most essential characteristic: his capacity to tolerate ambiguity in thought and behavior. Without knowing why, this society has tolerated the artist, because in being different, iconoclastic, defiant, blasphemous, and arrogant, the artist has also managed somehow to be incorruptible as well. To those who watch helplessly as this parable becomes reality, a true horror unfolds: the humanist Aztec tribes of the sixties are seen inviting the flashy and vulgar "gods" of technology into their sacred temples. Here the final abnegation occurs. Montezuma and his followers surrender willingly to the protagonists of technology; in one swift moment of history, they relinquish forever their most cherished heritage. Perhaps Richard Lindner's fetishistic painting *Angel in Me* hints at this interpretation. The brilliant contemporary sculptor Claes Oldenburg has created works that, in spite of their "tongue-in-cheek" nature, leave one with the uneasy feeling that all is not completely well when art and technology embrace.

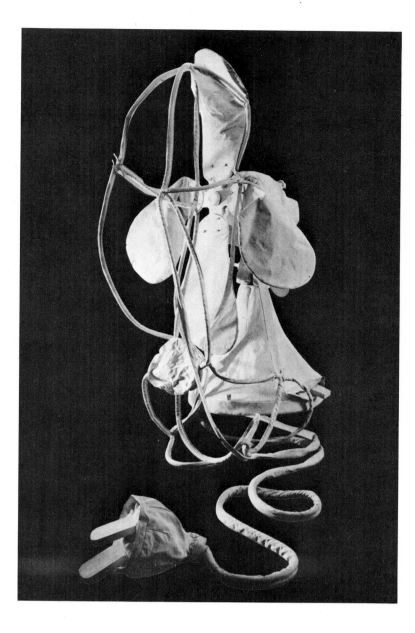

1-5. Sculpture by Claes Oldenburg, *Giant Soft Fan. Ghost Version,* 1967. Canvas, wood, foam rubber, 120" x 124" x 76". (Courtesy Sidney Janis Gallery, New York City; photographer, Geoffrey Clements.)

1-6. Painting by Robert Harvey. *Brother Home on Leave,* 1964. Oil, 48" x 48". (Collection, The Mead Corporation, Dayton, Ohio.)

In this nostalgic painting, based on an old photograph, the artist has transmuted the subject matter into a work of art. The impact here was the photograph remembered.

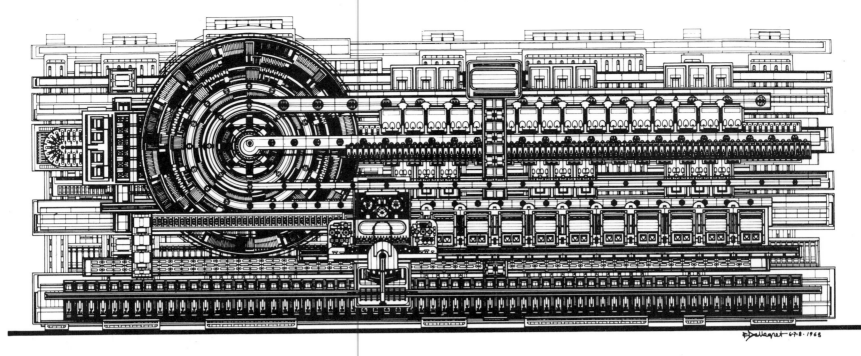

1-7. *Electronic Literature Machine,* patent 1963 by Francois Dallegret A whimsical machine drawn by the artist. Courtesy Waddell Galleries, New York City.)

1-8. A whimsical drawing done by a machine. (Courtesy IBM Data Processing Division.)

The computer as a new tool for artists. Pictures such as the one shown above were produced with the help of an IBM computer by Professor Leslie Mezei of the University of Toronto. This picture was drawn by a computer-linked graphic plotter guided by a set of instructions prepared by Mezei. (The "abstract" face resulted when the instructions were changed to draw the lines three-tenths of an inch apart.) Merely by altering the computer program, an artist may produce pictures ranging from realism to expressionism—and still be working with the same basic picture.
Professor Mezei points out that while the computer may have a dramatic effect on art expression, it will not usurp the creativity or originality of the artist. The computer, he said, will give the artist another powerful and versatile medium in which to work.

1-9. Versatile tools for the artist provided by technology. Computer graphics expert Janice Lourie at the controls of a graphic computer system she uses to create textile designs. (Courtesy IBM Data Processing Division.)

If some hold that disaster is the stepchild of this macabre union, an ever-growing segment of art-science protagonists has risen to challenge this premise. They argue with what at times approaches a Messianic vigor that the artist has always been a preeminent practitioner of technological innovation. Each art form has evolved, in this view, primarily through the advance of technical means. Certainly the history of art supports this view. Without the brilliance of the *cire-perdue* (lost-wax) bronze-casting process, the bronze Shang and Chou masterpieces could never have been realized. The later discovery of porcelain techniques permitted the creation of the Sung masterpieces. In the West, a similar phenomenon exists, with the innocent speculation that Jan van Eyck's enormous impact was inexorably linked to the technical innovation of the oil-paint medium.

In this conception of the functional value of technology for the artist, care has been taken to view technology as a vehicle but never a substitute for the creative act. Cézanne and Bouguereau were French contemporaries, the taste-makers of this century. Their use of the technique of oil painting exposed the mediocre practitioner for what he was, a panderer to the corrupted taste of the French bourgeoisie. In other words, Bouguereau's use of the oil medium could not hide the poverty of his artist's vision. Technique and technology are neutral; only the truly creative genius can supersede the lack of the medium. To update the analogy, the protagonists and the practitioners of science-art see their use of the most modern artifacts of science and technology as a logical extension of a long tradition. They argue that a Michelangelo or a Leonardo living today would probably employ film or videotape as a basic medium of expression. Certainly the argument has a strong viability: it is inconceivable that the giants of the Renaissance would realize their conceptions today in tempera, oil paint, stone, and mortar.

The basic purpose of this work is to allow the reader to determine the answer for himself. During the past four years, the author has taken an extensive tour of the realm of science-art. It has been his intention to maintain the posture and discipline of the journalist to allow the practitioners of these strange new media the opportunity to speak for themselves.

In order to accomplish this goal, two direct-recording devices were employed: the still camera and the sound tape recorder. Over ninety-five leading artists, engineers, scientists, and critics were interviewed and photographed in their particular environment. The approach to each interview was informal and open-ended; the intent was to convey to the reader as directly as possible how the conceptualizers of science-art responded on a given day. No conscious attempt was made to make the interview definitive or comprehensive, for, as the reader will see, the scope, diversity, and complexity of the persons interviewed certainly surpass the ability of this writer to synthesize everything into one brief and definitive whole. The reader

1-10. Versatile tools for the artist provided by technology. A portrait of Nam June Paik in his studio showing some of the electronic tools he uses for his light sculptures. (Courtesy John Brockman Associates, New York City.)

1-11. Versatile tools for the artist provided by technology. Jean Claude Risset, a visiting French physicist and composer, demonstrates a trumpet tune synthesized by a computer at Bell Laboratories, Murray Hill, New Jersey. (Courtesy Bell Laboratories, Murray Hill, New Jersey.)

Twenty listeners were unable to distinguish between Mr. Risset's computer tones and the real trumpet tones. Here he follows a trumpet composition on the board while listening to the computer-generated version played back on tape.

1-12. A portrait of Andy Warhol. Reprinted by permission of *Playboy* Magazine, © 1966, HMH Publishing Company, Inc. (Courtesy Hugh M. Hefner, Editor-Publisher, and Arthur Paul, Vice President and Art Director of *Playboy*.)

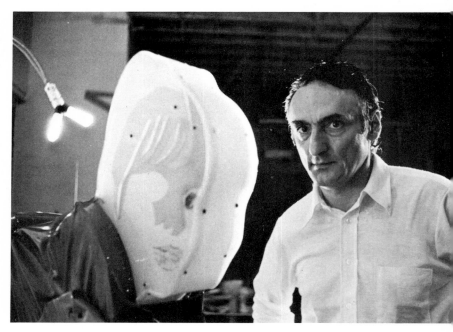

1-13. Portrait of Larry Rivers with a work commissioned for *Playboy* Magazine and rendered by Mr. Rivers. (Reprinted by permission of *Playboy* Magazine, © 1966, HMH Publishing Company, Inc. (Courtesy Hugh M. Hefner, Editor-Publisher, and Arthur Paul, Vice President and Art Director of *Playboy*.)

1-14. Portrait of James Rosenquist in his studio. Reprinted by permission of *Playboy* Magazine, © 1966, HMH Publishing Company, Inc. (Courtesy Hugh M. Hefner, Editor-Publisher, and Arthur Paul, Vice President and Art Director of *Playboy*.)

should consider this book a broad canvas; upon its surface is a collage of science-art.

Before we begin the tour of the realm, it might help the reader if we summarized the parameters of this vast subject and simultaneously indulged in a modest dose of recent science-art history.

During the sixties, there emerged several important artists who took the means of technology into the core of their aesthetic premises. As the movement gathered momentum, the mass media of television and print reflected this development. Perhaps the science-art movement had its most recent reincarnation in Pop Art. Major protagonists, such as Andy Warhol and James Rosenquist, took the most banal artifacts of a machine society and elevated them to the level of "high" art. Initially, the public reaction was one of outrage; however, in time the irony and pernicious truth of the Pop artist's idiom began to seep through the consciousness of its chastened critics. This process was exacerbated by the activities of major tastemakers such as Hugh Hefner. Early in 1967, he commissioned for his magazine a series entitled, appropriately, "The Playmate as Fine Art." In essence, the Pop artist had discarded the niceties of culture with a capital *C*.

The language of Pop was the litter from a machine-fed environment: the Brillo box, the ash can, the plastic girl, the jet plane, ersatz precooked spaghetti, and the atom bomb.

The effect of Pop on the direction of American art was twofold: first, it devalued the role of Brahman culture; and second, it focused attention on machine-made cultural artifacts. Its most talented practitioners, for example, as Warhol, advanced this preoccupation a step farther, for they began to concentrate their entire energies on the medium of film.

Technology had another major impact on the artist during the sixties: it extended the range of human visual perception from the smallest particles of inner space to satellite photographs of deep space. Primarily through the vehicle of sophisticated photographic techniques, science provided an insight into the nature of physical reality, which captured the imagination of a generation. The enormously successful venture of man into space was recorded through the mediums of still and motion picture photography. The greatest vicarious spectacular of the decade, however, was the live television transmission of man's first steps on the surface of the moon. This event, witnessed by more than half a billion people at the precise moment of its occurrence, was the most remarkable moment in the short evolution of the species. This triumph of communications technology could hardly have been overlooked by the artist; nor, for that matter, could the grab-

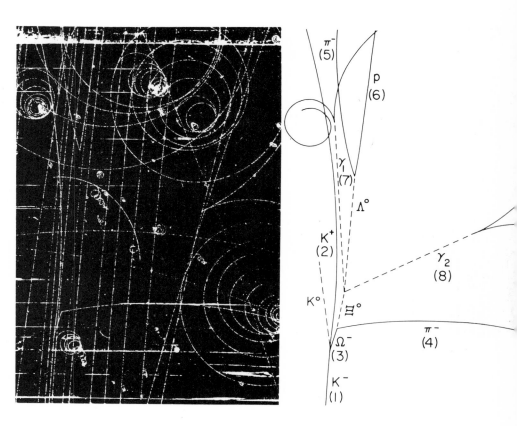

1-15. Extension of Man's Senses Through Technology: Inner space. (Courtesy Brookhaven National Laboratory, Upton, New York.)

Liquid hydrogen bubble chamber photograph showing the production of a negatively charged Omega meson by the interaction of a negative K meson (K^-) with a proton (a hydrogen nucleus in the bubble chamber). The sketch beside the photograph shows the proper assignments of a particle to each track. The paths of neutral particles, which produce no bubbles in the liquid hydrogen and therefore leave no tracks, are shown by dashed lines. The presence and properties of the neutral particles are established by the analysis of the tracks of their charged decay products or the application of the laws of conservation of mass and energy, or a combination of both. The photograph was taken in the 80-inch liquid hydrogen bubble chamber (the world's largest) at Brookhaven National Laboratory. For this experiment a beam of about ten 5 BeV/cK^--mesons entered the chamber every 2½ seconds. This beam was produced by allowing the circulating proton beam of the Alternating Gradient Synchrotron to strike a target and then separating the K^- mesons from the other particles produced and conducting them to the 8-inch bubble chamber by means of a very long (about 400 feet) array of magnets and electrostatic separators.

1-16. Extension of Man's Senses Through Technology: The penetration of three-dimensional space. Radiograph of a milkweed pod. (Photograph from *Medical Radiography*, published by Radiography Markets Division, Eastman Kodak Company.)

WHITWORTH COLLEGE LIBRARY
SPOKANE, WASH. 99251

1-17. Extension of Man's Senses Through Technology: The exploration of near space with the aid of photography. (Courtesy NASA, Houston, Texas.)

Apollo 9 EVA. An excellent view of the docked Apollo 9 command/service module and lunar module "Spider" with earth in background, during Astronaut David R. Scott's extravehicular activity on the fourth day of the Apollo 9 earth-orbital mission. Scott, command-module pilot, is standing in the open hatch of the command module "Gumdrop." Astronaut Russell L. Schweickart, lunar-module pilot, took this photograph of Scott from the porch of the "Spider." Inside the "Spider" was Astronaut James A. McDivitt, Apollo 9 commander. Land area in center of picture is the Mississippi River Valley.

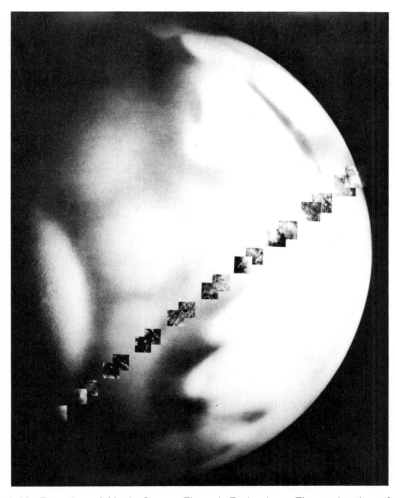

1-18. Extension of Man's Senses Through Technology: The exploration of deep space through satellite photography. (Courtesy NASA, Houston, Texas.)

This string of nineteen of the twenty-one photographs of the Mars surface taken July 14, 1965, by Mariner IV begins at about 30 degrees North latitude and moves in a southeasterly direction across the Martian equator to about 50 degrees South latitude. The Martian 180th parallel of longitude runs from top to bottom, roughly through the center of the lighted portion of the planet's sphere shown in this view.

bag of technological goodies dished up by a gadget-loving society. For example, it was inevitable that the artist would pick up the neon, the incandescent, the fluorescent, and the ultraviolet lights and do something with their inherent qualities. In Europe, Jean Tinguely and Nicolas Schöffer emerged as leaders in the integration of light with mechanical kinetic art. Tinguely's mad devices often were designed to destroy themselves, whereas Schöffer crafted his light-and-motion devices like a Swiss watch. In this

country, young artists created stainless steel, neon, and plexiglass totems to Times Square. It was as if the circle of derivation had been completed: Pop turned the public's attention back to the everyday scene and, in so doing, inadvertently redirected the attention of the new generation of artists as well. They were reaffirming what we had all known for some time: in its heyday in the fifties, Times Square was the best free environmental light show in the world.

1-19. The artist's response to technology: Kinetic light sculpture by Nicolas Schöffer, entitled *Chronos No. 7—1965.* 24″ high. (Courtesy Waddell Gallery, New York City; photographer, Studio Yves Hervochan, Paris.)

"Mr. Schöffer's kinetic sculptures continue to make those of most of his colleagues look like talented children's play. Mr. Schöffer is as different from Jean Tinguely, for instance, in spite of Mr. Tinguely's wittiness, as a space ship is from a wind-up toy. When Mr. Schöffer's beautifully constructed inventions get into action, they seem to turn metals into volatile fluids and light into escaping tinted gases. Their varying parts, starting, stopping, reversing directions, and operating at changing speeds, are connectable with such simple modern devices as automatic railroad semaphores and with laboratory apparatus so complicated that, for the layman, it ceases to have anything to do with science and becomes fantasy. Mr. Schöffer creates within the same range in his double capacity as engineer and artist." (Courtesy New York Times, *John Canaday review.*)

1-20. The artist's response to technology: *The Gates to Times Square—1966,* by Chryssa. Welded stainless steel, neon, plexiglass. 10′ x 10′. (The Albert A. List Family Collection; photograph courtesy the Pace Gallery, New York City.)

1-19

1-20

1-21. Visual simulation system created by NASA engineers, Ames Research Center, California. NASA engineer takes a fix on the moon with a sextant in an Apollo mid-course navigation simulator. (Courtesy NASA, Houston, Texas.)

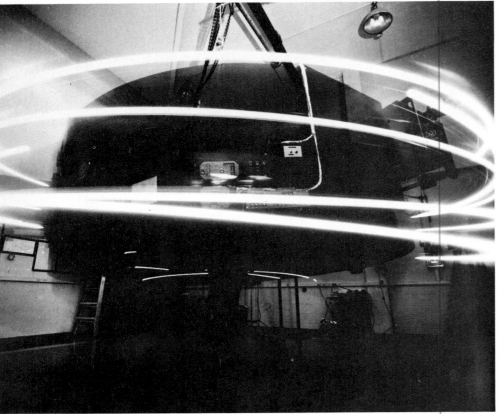

1-22. Kinetic simulation system created by NASA engineers. Lights streaks in Apollo test. (Courtesy NASA, Houston, Texas.)

Lights fastened to an air-bearing table produce this effect as the platform rotates and simulates characteristics of an Apollo spacecraft in flight. The Minneapolis Aeronautical Division of Honeywell, Inc., tests the stabilization and control system of the Apollo for the National Aeronautics and Space Administration.

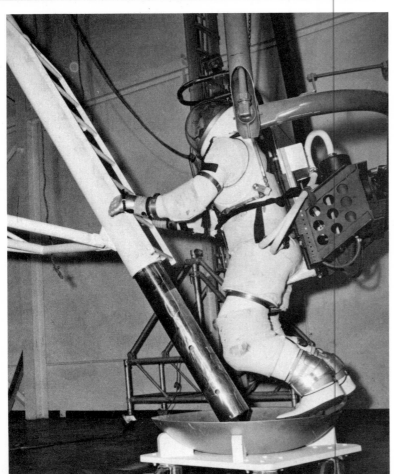

1-23. Physical simulation system created by NASA engineers. (Courtesy NASA, Houston, Texas.)

Houston, Texas, Hard Suit. An experimental hard suit, planned for possible lunar surface wear, is tested at the Manned Spacecraft Center by Jack Mays, Test Engineer, Crew Systems Division. Mobility of the suit is of special interest while he is strapped in a training device called the one-sixth degree of freedom simulator. A mock-up of the Lunar Excursion Module is used during the mobility tests. The Hard Suit is made by Litton Industries. (Courtesy NASA, Houston, Texas.)

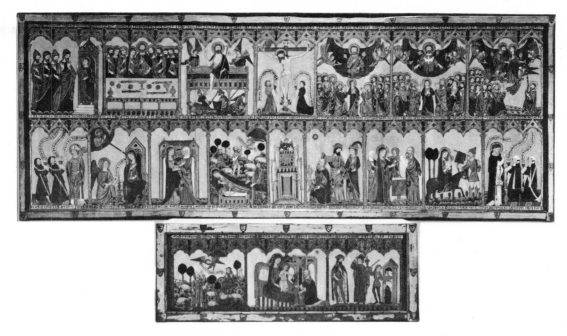

1-24. Environmental art as a very early phenomenon: *The Ayala Altar.* Tempera on panel. Altar 99¾″ x 251¾″. Antependium, 33½″ x 102″. Date, 1393. (Courtesy The Art Institute of Chicago. Gift of Charles Deering.)

1-25. A recent example of environmental art. Barn-door paintings by George Vander Sluis. View of the Floyd Randall 100-foot barn, Route 11, Homer, New York. (Courtesy George Vander Sluis.)

While all of this activity was involving the generation's leading science-artists, an unusual, yet totally independent parallel activity was developing in the land of the "squares," in Houston, Texas. There the National Aeronautics and Space Administration was busy planning the soft deposit of two live specimens of *Homo sapiens* on the surface of the moon. As we shall see, NASA scientists and their colleagues throughout the American engineering and scientific community were acutely aware that mere delivery of the organism to an alien environment was a small part of their task. They had to precede this event with the astronaut's total physical and psychological reorientation. This was no small task when we consider that the environment of space is alien, hostile, weightless, and fascinating. The solution was found in the new science of simulation. In the same manner that technology has offered a plethora of new tools to the scientist-artist, so too did it make its contribution to the conceptions of the engineer-simulator. NASA scientists took the tools of optics, photography, mechanical kinetics, and pneumatics to create a stupendous range of complex environmental simulators. In most cases, the simulators were under trainee control; in the parlance of the engineers, they

simulated "a nonprogrammed real world." Simply stated, this means that as the astronaut directed the controls of the simulator, he experienced both physical and optical conditions identical to the environment of space. The mechanical and optical aspects of the simulator were married to enormously complex computer programs. The computer interpreted the astronaut-controlled change to the optical and mechanical systems; the result was a responsive simulated environment. The reader may recall that, during the breathless eighteen minutes of man's first real descent to the surface of the moon, one exhilarated astronaut called out, "It's better than the simulator!"

If technology could lay claim to providing the hardware for better environmental illusions, it certainly must disown any claim to conceptual innovation. Environmental art is as old as the history of man; the Lascaux caves in France were filled with environmental art—perhaps designed to prepare the cavedweller for the perils of a hostile and dangerous world outside. In the fourteenth century, the idiom was transposed to the needs of an emerging Christianity; today, it may simply mean a more beautiful barn door.

During the sixties, two major figures emerged and de-

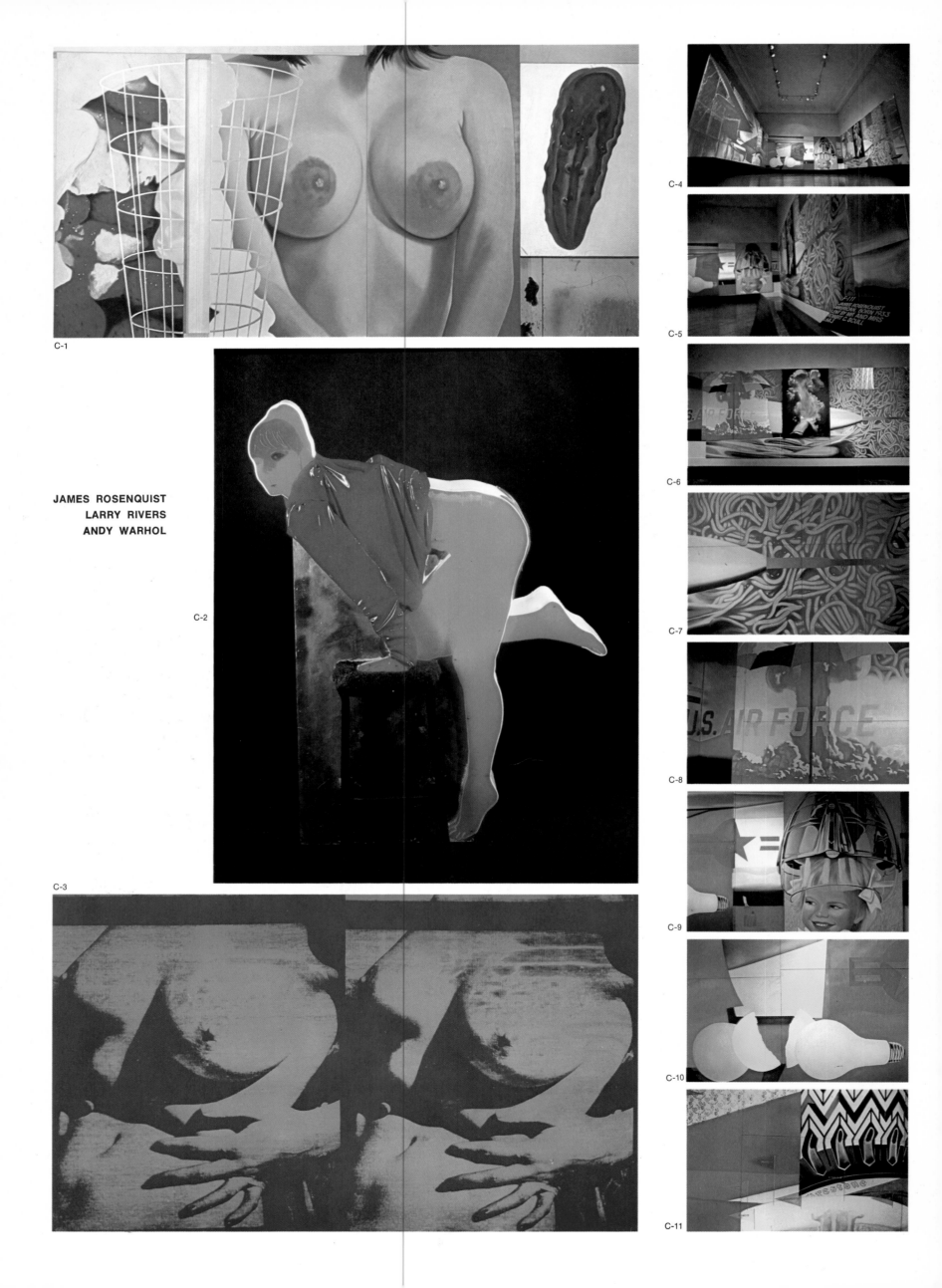

JAMES ROSENQUIST
LARRY RIVERS
ANDY WARHOL

C-1

C-2

C-3

C-4

C-5

C-6

C-7

C-8

C-9

C-10

C-11

opposite
C-1. Painting by James Rosenquist. Rosenquist's Playmate juxtaposition of girl, wastebasket, pickle, and strawberry shortcake fills two canvases, which together measure 7' x 16'. (Courtesy *Playboy* Magazine, Copyright 1966, HMH Publishing Company, Inc. Hugh M. Hefner, Editor-Publisher; Arthur Paul, Vice President and Art Director.)

C-2. Five-foot tall plexiglass and metal Playmate construction by Larry Rivers. (Courtesy *Playboy* Magazine, Copyright 1966, HMH Publishing Company, Inc. Hugh M. Hefner, Editor-Publisher; Arthur Paul, Vice President and Art Director.)

C-3. Painting by Andy Warhol designed to be viewed when illuminated by ultraviolet light. (Courtesy *Playboy* Magazine, Copyright 1966, HMH Publishing Company, Inc. Hugh M. Hefner, Editor-Publisher; Arthur Paul, Vice President and Art Director.)

C-4—C-11. James Rosenquist's environmental *F-111*. (Collection Mr. & Mrs. Robert C. Scull; photographer, Michael Fredericks, Jr.)

1-26. Portrait of Allan Kaprow. (Courtesy John Brockman Associates.)

1-27. Dr. Billy Klüver *(left),* preparing for the *Nine Evenings* intermedia performance. (Courtesy Bell Laboratories, Murray Hill, New Jersey.)

1-26

1-27

liberately committed their activities to finding a viable synthesis between science and art. Billy Klüver, a laser scientist at Bell Laboratories, became fascinated with the possibilities of a direct collaboration between the artist and the scientist. His interest was stimulated by his friendship with Robert Rauschenberg; together they created the first major collaborative science-artwork, which they entitled *Oracle.*

At the other end of the spectrum was Allan Kaprow. He participated in the development of the spectator-participant environment, which he called a "happening." The happening became a series of events prepared for a new audience and a new art form. The walls between the artist and the spectator were destroyed; in the act the spectator merged with the experience of art at the moment of its creation. At times the environment was benign and a kind of maze in which the participant began to re-experience light, space, sound, and touch. As more artists began to practice spectator-oriented art, however, new premises were brought into play. Some environmental artists employed the paraphernalia of light and sound as a technological smorgasbord designed for sensual overkill. The overt desire was to break through the blasé facade of the spectator to affect his subconscious and unconscious urges. At these happenings the spectator was often used and misused, bombarded, jiggled, shaken, bounced, and generally humiliated in a thinly veiled expression of hostility.

1-28A. Gyula Kosice's *Mobil Hydromural*. 53' x 19½'. (Embassy Center, Buenos Aires. Courtesy Galleria Bonino, LTD. New York City.)

1-28B. Jesus Soto, *Untitled*, 1963. Wood and duralumin composing a five-walled room 9'10" x 29'17". (*Plus by Minus: Today's Half Century Exhibition*, March 3-April 14, 1968. Courtesy Albright-Knox Art Gallery, Buffalo, New York; photograph by Greenberg & May, Inc.)

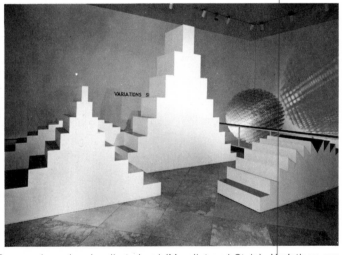

1-28C. *Groupe de recherche d'art visual* (Morellet and Stein). *Variations sur l'Esclade* and Morellet's *Sphere Webs*. (*Plus by Minus: Today's Half Century Exhibition*, March 3-April 14, 1968. Courtesy Albright-Knox Art Gallery, Buffalo, New York; photograph by Greenberg & May, Inc.)

1-28D. Lucas Samaras, *Mirrored Room*. Example of environmental art that envelops spectators by using light and mirrored surfaces. (Albright-Knox Art Gallery, Buffalo, New York, Members' Review, December 15, 1966. Courtesy Albright-Knox Art Gallery, Gift of Semour H. Knox. Photograph by Greenberg & May, Inc.)

More often than not, the means employed were less than the conception—in other words, true environmental involvement requires very sophisticated hardware, expensive projection and sound systems, and large and flexible floor space. In general, most private art galleries were too small to accommodate the new art, commercial space was too expensive for such ephemeral activities, and the museums were too poor to underwrite these complicated technological experiments. Even when the large museums did sponsor science-art environments, the results often disappointed. In certain rare instances, enterprising small museums, such as the Finch College Museum of Art and the Museum of Contemporary Crafts in New York City, surprised and surpassed the efforts of their big and prosperous neighbors. Elayne Varian at the Finch College Museum of Art and Paul Smith at the Crafts Museum have

consistently created impressive environments in exhibitions devoted to a singular emphasis, such as light, projected art, touch, sound, or smell.

Environmental art found its milieu in the great international exposition prepared by the Canadians at Montreal in 1967. Here the essential ingredients coalesced: money, space, time, and talent were collected by titans of industry and ministries of culture. With Expo '67, however the usual international exposition mainstay—vulgarity—was somehow omitted. In its place, the tradition of architecture was extended in the remarkable environments created by Buckminister Fuller for the United States; and by Josef Svoboda and Emil Radok for Czechoslovakia. The tradition established at Montreal was transposed to Osaka, Japan, and Expo '70. The most talented environmental artists were recruited to develop works for these public gathering places. The full language of intermedia, multimedia, and environmental art was explored to a degree not previously realized in one place at one time.

The development of spectator-participant art in the decade of the sixties owed much to the technology of photography, optics, and light, but the essential ingredient proved, as it always does, to be the presence of the talented artist. His interest had been captured by the stuff of technology; the direction of this fancy took a personal turn. Alwin Nikolais, Carolee Schneemann, and Elaine Summers all use light, movement, mixed media, and contemporary sound. Yet their expressive use of the language of intermedia is personal and unique.

And so, with the decade of the sixties closed, and we are well into the decade of the seventies, perhaps we can ask, as some critics have asked, "Is this movement merely a monstrous Dadaesque mockery of *Art* and a not-too-subtle putdown of the spectator? Or does it reflect the beginning of a totally new synthesis of art and science?" This writer favors the latter premise. It is always dangerous to prognosticate about the future of any movement in the arts, particularly when a large segment of critical thought hardly accepts this movement as worthy of such a designation in the first place. In essence, the contention here is that the movement toward a continuing synthesis of art and science is already inexorable. The argument in favor of such a conclusion stems from a fundamental prognosis for our culture; our lives have encompassed the revolution, from the necessity for functional work in order to survive to the realm of custodial activity so that the society may remain ordered and hence survive. In such a near-future society, the very meaning of human activity will undergo a profound transformation. In its most frightening form, the new society may include an intellectual-scientific elite who will govern the benign masses with the active cooperation of the political elite. The function of "work" will be custodial. An alternate scenario more palatable to this writer is that the near-future society will begin to utilize the full potential of each area of human activity. Computer information banks will update the scholar minute by minute. The artist and the scientist will emerge as the most creative and significant societal members. With an active interaction with technology, true collaborative works of science-art will emerge. Perhaps the Museum of the Media will project holographic images of the ancient protagonists of this collaboration admiring their work: Robert Rauschenberg and Billy Klüver will be standing shly in front of *Oracle*. Multichannel sound will record their thoughts for a mildly amused audience. They will see this first effort with the same whimsey with which we today watch the experiments of the Wright brothers, or the early motion pictures of Lumiere. In this future society, instantaneous visual, audio, and pseudophysiological communication will enable a hopefully enlightened mass culture to experience, in a total environmental synthesis, the meaning and import of the science-art experience. As for the

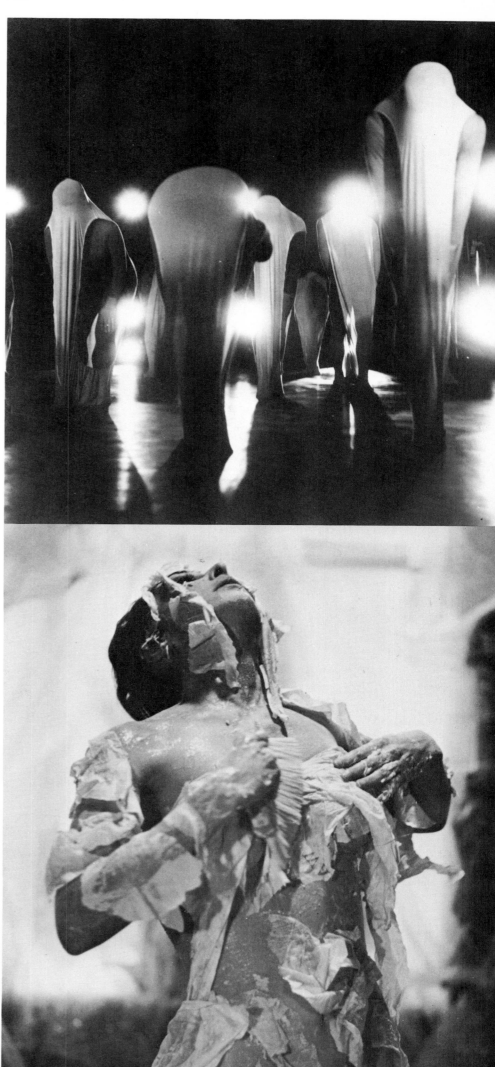

1-29A. Transformation of the human figure through costuming and the use of light. Scene from the dance theatre-piece *Sanctum* by Alwin Nikolais. (Courtesy Alwin Nikolais; photographer, Ken Kay.)

1-29B. Intermedia performance by Carolee Schneemann. (Courtesy John Brockman Associates.)

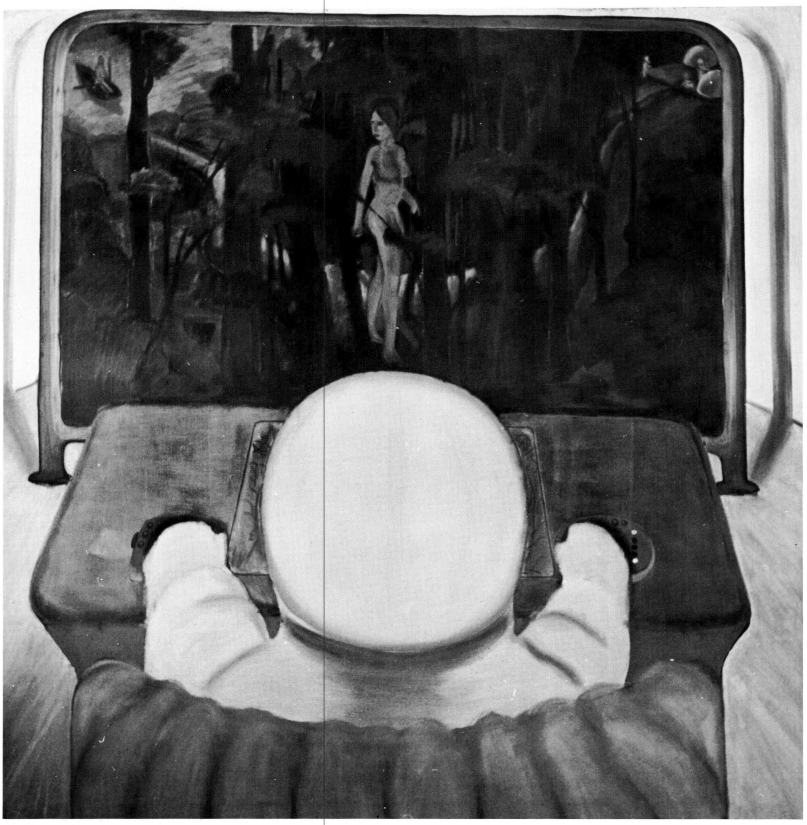

1-30. *Android Trying to Paint the Way it Was* by West Abrashkin. (Courtesy the artist.)

proponents of the science-art syndrome, the near-future will undoubtedly lead to an extremely high level of functional cooperation between the artist and the scientist.

And then again, perhaps a young unknown American artist, West Abrashkin, has eloquently expressed the alternate scenario in his painting entitled *Android Trying to Paint the Way it Was.* In describing his work, Abrashkin has said, "The Android (robot) is piecing together racial memories of man. He portrays man's path to the beginning of the Android era. He also obviously sees the woman as object of desire (as he has heard she was). His painting equipment can be seen on the 'desk'—the painting, in line form, can be seen partially covered by the Android's head—color controls are on the right."

How will it all end? Certainly the answer lies beyond one little decade. In the chapters that follow, the reader can tour the realm of science/art. He should bear in mind that the great, the near-great, and the talented—artists, engineers, scientists, and critics—are all intermixed. Their statements and involvement are in themselves a full commitment to the craft; best we listen, for this remarkable group and its interest tells us something about our time, our values—our peculiar and ecstatic passion for the machine, for things that buzz, whir, grind, blink on and off, and do magical things.

(See color page 26 for reproductions of Rosenquist, Rivers, and Warhol paintings.)

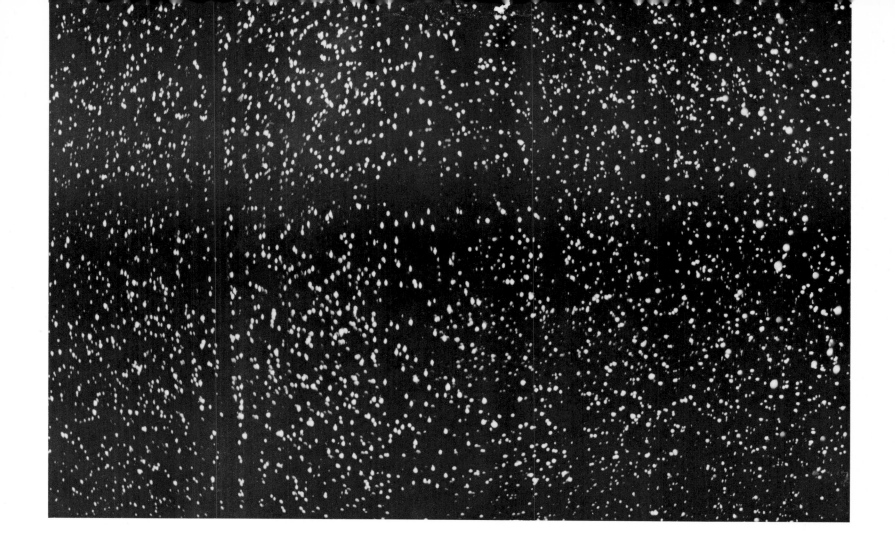

1-31. Environmental *Walk-in Infinity Chamber* by Stanley Landsman. (Courtesy Nelson Gallery of Art, Kansas City, Missouri; photograph from the book *The Magic Theatre* by Ralph T. Coe, Circle Press, 1970.)

Landsman's Walk-in Infinity Chamber. *From the space-defined activities of the Seawright peristyle one passes here into pure space itself by walking up the stairs into Landsman's double-walled chamber (visitors are asked to don the shoe coverings provided at the entrance in order not to damage the glass-floored interior). The outer wall is of standard black plywood. It supports an inner facing of standard mirror pierced by six thousand separately drilled holes. Six thousand miniature lights are mounted on all but invisible stalks set into the holes. Facing this light-filled double-walled chamber is an inner wall of miropane (see-through mirror) through which the visitor peers when he enters the center chamber (a cube six and a half feet to a side). Floor and ceiling are of the same transparent mirrored construction. Spectators will stand within a complete infinity experience, contemplating the six thousand lights as each is reflected forty to fifty times in a never-ending playback between the solid and see-through mirrors.*
Sources as far away as Toledo, Ohio, and Fort Smith, Arkansas, donated the glass. Drilling of the glass, wiring, fabrication, and assembly were worked out locally. The purity of concept belies the effort and complexity of construction which involved such steps as inventing a machine to split plastic wire connectors or allowing three-eights inch difference in spacing certain drilling operations to corner the mirrors properly. There is an extraordinary relationship between this finite box and the viewer who beholds in it an infinite concept, beyond his dreams, which the mind cannot really grasp or measure. Landsman has created a work of art larger than itself. The viewer leaps straight into the fourth dimension—what the astronauts have described as space-walks set down into a format of unbelievably compact aesthetic concentration. From the finite, sculpturesque connotation of Antonakos's neon "bridge," to the space-controlled sensations of Seawright's "garden" we have now entered farther into infinite space. Now, conditioned to pure psychic extension, we are free to stroll into even less material precincts of the Magic Theater. (Taken from the exhibition program of *The Magic Theatre* by Ralph T. Coe. Nelson Gallery of Art, Kansas City, Missouri.)

1-32. Close relationship between the work of the artist and the scientist. Kinetic light images created by R. Wayne Anderson. (Courtesy R. Wayne Anderson, Research Photographer, Dow Chemical Company, Midland, Michigan.)

2 progenitors of science-art

Every movement in the arts finds its origin long before its actual manifestation in the genius of a few seers and believers. Certainly the collaboration between art and technology has ancient roots. The artist has always worked with the tools of his time. In his famous mural *The Last Supper* Leonardo da Vinci used a new tempera technique that proved to be unstable. Restoration of the painting began in the artist's lifetime and is still going on.

Why did this artist-scientist, one of the geniuses of history, turn to a completely new medium instead of staying with the traditional fresco medium? The answer lies in the nature of the artist, who is essentially an iconoclast and innovator. Perhaps the true genius of the creative mind is in finding new analogies in the artifacts of daily existence, analogies that lead to fresh insights into man and his society. The impact of these insights can be enormous. It is no accident that David and Delacroix, identified so closely with the French Revolution, were considered enemies of the state. The activist artist can be, without doubt, a threat to the established social order.

Today's artist is responding to the technical revolution that surrounds us. In this context, we should also consider that the ultimate frustration and humiliation for the artist is to have his work ignored by the public. Needless to say, he has found through experience that, in order to engage the attention of this capricious group, his work must be relevant to societal preoccupations. Partially in an attempt to accomplish this, the contemporary science-artist has turned his attention to the most compelling phenomenon of our time—the cornucopia of technology and the methods that have made its fecundity so pervasive.

The collaboration between the arts, science, and technology did not miraculously reappear like a fresh lotus at the dawn of a new Kalpa blossoming from the ample navel of a latter-day Vishnu. As is usually the case with a rediscovery of the ingenious past, this exciting contemporary movement has its roots in the lonely work of its founding progenitors. The groundwork for art-science collaboration was laid in the early decades of this century—only now can we realize the significance of these independent efforts. In general, the most significant characteristic of these art-science progenitors was any lack of embarrassment as to the relevancy of such a synthesis. They early saw and understood the artist's search for relevancy through use of scientific and technological means.

In the author's tour of the realm, a few men emerge as the true progenitors of the science + art movement. In one way or another, as scientists, artists, teachers, and entrepreneurs, they have fostered and furthered a profound interaction between two seemingly independent strains of human activity.

Gyorgy Kepes

Massachusetts Institute of Technology, historically devoted to training scientists, has established a Center for Advanced Visual Studies, with Gyorgy Kepes as director. In doing so, MIT marks a trend on the part of scientifically oriented colleges and universities to add studies designed to develop in their students an awareness of the world of the humanities. Perhaps this insight on the part of educators grew out of the collective guilt members of the scientific community experienced over the effects of research in the areas of the destructive power of atomic energy and biological and ecological weapons.

Gyorgy Kepes is an artist, writer, lecturer, and teacher. His early work *The Language of Vision* reoriented our ways of visualizing reality, and *The New Landscape* encapsulated the significant visual experiences in our physical environment and their origins in technology. His most recent six-volume *Vision and Value* series is probably the most important collection of papers on art-science published to date.

Art, science, and technology have inexorably drawn closer together under the leadership of Kepes at the MIT Center. Grants for artists-in-residence enable students to work intensively in the use of technology to extend the aesthetic experience. The center for Advanced Visual Studies at MIT is a remarkable conception. Kepes has established a series of grants in which artists, engineers, and media experts can work collaboratively. In the course of his work with this group, Kepes has stimulated numerous plans for the creation of highly ambitious environmental sculptures and works designed to embellish the planned 200th-anniversary of the U.S. celebrations in the Boston area. A fundamental premise established by Kepes is that the science-artist-in-residence must work on joint projects. His success has been based on his remarkable ability to create a project of sufficient scope and scale to challenge a group of highly individual and successful science-artists to work collaboratively on a major project. The thinking behind this collaboration stems from a basic perception of the process itself; namely, that the individual disciplines of engineering, electronics, physics, optics, visual imaging systems, audio components, and related disciplines, are simply too complex for one person to practice and master. Furthermore, these disparate activities engage talents far removed from those commonly associated with the creative artist.

Collaborations among individual artists and scientists flourish, too, in the Center environment. Undergraduate students in the university may enrich their studies by taking elective courses in design and aesthetics. Kepes pursues a vigorous exhibition program in which the advanced work of kinetic light, mixed media, and intermedia artists is presented.

Thus, on both conceptual and practical levels, artists, scientists, and technologists grow in understanding of one another and move collaboratively toward the creation of an imagery appropriate for our time.

Thomas Wilfred

The first expression of kinetic light as an art form in the twentieth century was called *lumia* by its originator, Thomas Wilfred. Today he stands as the patriarch of this conception, in which light is used as the sole medium for the artist.

Wilfred molded light by optical means, and then added color and motion. He accomplished this with his invention, the Clavilux, an organlike console that enabled him to project optical combinations of light, color, and motion on a huge screen.

At the time of his death, August 15, 1968, Wilfred was still active as director and artist-laureate at his Art Institute of Light in West Nyack, New York. His entire adult lifetime was devoted to developing and perfecting lumia, "the art of light," which he regarded as the "eighth major fine art." Wilfred saw his addition of movement to form and color as the essence of lumia.

The word "Clavilux" means light controlled by key. A broad, slotted keyboard allows the operator to achieve a wide range of optical combinations, using a battery of powerful projectors. Wilfred's concept of lumia included two distinct performance levels—a live interpretation of a composition devised by the lumia artist, and automatic programming, which is presented mechanically in a lumia box.

Wilfred did not aspire to use light in the traditional manner employed in photography or motion pictures. These programmed or "canned" mediums did not satisfy the immediacy that Wilfred could achieve through the direct manipulation of his Clavilux. His light-generation machine had unique properties, the most significant being that it could be played in a manner similar to that of a concert organ. By manipulating numerous sliding levers on the "keyboard" of the Clavilux, Wilfred could change at will the focal plane of powerful lamps enclosed in the Clavilux cabinet. This action enabled the performer to modulate with great sensitivity delicate nuances of light intensity, color, and shape configuration, which were in turn projected on an enormous auditorium screen. If we recall that these lumia performances antedated color motion pictures by at least two decades, it is possible to estimate their impact on a theatre audience of the time. The lumia performance had another important aspect: it was extemporaneous, in the manner of theatre and ballet. The artist could, with this medium, sense audience reaction and modulate his performance accordingly.

To preserve these compositions so that they might be played again, Wilfred developed a system for making visual notations of how lumia compositions should be performed. Wilfred has said:

Just as music is built on a foundation of silence, so is lumia built on a foundation of darkness. The lumia artist first visualizes his composition as appearing out of an infinite dark space, and then reproduces it in such a way that the concept will appear to the spectator as the artist first imagined it.

The art is not entirely dependent upon a lumia artist's ability to control the keys of the Clavilux. Wilfred also developed a mechanical programming system so that compositions could be projected automatically in a lumia box. *Lumia Suite, Opus 158,* on display at the Museum of Modern Art, illustrates this development. This work, commissioned in 1963 for the Museum, is projected on a six-foot by eight-foot screen. It is a series of three suites, each of which lasts for approximately twelve minutes. Each movement establishes a theme with variations and interpretations of the dominant theme.

Automatic projection is a great advantage to the medium, although it lacks the spontaneity of a live performance. It means that in addition to being used in a museum gallery, a composition can be exhibited as a wall mural. Long before its contemporary vogue, Wilfred designed lumia works for clients, such as the Clairol World Headquarters, 1200 Avenue of the Americas, New York City. Here a large lumia composition entitled *Study in Depth, Opus 152* recalls his early leadership.

As early as 1929, Wilfred envisioned the possibility of a lumia projection from the top of a skyscraper—which he employed for General Electric's World Headquarters in New York City.

Impressive as these pioneering mechanical uses of lumia may be, the art is undeniably most effective when operated by an artist who can personally conrol the projections on the lumia screen. Something of its distinctive value is described by Wilfred:

In lumia, the art of light, the lumia composer may freely write a rapid passage with the assurance that the interpreting artist at the Clavilux keyboard commands the uninterrupted and even flow of motion at any velocity, the motion being effected by the player's own hands at the time it is seen by the spectator. We have so far used rapid motion sparingly as lumia, but it is there at our command.

As an example, I shall take one of my own compositions, "Unfolding, Opus 127." At the climax, a slender curved tendril of light travels from the bottom of the screen to its top in less than a second and the result is a graceful, spirited sweep, as of a soaring bird, easily followed by the eye, sharp and distinct throughout. A motion picture of this passage—for simplicity assuming the screen to be twenty-four feet high—would transform the continuous motion into twenty-four good jumps, and worse, the visual impression of a form in one location would remain on your retina for a moment after its appearance in the next, one foot higher up, the visual effect being similar to that of a flashlight beam, sweeping up the rungs of a ladder. (Thomas Wilfred, *The Journal of Esthetics and Art Criticism,* Vol. VI, No. 3 (March 1948), p. 272.)

Lumia artists, such as Tom Douglas Jones, Jackie Cassen, Rudi Stern, Robert Fisher, and Christian Sidenius, to mention a few, acknowledge Wilfred as an innovator, a consummate genius, and one who created a unique twentieth-century art form.

Len Lye

If Gyorgy Kepes provides the fundamental link between the theoretical and the practical applications of art and technology, and Thomas Wilfred pioneered in the use of light as an art form, an equal role as a progenitor of science-art must be assigned to Len Lye for his exploration into the use of motion.

"I had only one idea—composing motion," he said. "I didn't care how I did it. If I got juice from the moon, or the depth of the ocean, it didn't matter what happened on the technological side, so long as you can control the stuff."

Len Lye, a dynamic and ubiquitous artist, was obsessed by the beauty of motion from the early age of fifteen. Coupled with this basic preoccupation was an inherent sense of propriety and craftsmanship in the use of his materials. The leading early figures of this movement tended to employ metal as their basic building block. This choice was dictated in no small matter by the necessity to articulate the movement of the sculpture with mechanical means. At one extreme, Alexander Calder used the subtleties of wind currents to give motion to his delicately counterbalanced mobiles; at the opposite end of the spectrum, Jean Tinguely created mechanical monsters that were designed in some extreme Dadaesque moments to shake themselves literally to pieces. Len Lye's work reaches both ends of the scale: at times his work is designed to be articulated by air currents, at others by the spectator's hand, and, in certain applications, by electric motors and complicated gearing.

Lye's interest in motion led him to a related concept: the role of function of the spectator to kinetic sculpture. More and more, his works began to include the spectator in the experience—directly as we have noted in the sculpture articulated by the spectator's hand, and indirectly as an active part of the total aesthetic experience. The term "spectator" begins to lose its passive meaning, and unless the spectator, by his presence or movement, activates it, the work is not complete. By his action, the participant becomes essential to, and functionally a part of, the work of art.

This is not a kind of side-show activity in which the layman is a part of the spectacle. Serious intermedia or mixed-media artists are deeply committed to creating art that will be more fully experienced by the spectator-participant. Their ideal is the opposite of the traditional salon art of the late nineteenth and early twentieth centuries. The Greek temple-museum, aloof and austere, became a symbol for the preservation of the artifacts. The concept of the work of art as an artifact, to be cherished and admired but not touched—by all means, not touched—is perhaps the heart of the intermedia artist's challenge. His work is meant to be touched, felt, and—especially—set into motion. Adults trained in the "thou-shall-not-touch" school of art appreciation are reluctant to accept the invitation. At a recent Whitney Museum of Art show, sculptures on display had been expressly designed to be fondled, caressed, banged, and thumped. It should not surprise us to learn that the most uninhibited visitors were the children. They did not pass up any opportunity to become a part of things. Their more timid elders, observing this, began to emulate their more adventurous charges and proceeded to caress, fondle, thump, and bang these exhibition pieces themselves.

Lye mulled over his preoccupations with motion from the time he was 15 years old to his maturity at 21. He celebrated this event by leaving his native New Zealand in August of 1922 to study film animation in Sydney, Australia. Later, as he developed his powers, he left for the excitement of London, where he gained recognition for his cartoon *Tusalava,* in 1928. It was not until 1935 that he directed his first film, but his innovative work in animation influenced a whole subsequent generation of film artists, such as Norman McLaren of the National Film Board of Canada and Carmen D'Avino in New York City. Kinetic sculpture was a natural step from this early activity. Later, Lye came to the United States. Boyd Compton persuaded him to come to his Intermedia Program at New York University to teach a new generation of artists. Lye was able to work with Thomas Tadlock, Anthony Martin, Morton Subotnik, and others during the years this group held together.

In the school studio Len Lye had, among other exotic paraphernalia, a model for a proposed monumental sculpture, entitled *Gateway.* His vision of this work, as well as his energy, his genius, comes through best in his own description, as related to me in our recent interview:

Well, this model is called *Gateway,* and it is designed as part of a Kinetic Park. Really, to give you an entirely new type of sensory experience. You go through a big gateway—this loop. It will be 90 feet wide and 60 feet high. See the little figures going up the ramp. They will be on automatic skis which will take them up the ski run. They'll go through a big twisting flip—this oval-shaped thing that the ski run passes through. It's part of the sensory experience you get when this thing flips around you. There are guards on the sides of it so you won't get your hands out. Now, when you go up, there will be a whole avenue of twisters. Then the motor is stopped that's twisting them, and they coast. As they coast, they elongate. The electromagnetic brake is put on. They brake to a stop, and when they stop, the sudden stress of unraveling makes a fantastic racket, makes a wonderful cascading astringent sound, and you'll be going through these—a whole avenue of them. Lots of things will be differently proportioned because of the landscape wherever it is done. This was the concept of Death Valley, where metal doesn't corrode and you can have stainless steel finished quality.

Instead of going to a cathedral for your sense of being, you would go to places like this. It takes the place of religious experience. When you get through to the top, there is a rotating harmonic rug. You will be taken round and round on your skis, and around, and then you will come down the escalators and have your mint julep when you get down below. And recover. That's about it.

I asked Len Lye if he thought that this environment might ever be actually realized. His answer was characteristic: "Oh, I couldn't care less. As a matter of fact, I can't spare my time worrying about anything like fabrication. There are plenty of guys who like doing that."

Alwin Nikolais

Len Lye shapes steel to articulate space. Alwin Nikolais, the modern choreographer, transforms the human body with light and sculptural costuming for the same purpose. Stretched fabrics extend the illusion of moving bodies, and surrealistic shapes, encasing them, cast strange shadows. Projected images fall on the figures of the dancers and other surfaces. Nikolais makes use of ultraviolet light and other advanced techniques in "dance theatre-pieces."

His approach to music is equally revolutionary. He composes his own sounds, mixing traditionally composed and performed music, electronic music generated on the Moog synthesizer, and tapes played at differing speeds. The variations are infinite. Positioned speakers at his operational home, Henry Street Playhouse, place the multichanneled sounds to correspond with the varying movements of the dancers.

For all his concealment of the human form in some of his dance theatre-pieces, the dancer's form is the elemental motif of Nikolais' work.

"I don't think of my creatures as mechanical men at all," he said. "As a matter of fact, you only have to see a bunch of poor dancers do the pieces to realize the great difference between these things being performed by a sensitive artist as against, let's say, a fellow who really mechanizes it. Mechanism isn't the answer. It's the sensitivity of that mechanism to allow a greater dimension to something that can't be shown otherwise."

However, the unique ability to synthesize movement, light, sound, and color into a new and compelling organization of space and time depends, in the final analysis, on the choreographer's understanding of the dancer himself. In this sense Nikolais proved to be a competent teacher. At the Henry Street Playhouse he trained a new generation of dancers sympathetic to and aware of his

revolutionary concept. He taught his dancers to develop the ability to respond to the enormous demands of total integration into a synthesis of sound, light, and movement. It is in this aspect that Nikolais surpasses his imitators. Traditional choreography tends to focus on the individual dancer as the protagonist of the choreographer's intent. Although Nikolais demands and uses this aspect of the dance frequently, the most remarkable aspect of his achievement is that he has been able to encourage and train his dancers to become part of the total visual unity. Nikolais' ingenious use of lighting and costume design often cannot be appreciated by the individual dancer; it is apparent only to the choreographer and his audience. This brilliant ensemble work and total visual unity distinguishes Nikolais' ballets and have brought him critical acclaim. It should be noted, however with some real sadness, that while Nikolais' work has been ecstatically received abroad (where he has been hailed as one of the most original minds in dance), in this country he has to struggle marginally to keep together a modest company in the Henry Street Playhouse.

Nikolais' role as an innovator was recently reasserted when he wrote and choreographed the electronic ballet *Limbo* for the Columbia Broadcasting Company. In collaboration with the producer, Ray Abel, and a brilliant electronic engineer, Herb Gardener, Nikolais developed a videotape ballet that could only be realized in this medium. The videotape ballet was realized with Chroma Key switching. Chroma Key switching enables the director to transform the screen into two or three totally independent visual fields. For example, a dancer's face and hands may appear as visible elements recorded from one studio camera. The dancer's body, however, can be visualized with input from a second camera. The "background" can then be realized by switching to the input from a third camera. This flexibility enabled Nikolais to create a "ballet without gravity, the ultimate realization of the choreographer's dream."

Dr. Billy Klüver

Dr. Klüver is a widely respected scientist who has achieved international renown by developing advanced concepts in laser research at Bell Laboratories. On the face of it, he is an improbable candidate as a leading protagonist of collaboration between scientists and artists; however, his lifelong interest in art brought him into contact with the restless energy of the experimental American painter Robert Rauschenberg, during the decade of the sixties. At the time, Rauschenberg was devoting his prodigious talents to creating spectator-activated works of art. The traditional tools of the painter were inadequate to the task; more and more, he found his interest turning to the hardware of the electronics industry. It was here that his conception surpassed his technical competence. It was a short step to seek the advice of his friend, the laser scientist. This association led to one of the first direct collaborative science-art projects by major protagonists of these contrasting disciplines. Together, Rauschenberg and Klüver created a prototype electronic sculpture consisting of five pieces; each section contained an independent sensing device coupled to advanced audio components. As a spectator passed a section of the sculpture, his movements would trigger a motley but provocative collection of electronic sounds. When the work was completed, Rauschenberg prophetically entitled it *Oracle* and asked Klüver to join him in co-signing the work. This act was a significant milestone inaugurating an era of science-art collaborative works.

From this collaboration came a show, now famous, held at the 69th Street Armory in New York City during October 1966. The show was called *Nine Evenings: Theatre and Engineering,* and it drew upon the talents of ten well-known artists and thirty outstanding engineers recruited primarily by Rauschenberg from the artistic community in New York City and by Klüver from the scientific community at Bell Laboratories.

The original aim was not to produce the show, but to achieve participation by the American artists in the Stockholm Festival of Art and Technology, scheduled for October 1966. To this end, the artists met in January 1966 to discuss the technical aspects with Klüver and the engineers. In time, negotiations with the Stockholm group deteriorated and the plan to produce the *Nine Evenings* came into being. The planning and some of the immediate problems become apparent in the following description by Klüver:

The *Nine Evenings* was a deliberate attempt by ten artists to find out if it was possible to work with engineers. Their investment in terms of putting-yourself-on-a-limb was considerable. For ten months they worked with thirty engineers and were able to make a series of beautiful performances out of the collaboration. I believe it was John Cage who remarked that the *Nine Evenings* "was like the early movies" where the camera, the stage, the literary content were all separate and easily identified elements. An unmixed media—the horseless carriage—the wireless microphone—theatre and engineering.

At first rather sophisticated technological processes were the focus, but as the project approached actual performance the decisions were toward simplification. "We created a deliberate group therapy situation," Klüver explains. The engineers began to lose their suspicion of the artists, who had at first seemed both impractical and not very clear in their ideas. Klüver comments:

It is inevitable that the engineer's work has to precede that of the artist.* This makes any collaboration highly imbalanced, but when all is fused together there are great possibilities for give and take. It was on the simple practical level that the best results of the artist-engineer relationship were achieved; our best experiences came from the projects where the artists had worked with the same engineers from the first idea to its realization.

*Dr. Klüver no longer believes this: "Even a relay has its own aesthetics."

There were over 8500 engineering hours of work that went into the *Nine Evenings*. This makes a total of more than four man-years of work for the 30 engineers involved. A low estimate of the value of engineering time is $150,000. During the 16 days in the Armory 19 engineers worked more than 2500 hours and three of them worked more than 250 hours each. The audience was a little over 10,000. (Billy Klüver, "Theater and Engineering—An Experiment. 2. Notes by an Engineer," *Art Forum,* Vol. 5, No. 6 (February 1967) pp. 31, 32)

The *Nine Evenings* was not theatre. It was a series of compositions created from the imaginations of artists working in the new forms of intermedia, multimedia, and kinetic light. Although there were technical failures, difficulties in production due to the use of the Armory, a disappointing reception from conservative critics and a suspicious public, the *Nine Evenings* was not a failure in its purpose: to test the ability of two different disciplines in two unrelated fields to work and achieve results together.

The project had far-reaching after-effects. Out of it grew an organization that Klüver, together with Robert Rauschenberg, Robert Whitman, and Fred Waldhauer, was active in founding and for which he now provides active leadership: Experiments in Art and Technology (E. A. T.) in New York City.

Howard Wise

Often the progenitors of a new art form atrophy from lack of sponsorship. In spite of the great progress we have made in rewarding initiative in politics and industry, unfortunately this functional societal ability has never been extended effectively to the arts. Like vintage wines, our artists are accepted long after the grapes are pressed.

Early in the life of the science-art movement, Howard Wise lent the prestige of his gallery in New York to a series of experimental exhibitions focused on this controversial art form. He has encouraged the patriarchs of the movement in exhibitions for Len Lye and Thomas Wilfred; at the same time he encouraged the young intermedia artists from the USCO cooperative; and he offered a forum for scientists such as Bela Julesz, Michael Noll, and Gerald Oster. Wise summarized his early pioneering interest with an exhibition entitled *Lights in Orbit,* which took place from February 4 to March 4, 1967, at his gallery. It was no easy undertaking. The gallery had to create conditions under which a number of intricate compositions could be shown to advantage. High-voltage electrical installations, as well as other complex electronic facilities, had to be accommodated.

Howard Wise's early and unwavering support of intermedia ranks him high in the category of progenitors of science-art. *Lights in Orbit* summed up the history of the movement to that time. Since then Wise has devoted his full time to providing a stage for the intermedia, mixed media, kinetic lights, and environmental artist. Wise's influence has extended far beyond the traditional gallery owner's preoccupations. An example can be found in his personal sponsorship, providing encouragement and, more significantly, funds to secure the development of talented young artists' creative work. Even after he closed his 57th Street gallery in New York City, he funded gifted young artists, such as Eric Siegel. Siegel wanted to design and perfect an electronic synthesizer that would permit him to make unique television images. (See color illustrations C-157 and C-158, page 278.) Mr. Wise gave the young artist the necessary funds.

Boyd Compton

Intermedia is a way of life to Boyd Compton, former head of the Intermedia Program at New York University. Five years in Java, Bali, and Sumatra made him aware of the richness of lives in which song, dance, community activities, and family relationships are interwoven. The arts of music, fantasy, dance, and living seemed to him to be of one fabric. In these "primitive" societies he observed the constant intimacy of adults and children in shared activities. During an interview with the author, he contrasted the warmth of these family groups with the loneliness and alienation of family life in Western society. To Compton the life he observed in the Far East defined his concept of a natural intermedia experience.

His empathy with Far Eastern life grew out of his studies at Princeton University, where he found Chinese art history the most interesting of his courses. During World War II he spent two-and-one-half years in China as a member of the Marine Corps. On returning from the service, he earned an advanced degree in Chinese studies. He translated a book by Mao Tse-tung, but could not accept a fellowship to study in China because Peking had fallen. He went to Indonesia on a fellowship from the Institute of Current World Affairs. After his five years there, he went to the Netherlands, where he spent two years because he "wanted to see what the Dutch were like. After all, they had ruled Indonesia for 300 years."

The Institute of Current World Affairs allows its fellows great leeway in delving into the culture of the countries to which they are assigned. Compton explains that "the only rules of the game were: don't mix with the foreign colony, travel widely, live in the culture and in the language."

Compton found that often persons in Java or Bali lived an entire life without ever having been physically alone. In his opinion, people in such a society produce a life style, interpersonal relationships, theatrical dance, and visual drama that become their intermedia. In this context, Compton feels that for art to stand alone is almost unthinkable in a communal society.

Later, after a period with the Rockefeller Institute back home, Compton set out to provide an environment for intermedia artists that would approximate the life-in-art and art-in-life experience of the Far East. For the new School of the Arts Intermedia Program he recruited a faculty whose patriarch was Len Lye. Lye, in turn, was joined by younger intermedia artists, such as Anthony Martin and Morton Subotnick.

Interviews

Interviews with the personalities discussed in this chapter follow. Photographs illustrate the subject matter of the interviews and the theme of the chapter.

GYORGY
kepes

DIRECTOR, CENTER FOR ADVANCED VISUAL STUDIES, MASSACHUSETTS INSTITUTE OF TECHNOLOGY, CAMBRIDGE, MASSACHUSETTS

Yes, MIT is a most exciting and rewarding environment for an artist working here. But it is not always an easy environment, particularly at the first encounter. When I first came here I had an inflated and distored notion of my role as an artist. The world of science and engineering was for me a distant unknown land that I knew only from a few books (rather inadequate maps); so when I arrived here it was like facing a new country, unable to speak the language or understand the mores of its people. I was defensive and critical. But through personal friendship with some of the scientists and engineers I began to understand our different vistas and values and discovered essential common denominators. As a consequence, I had to look into myself and restructure my own values and look outside and seek contact points between my own involvements and those of the scientists and engineers working at the Institute. It was not an easy time, but it was the most important in my life.

Just a few words about my background. I studied painting at the Art Academy in Budapest, and belonged to the second generation of the avant-garde. But as Hungary was in no way in the center of the world, we young artists received only echoes of the echoes of the fast-shifting phases of artistic movements. Sometimes we picked up signals without knowing their true meanings or origins. Living in a country that was deeply troubled by social conflicts (it was the time of the Depression), I could not escape being involved in a search for social solutions. Having a deep sympathy with the Hungarian peasants, who had less than a fair share in life, I felt that I could not pursue with a clear conscience my artistic interests in exciting morphological explorations without a search for new ways of creative involvement that could combine my joy in visual values with an expression of my social beliefs. Filmmaking seemed to be the answer, for films could offer a vital complementary unity of personal and social needs. Personal and historical circumstances canceled my hopes of becoming a filmmaker. However, my belief in the significance of what filmmaking stood for did not disappear, but, on the contrary, deepened and intensified. For in filmmaking there was a convergence of values of sensibilities, social responsibility, cooperative work patterns, and utlization of advanced scientific and technological tools. This belief in the possibility of these four essentials served as the seed for all my later creative interests and hopes.

MIT offered the fertile ground for this seed. First, it gave me a new sense of reality, at least a glimpse of a new landscape opened up by contemporary science and technology—a stimulating new world for the sensibilities.

Second, MIT gave me a new perspective of the social and ecological horizon. I learned here that to be angry or unhappy is not enough. To give reality to one's social beliefs and sense of solidarity with fellow men, one has to know the precise concrete particulars of the world we face. A disciplined, clear interpretation of the human condition is a must.

Third, observing the intense and inspired collaboration between scientists here at MIT, I began to fully realize the significance of such cooperation.

And last, here I learned to recognize that in order to be effective in this new explosive scale of knowledge, power, and human conflicts, the artist has to learn to understand and utilize new scale tools commensurate with the new reality—and thus accept scientific technology as an ally.

The Center for Advanced Visual Studies was the concrete focus of all these convictions and aspirations. It was formed with the belief that it would be a congenial

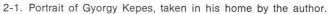

2-1. Portrait of Gyorgy Kepes, taken in his home by the author.

2-2. *Lift and Equilibrium,* by Otto Piene. (Photograph by Bob Lyon, Center for Advanced Visual Studies, MIT, Cambridge, Massachusetts.)

place for those few artists who are ready for it—a place where they could bring into common work-focus their personal artistic needs and shared major creative goals. The essential objective at the Center is not merely to develop new artistic idioms that utilize sophisticated technology, but rather to innovate new creative objectives suggested by our new life conditions. Ours is an uphill struggle for many reasons. First, we all carry within us the inhibiting weight of our ego investments. We have different basic appetite and idea orientations that do not always fit within a single common goal. We also lack public sponsorship, though the task we have in mind has an ambitious scale that requires generous civic support. Nevertheless, after four years' existence there are results.

The Center's idea profile is now clearly legible. It is a singular cooperative commitment to a new relationship between art and our common life. Among our ambitions is to find new vital formats for artistic creativity in which artists could intensify and enrich our inner and outer environment; formats that move beyond the gallery or mere facelifting of the cityscape with large sculptures. But we are not unmindful that the search for new formats of art on a civic or public scale cannot be done without tapping the inner resources of the individual sensibilities.

Parallel with the exploration of common creative goals, each artist working in the Center pursues his own individ-

ual realms. For whatever broad context we hope to act in, the work has to begin with a return to the individual. When the American, Glenn, and the Russian, Gagarin, astronauts returned from their respective historic orbits made possible by the combined wealth of contemporary scientific technology, their first few words commenting on the trip were significantly personal and poetic. Both these men spoke with real awe of the bluest blue they had ever dreamed of and, shedding all their technical language, spoke with spontaneity of their deep personal involvement. Whatever we try to do here at the Center and however lucky we are in creating urban scale physical structures, or in communicating ideas in the scale of the medium, we recognize the complementary roles of the personal and the public as basic. To put it in other words, we are not technological fetishists. We hope to use technology in art only in scale with our feelings and genuine needs. We know that the rich but troubled life of today is pregnant with immense creative potentials. These creative tasks cannot be realized without being truly human and truly contemporary. To be truly human implies that we never lose our personal sense, nor our link to our fellow man. To be contemporary implies a clear awareness of the problems of today, as well as a genuine knowledge and competence in the use of twentieth-century scientific technology.

2-3

2-4

2-3. Model of a kinetic light tower, by Michio Ihara. (Photograph by Nishan Bichajian, Center for Advanced Visual Studies, MIT, Cambridge, Massachusetts.)

2-4. Caustic curves reflected—from giant mirrosited spherical buoys, by Gyorgy Kepes. (Photograph by Nishan Bichajian, Center for Advanced Visual Studies, MIT, Cambridge, Massachusetts.)

2-5. Video-lumined light wall, by Ted Kraynik. (Photograph by Nishan Bichajian, Center for Advanced Visual Studies, MIT, Cambridge, Massachusetts.)

2-5

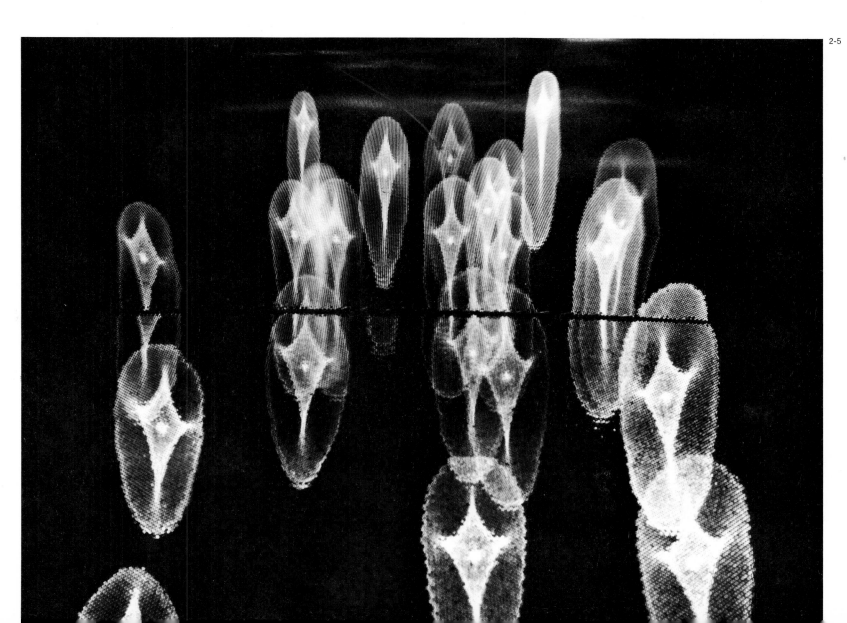

2-6

2-6. *Cybernetic Sculpture #4127* by Tsai. Stainless steel, stroboscopic lights, and electronic feedback control system. (Collection Addison Gallery of American Art, Andover, Massachusetts, 1969. Photograph by Nishan Bichajian, Center for Advanced Visual Studies, MIT, Cambridge, Massachusetts.)

2-7. Frame from a computer film, Stan VanDerBeek. (Courtesy Center for Advanced Visual Studies, MIT, Cambridge, Massachusetts.)

2-7

THOMAS
wilfred*

LUMIA ARTIST

Although the author had telephone conversations and correspondence with Thomas Wilfred, he did not meet the great artist before his death in August 1968. A warm, nostalgic portrait of the artist emerges, however, from interviews with Christian Sidenius and Jackie Cassen, admirers and emulators of his work. Sidenius was interviewed at his Theatre of Light, Sandy Hook, Connecticut. Christian Sidenius:

Thomas Wilfred is probably the most important pioneer in the history of lumia, although he does have predecessors, men who worked with the idea of large-screen color organs designed to saturate the eye. Their concern was not graphic, but with just pure colored light in various intensities, saturation, and so forth.

Wilfred's first performance was, I believe, at the Provincetown Playhouse in Greenwich Village, in 1922 or 1923. His performing instrument was essentially a transformation of filter images. He had electric light bulbs made with filaments shaped in triangular, square, or more complex forms. He would project these images through various lenses, tilting the lens, throwing it in and out of focus. He would transform this image somewhat near the nodal point, where the beam of light converges after it comes out of the lens.

With lumia performances, we are not trying, as is the case in classical physics, to get the best image. We are using all the aberrant optics. We use all the things that classical physicists don't want. We use chromatic aberration to give fringes of color. The same thing for the mirror projector. Rather than work with a flat-plane, first-surface mirror, as the physicist would, we use a bent, twisted mirror. We find that everywhere we turn, a new projector can be made out of what is essentially bad optics. But it makes very interesting imagery and, used creatively, it becomes an art form.

Wilfred continued making instruments right up to his untimely death. His performances went all over the world. He built a theatre in the Grand Central Palace in New York City, where he performed regularly. At the beginning of World War II, the place became an induction center, and his theatre was demolished. His apparatus now is dismantled and somewhat cannibalized. It is stored in West Nyack, New York.

He called his instrument the Clavilux. It was controlled both mechanically and electrically. The electrical controls were for dimming lamps, varying the speed and direction of motors. The mechanical controls were to lift slides, tilt

*From interviews with Jackie Cassen and Christian Sidenius.

lenses, change the focal length of lenses, and to focus and raise the various optical devices in and out of the beam of light.

This is essentially what I do, because it allows you to hand-perform by using compound mechanical advantage. With an arm stroke of about 20 inches you can, by mechanical advantage, reduce this down to one-half inch or an inch of actual movement in the focal plane. This allows you to introduce time elements which motors can't do for you. Now Wilfred actually performed silent visual music, to which dancers performed. Ted Shawn and Ruth St. Denis performed, as he beat time with his Clavilux. The image is moving according to his hand and his use of time. So he was able to divide the time visually, instead of audibly. The dancers moved to that rather than to the beat of the music.

He preferred to perform silently because of the difficulty of getting music, getting permission to use the music, then being chained to the music. So he found it much more satisfactory to work silently. He could use time as creatively as he wished.

2-8. Photograph of the late Thomas Wilfred at the Clavilux, taken when he was a young man.

2-9. Drawing by Thomas Wilfred illustrating the concept of lumia, "the eighth major fine art," a term he coined.

Jackie Cassen on the importance of Thomas Wilfred as an artist:

Thomas Wilfred's contribution to the art of light was so enormous that one day the entire field of visual performing arts, which includes video and the synthesizer, will acknowledge the debt to him. The idea of light as a medium covers the whole spectrum of what we are all doing. His ideation of an individual composition—the months and months he spent in evolving each permutation of form—is still beyond anything we are doing. One of his great dreams was that every new artist would be influenced in this direction, leaving the past to the past, working with electronics, working with light. He was a great genius, one of the truly great geniuses of all time.

2-10A. *Four Moments from Unfolding,* Opus 127. A lumia composition by Thomas Wilfred. "A nucleus of tendrils detach themselves from a rising core of light"—Thomas Wilfred.

2-10B. *Four Moments from Unfolding,* Opus 127. A lumia composition by Thomas Wilfred. "The tendrils elongate and drift away, followed by the also elongating core, until they both disappear in the distance"—Thomas Wilfred.

2-10A

2-10B

2-10C

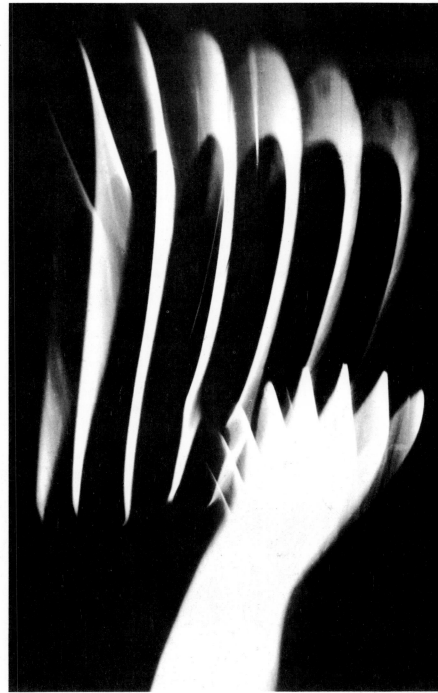

2-10D

2-10C. *Four Moments from Unfolding*, Opus 127. A lumia composition by Thomas Wilfred. "The tendrils separate and drift upward and outward as the core also expands and rises"—Thomas Wilfred.

2-10D. *Four Moments from Unfolding*, Opus 127. A lumia composition by Thomas Wilfred. "A new cycle begins. A heavier and more intense core releases another nucleus of rising and separating tendrils. This time the whole mass rotates in space as it expands and vanishes upward and outward"—Thomas Wilfred.

2-11. Reproduction of a light projection display apparatus patented by Wilfred in 1931. This diagram illustrates Wilfred's long interest in lumia and light sculpture. (All photographs courtesy of Thomas Wilfred.)

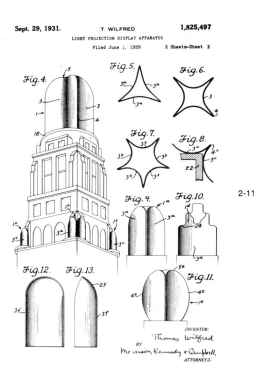

2-11

LEN
lye

Listening in on Len Lye's class in his Bleecker Street Studio. He is talking to his students. There are questions and answers, which slip through torrents of words. Colloquial, profane, learned, the session ranges over a life, a philosophy, a way of work, failure, success, adventure, descriptions of the technicalities of conceiving and producing kinetic sculptures, so detailed and complicated that the tape gives up, and gasps. The work itself, on display, is beautifully coherent.

(*He was only 15 when he ticked off about motion.*) I was up on a hill looking at the clouds. I had read that Constable tried to simulate the clouds' motion in oil sketches. It suddenly struck me. I got this feeling, this very strong feeling that motion was the great thing to think about, and why couldn't it be composed as a composer composes sound?

I had only one idea, composing motion. I didn't care how I did it. If I got the juice from the moon, or the depth of the ocean. It didn't matter what happened on the technological side, so long as I could control the stuff.

It is my belief that in art, in photography, in music, there's some distinctive quality which is uniquely part of the creator. It applies even in an utterly mechanical thing. If you are working with a team, a film crew, they see what you want, they get a feeling of what you are trying to

2-12. Portrait of Len Lye, taken by the author at Lye's Intermedia Studio at New York University.

achieve, they get into the exact same spirit. And this is how you work with the mechanic. You get a quality, over and above the utility.

I just want to get the feeling of myself, my essential self, into what I am doing. I don't get it by formula.

I know there are only two guys entirely preoccupied with the pursuit of truth. One is the scientist, who wants the facts, and one is the artist, who wants the emotion. Emotional truth and factual truth—there are only these two people who are after those truths for their own sake.

When the scientist has isolated a fact that can be demonstrated, verified, etcetera, it's a marvelous revelation. Next week, there's something out and added to it, and that marvelous revelation is now one of the links in a long chain of knowledge. . . . The artist isolates some essential quality of life . . . ; once that is isolated, it's unique. It attains this intrinsic value of the essence of somebody's individuality. Retains it forever. You can throw away the arms or limbs, leave half a face, and still feel the quality of work that went into that thing. It's a good art as it was in the first place.

The aesthetics of motion—all kinetic aesthetics—is such a new thing that anybody can get into it and discover something. People using technology are finding that out, and having a ball. Art is the one way that you can isolate the absolute, essential part of your individualities, the essence, the temperamental essence that has gone on in art since the year One. This is what will always make art great: the essence of individuality that's isolated in the work—the enhancement, the sharpened wits, the finalized creative urge, the perfection, the contentment of that oneness with self that the artist gets into his work. That's what makes art great, irrespective of whether it's done with mercury, or electronic whiz-whams, paint, whatever. If you can get this quality into it, that's all that matters. . . . For the artist, the by-product is satisfaction, and you want to do it again. . . .

The kinetic image is the most emphatic image for the immediacy of empathy, involvement. There is no other image that will immediately alert your attention, that you'll observe over everything else that's involved (in the situation). This thing is an act, and you are going to watch it in preference to watching a finish on the floor or the color of a sunset. This thing is wagging around, the bird is darting, this boat is capsizing. You've got to watch it now. This is very important. On Sunday, come Utopia, you'll want your whole sensory self completely stimulated and

2-13A. Len Lye's model for his intermedia environmental sculpture entitled *Gateway*.

This is a photograph that shows the proposed intermedia kinetic sculpture Gateway. *In the foreground, a huge kinetic band of stainless steel envelops the spectator. This band is articulated by the wind and strikes a rotating ball above the band and to the left. As the spectator is propelled on skis along the ramp in the center of the band, he passes kinetic sculptures as he moves toward the elevated shrine in the background at the base of the mountains. This intermedia environment has all of the classic elements of the Egyptian temple shrine, using the outdoor setting against the mountains as a device to increase the monumental feeling of the environment. It has a second purpose of integrating the man-made elements of the environment with sculptural elements from nature, such as the mountains shown in the illustration.*

2-13B. Closeup of a kinetic piece articulated by the wind.

involved in some kind of ritual, and not only that, but the control of the sensory impact. You'll combine visual action with sound, with verbal stuff, with escalator things that move you, that take you from one viewpoint to another. All this will make old-time religion seem a little inadequate. We'll have new-time religion, and the kinetic image will be one of the images of this time. And what is the matter with the time now? We're beginning it right now. They are messing around on the football level, but when it gets to the fine-art level, that will be great.

2-13C. Model of spectators on movable ski ramp with kinetic sculptures on both sides.

2-13D. Approach to the elevated shrine through a large kinetic ring.

2-13F. Closeup detail of the shrine sculpture.

2-14. Closeup of Len Lye incising rhythmic abstractions on a photographic film. (From the film *The Walls Come Tumbling Down*, written and produced for CBS-TV by Merrill Brockway. Executive Producer George Dessart.)

In discussing his direct drawing on film for his Free Radicals *motion picture, Len Lye stated: "In my work, I try to get a—some essential business going on. I call it, in my instance, a kind of 'jizzy' quality. And I just say that my work has a kind of 'jizz.'*
"You drip the needle, and you put it into the celluloid, and you scratch a design. Now, that design has to be repeated twenty-four times to give you a second of animation, a second of picture. So, you do twenty-four in succession. And it is—once you get into the knack of it—it's as simple as writing your signature twenty-four times."

2-15. Closeup of Len Lye examining scratched film from *The Walls Come Tumbling Down.*

2-13E. Closeup photograph of the kinetic shrine with exit staircase at right.

2-14

2-15

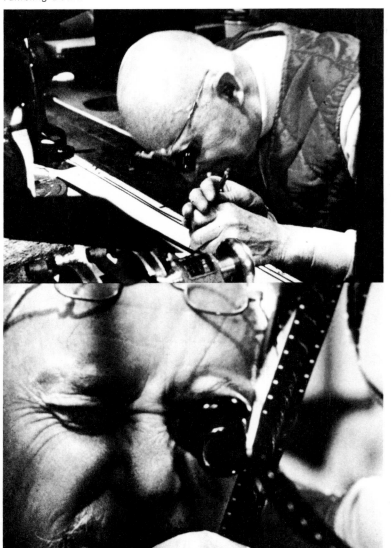

ALWIN
nikolais

CHOREOGRAPHER—DIRECTOR, HENRY STREET PLAYHOUSE, ALWIN NIKOLAIS DANCE THEATRE, NEW YORK CITY

Alwin Nikolais is distinctly a man in his time and very much aware of it.

Man is no longer content to perceive his world through the sensory dominance of the eye and the ear. Young people do not trust the one sense. We suspect that we are being coerced by Madison Avenue, by newspapers, by things people say. We want a total perception of our world. We're not content only to see or hear; we want to smell, we want to taste, we want to feel our whole relationship to environment, and world, so that we can decide through perceptions accumulated through all the senses what is the *fact* of the matter. We all want to regain some of the sensory vitalities inherent in our animalism, which civilization has dulled.

Dance is not only a kinetic art; it is also a visual one. Years ago I began to use the processes of the sculptor and the painter in much more integral relation to dance than before. The dancer has to have more than kinaesthesia to move. He has to have sight; he has to have balance; he has to have feeling for a sense of space, a sense of timing. He uses many more of his senses than we earlier believed. But the dancer wants to move (they've got to get a hernia, you know, to be happy), and to hold him down to a visual component is often difficult.

I was always interested in music as the art of sound, not as the art of scales and harmony and melody. I studied dance really to learn about the accompaniment, and this in turn unified the two. When I taught dance after that, I taught the dancers to make their own sound. With the invention of the tape recorder, it was possible to put these sounds on tape. Of course, sometimes the tape would break or be put in backward. I'd say: "Well, it sounds better that way." Or we might by mistake put on the slow speed, instead of the normal speed, and I discovered in this way that it was possible to manipulate the tape. So, innocently I became a tape composer. . . . When electronic equipment came along, I switched to electronic sources.

I am a frustrated film man, in a way, because I try to treat my stage as a 3-D canvas. And gravity is an awful nuisance; it always pulls action down to the bottom. It keeps the figure anchored on the floor in one level, whereas in television or film he can go anywhere. You can put him out of gravity. One of the significant things about art is reaching for freedom. Technology is breaking another barrier. Gravity is one of my barriers in choreography. Now, technology is helping me to break that bar-

rier, and this excites me very much. We have men up in space. We have a feeling for nongravity just out of the fact that we've seen someone walk in space up there, free of the gravity pull. Our whole sense of presence in the universe has been greatly shaken by new discoveries in science. . . . The artist has a feeling about this. Science and technology express our time, but, more than that, they offer us new means to express it.

The old Aristotelian rules of time and reality no longer serve our field of vision. We need to see beyond reality into the mysticism of what is beyond that. . . . We still have that portion that says we don't know where we came from and where we're going. The body is a magical instrument. I can show you my hand—a fleshly physiological reality. That's a sculptural thing. It's a shape, but the moment I do this, it's a deer running. From reality we can, in a fraction of a moment, transcend into an illusion of something else. The dimensions that the body can operate in are infinite. . . . When we get scientific machinery to make finer and finer decisions and work out a memory process of detailed sensitivity, we're only trying to duplicate what man has already done. . . . Perhaps technology will give him more freedom to live and perceive in greater depth his own reason for being.

(Scenes from Nikolais' ballets *Echo, Somniloquy,* and *Tent* are shown in color on page 51. Also see the Ray Abel-Herb Gardner-Alwin Nikolais collaboration *Limbo* in chapter 8, and *Limbo* scenes in color on page 190.)

2-16. Alwin Nikolais in his office at the Henry Street Playhouse, New York City.

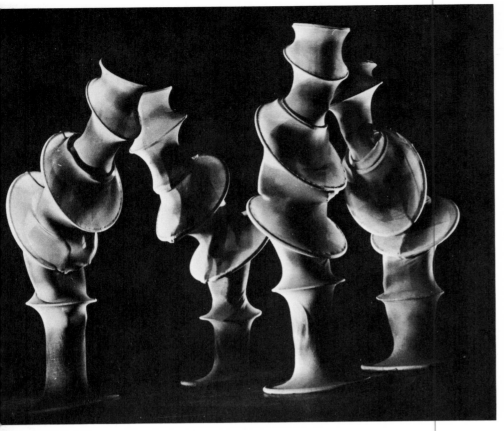

2.17. *Allegory*, a dance theatre-piece by Alwin Nikolais. The human forms of the dancers are restructured into surrealistic images. The sense of unreality is enhanced by the accompanying electronic music. Courtesy Alwin Nikolais; photographer, David Berlin.)

2-18. Brilliant use of props and dancers in the dance theatre-piece *Vaudeville of the Elements*. (Courtesy Alwin Nikolais; photographer, Susan Schiff-Faludi.)

2-19A. Elastic shrouds enveloping dancers create beautiful abstract patterns in the Alwin Nikolais dance theatre-piece *Sanctum*. Designs reminiscent of a Hans Arp painting or Henry Moore sculpture open and close in the fluidity of the dancers' movements. (Courtesy Alwin Nikolais; photographer, Susan Schiff-Faludi.)

2-19B. Elastic shrouds enveloping dancers create beautiful abstract patterns in *Sanctum*. (Courtesy Alwin Nikolais; photographer, Susan Schiff-Faludi.)

2-19B

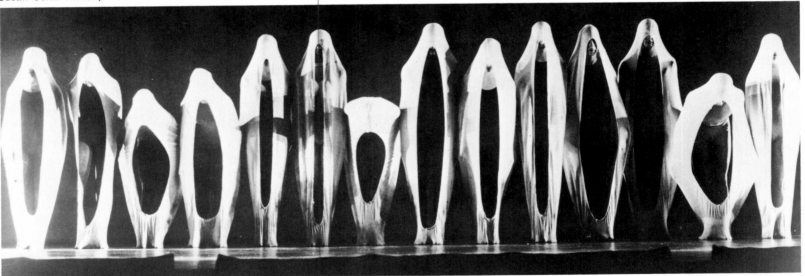

C-12

C-13

C-14

C-12. Scene from the Nikolais-Louis Dance Company ballet *Echo*. (Courtesy Alwin Nikolais; photographer, Susan Schiff-Faludi—Three Lions.)

C-13. Scene from the Nikolais-Louis Dance Company ballet *Somniloquy*. (Courtesy Alwin Nikolais; photographer, Bob Moreland.)

C-14. Scene from the Nikolais-Louis Dance Company ballet *Tent*. (Courtesy Alwin Nikolais; photographer, Bob Moreland.)

C-15. Another scene from *Tent*. (Courtesy Alwin Nikolais; photographer, Bob Moreland.)

C-15

2-20A. Ultraviolet light produces enigmatic disembodied figures in the dance theatre-piece *Galaxy*. (Courtesy Alwin Nikolais; photographer, Susan Schiff-Faludi.)

2-20B. Scene from *Galaxy*. Ultraviolet light on dancers' bodies. (Courtesy Alwin Nikolais; photographer, Susan Schiff-Faludi.)

2-21. Kite-shaped forms extend the range of dancers' movements in the ballet *Imago,* by Alwin Nikolais. (Courtesy Alwin Nikolais; photographer, Herbert Migdoll.)

DR. BILLY
klüver

PRESIDENT OF THE FOUNDATION EXPERIMENTS IN ART AND TECHNOLOGY (E.A.T.), NEW YORK CITY

Billy Klüver is a living collaboration between science and art. He was working in the laser field at Bell Telephone Laboratories—after a number of years in microwave theory and electronics—when he decided to organize and head Experiments in Art and Technology, making permanent a love affair with art begun in his student days in Stockholm. There he ran the University Film Society. From films he became interested in painting. Around 1959-1960, he was involved in a group around Alfred Leslie. Later

he worked with Jean Tinguely on a machine that destroyed itself. "That," he says, "was the first experience of what we now call collaboration." And then there was *Oracle*, an environmental sculpture on which he worked with Robert Rauschenberg for three years. Both signed the piece. "In a way, we established a precedent, which I can see now was important because the engineer's contribution is recognized."

2-22. Participants in the *Nine Evenings* intermedia program held at the 69th Street Armory in New York City. (Courtesy Bell Laboratories, Murray Hill, New Jersey.)

This photograph appears in the program for the Nine Evenings *performance. Reading left to right, zigzag: Top row: Joe Fallica, Ulla Lyttkens, Phillip Idone, Ron Hobbs, John Cage, Jennifer Tipton, Beverly Emmons, Irfan Camlibel, Jacky Grant, Bob Kieronski, Sönen Brunes, Witt Wittnebert. Second row from top: Jeff Strickler, Alice Schwebke, Ulla Wiggen, Alphonse Schilling, Howard Marks, Herb Schneider, Oyvind Fahlstrom, Larry Heilos, Jim McGee, Per Biorn, Yvonne Rainer, R. Whitman, Clark Poling, Simone Whitman, Gloria Bryant. Bottom row: David Long, Nancy Chandler, Billy Klüver, David Anderson, Deborah Hay, Franklin Königsberg, Fred Waldhauer, Lucinda Childs, Robbie Robinson, Robert Rauschenberg, Ralph Flynn, Bruce Glushakow, Pontus Hultén, Alex Hay, Cecil Coker, Larry Leitch, Steve Paxton.*

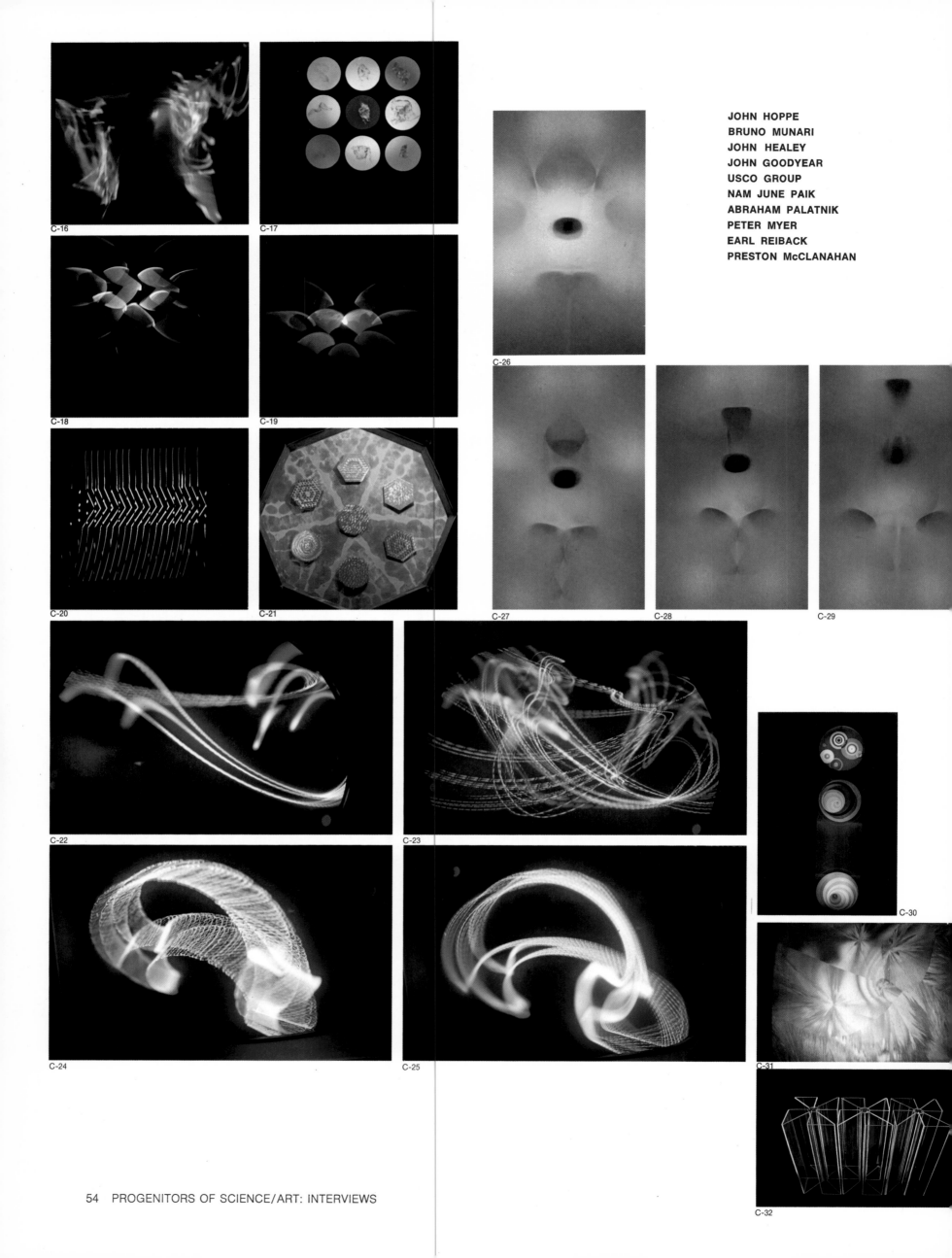

C-16

C-17

C-18

C-19

C-20

C-21

C-26

C-27

C-28

C-29

JOHN HOPPE
BRUNO MUNARI
JOHN HEALEY
JOHN GOODYEAR
USCO GROUP
NAM JUNE PAIK
ABRAHAM PALATNIK
PETER MYER
EARL REIBACK
PRESTON McCLANAHAN

C-22

C-23

C-24

C-25

C-30

C-31

C-32

opposite

C-16. John Hoppe, *Mobilux Suspended* projection, 1967. Series from Hoppe sequence shown at The Howard Wise Gallery.

C-17. Bruno Munari, *Polariscope #12*, 1966. 20″ x 20″ x 6″. Static patterns of light slowly changing colors.

C-18, 19. John Healey, *Box 3*, 1963. 25½″ x 38½″ x 13″. Shapes of light appear, grow, and dissolve, forming continuously evolving patterns of continuously changing color.

C-20. John Goodyear, *Bent Wave Pattern*, 1967. 24′ x 24″ x 9″. Rhythmic parallel lines of colored light are intercepted by swinging plastic grid to form moiré patterns. (Collection, The Milwaukee Art Center.)

C-21. USCO Group, *Seven Diffraction Hex*, 1967. 26″ x 37″ x 31″. Programmed hybrid of solid-state and electrochemical technology. The basic interaction is between motorized diffraction gratings and strotoscopic light.

C-22. View from Nam June Paik's color television program *Electronic Blues*, 1966. 30″ x 25″ x 20″.

C-23, C-24, C-25. Changing sequences from Nam June Paik's *Electronic Blues.*

C-26. View of Abraham Palatnik's *Sequencia Vertical S-30,* 1965. 44″ x 27″ x 8″. Organic shapes of changing color slowly form and disappear. Programmed, ten-minute cycle.

C-27, C-28, C-29. Three changing sequences from Abraham Palatnik's *Sequencia Vertical S-30.*

C-30. Sequence from the Peter Myer's kinetic *Transit Orb,* 1967. 72″ x 19″ x 6″. Changing patterns of iridescent colors formed by polarized light move over a plastic disc. (Collection, The Colorado Springs Fine Arts Center.)

C-31. *Luminage Projector,* 1967. Earl Reiback. Changing shapes of iridescent colors slowly evolve and dissolve. Various surprises greet the viewer.

C-32. *Cloverleaf,* 1966. Preston McClanahan. 24″ x 32″ x 10½″. The edges of the transparent plexi forms glow with changing programmed colors. (Collection, The Walker Art Center, Minneapolis, Minnesota.)

(Courtesy The Howard Wise Gallery.)

2-23. Billy Klüver at the 69th Street Armory during preparations for the *Nine Evenings* performance. (Courtesy Bell Laboratories, Murray Hill, New Jersey.)

Experiments in Art and Technology grew out of the isolation of the artist from the technical world. He did not have any direct access to the engineer, to the scientist. He did not know how to get in touch with them.

After two or three years of work on our part, this has changed to the point that spontaneously, all over the United States, and even in other parts of the world, artists and engineers have begun to work together. As we ourselves predicted in our first E.A.T. Newsletter, we are being phased out of the operation. At present we are at a point where we would like to turn it over to some other institution. We feel that it has its own momentum. In other words, it has become an acceptable thing. People know the language. There are articles in the technical press about engineers who, in one form or another, are working with artists.

I have a feeling that future problems are not going to be on this level at all. The problems associated with just the physical thing of getting artists and engineers together, which was the *raison d'être* of E.A.T. six years ago, simply don't exist any more. The engineering schools are setting up art classes, and the art institutes are setting up engineering classes, and so on.

My feeling is that artists' use of technology is here to stay, but that now the real work begins. Some real aesthetic breakthroughs have to happen. If there is to be a viable collaborative situation, art has to be the result. Earlier, we were looking at the problem as functional or social. Now that the change has happened, it has to translate itself into aesthetic expressions.

Of course, it's okay for an engineer or scientist also to be an artist; but he has to produce valid works. It is very hard to make art. It's even harder if you have already spent ten or twenty years of your life being an engineer or scientist. First, he discovers he can make art. After a

while, he finds out that it isn't really that easy; but there is a genuine desire to be creative. The engineer and the scientist often move into the field with great enthusiasm and generosity, but like everything in life it takes time and it's tough.

Collaboration can yield a lot more, has greater potential than working alone, but it is also much harder. It will have to evolve its own form. There isn't any form for the collaboration yet. It happens on a personal level and when it is successful we don't know why.

As for the role of E.A.T. in the future, in the last two years we have become more and more project-oriented. We commit ourselves to a finite project with a specific aim in mind, where the artist's input is important. These projects are in areas with a strong aesthetic component. For example, we are very interested in finding new methods for television programming. We are very interested in developing countries, where technological change superimposed on the old culture creates cross-cultural tensions, where some form of information is needed to alleviate the transition.

In dealing with unknowns and experimental projects, you always have problems, and they are always different. You tend to assume good will and respect for the artist; then you find that people generally misunderstand what he is doing and how he behaves. You either have to start defending him, or explaining what he's really doing. And you get into any number of jams.

In *Oracle,* we were absolutely committed to having the project turn out as a work of art. As it stood when we left it, nothing had been changed. Everything was exactly as the artist wanted it. It came about through a tremendous amount of work and effort on our part, a real collaboration of artist and engineer.

2-24. Robert Rauschenberg's performance at the *Nine Evenings*, entitled *Open Score*. (Courtesy Bell Laboratories, Murray Hill, New Jersey.)

2-25. Scene from Alex Hay's "Grass Field" at Nine Evenings. (Courtesy Bell Laboratories, Murray Hill, New Jersey.)

2-26A. Scene from environment entitled "Physical Things," by Steve Paxton, *Nine Evenings* performance. (Courtesy Bell Laboratories, Murray Hill, New Jersey; photographer, Robert R. McElroy.)

2-26B. Photograph of Steve Paxton's "Physical Things" environment, *Nine Evenings* performance. (Courtesy Bell Laboratories, Murray Hill, New Jersey; photographer, Robert R. McElroy.)

2-26C. Detail of spectator-participant in Steve Paxton's "Physical Things" environment, *Nine Evenings* performance. (Courtesy Bell Laboratories, Murray Hill, New Jersey; photographer, Robert R. McElroy.)

2-26D. Steve Paxton's "Physical Things" environment, *Nine Evenings* performance. (Courtesy Bell Laboratories, Murray Hill, New Jersey; photographer, Robert R. McElroy.)

2-27B

2-27B. Mirror Dome, E.A.T.-designed Pepsi-Cola pavilion, Expo '70, Osaka, Japan. (Courtesy Dr. Billy Klüver; photographer, Shunk-Kender.)

2-27A. E.A.T. Osaka Pavilion at night set off by lightframe. (Courtesy Dr. Billy Klüver, President, E.A.T. (Photographer, Shunk-Kender.)

2-27C. E.A.T.-designed Pepsi-Cola pavilion Expo '70, Osaka, Japan. (Courtesy Dr. Billy Klüver; photographer Shunk-Kender.)

2-27D. Spectators at E.A.T.-designed Pepsi-Cola pavilion, Expo '70, Osaka, Japan. (Courtesy Dr. Billy Klüver; photographer, Shunk-Kender.)

HOWARD
wise

FORMER DIRECTOR, THE HOWARD WISE GALLERY, NEW YORK CITY

Contemporary art is to the art of the past as current events are to history.

This working relationship of artist and technologist or scientist is a very important direction for art because it is so readily communicable to an uninitiated person. . . . When an artist uses some of the natural phenomena, with which science has made us familiar and enabled us to either visualize or in some other way to materialize the the invisible forces that govern our universe, this serves as a bridge and takes art out of the sort of esoteric area that is above a normal person's comprehension and into an area that is readily available to a normally educated person.

A child, for example, is fascinated by motion. You take a child through any art gallery and it may respond to a certain degree, but let there be something moving or flashing, or a kinetic manifestation of one sort or another, and the child will immediately be attracted to it. Now this is the sort of thing that happens with so-called kinetic art. It appeals to all of us.

Art shouldn't be something that is way off on a mountaintop . . . ; the thing that interests me about art is that it is happening today. We always think of the great masters, but at the time they were creating, they were contemporary. As a rule they were not held in very high esteem either. . . . Because something was created that was strange and seemed strange to people, they resented it; most people do resist change. Now, with this new kinetic art, it seems to me that the artist is making use of natural phenomena, such as magnetism and flow of liquids, flow of gases, air, light, energy—all sorts of things that we know surround us in our universe and hold it together. Yet they are mystical, too, because we cannot see them.

Really, I think that anybody who creates something of value in this area, or in the visual area, is an artist. There are many, many factors in common between artists and scientists. Some of the qualities that make for a good research scientist are the very same qualities that make for an artist. In other words, imagination. . . .

I think that Len Lye is the king of kinetics. He is going down in history. This idea of energy is imbued in him, and he is so full of it he is literally a bouncy fellow. What he is trying to do is to make motion or energy tangible, as he calls it, or felt. Here is energy or abstract force, not visible and yet we know it exists . . . . By the way, he is no scientist whatsoever. He doesn't even drive a car. But he has an

intuitive feeling for the qualities of his materials, which are mostly metal, stainless steel, or aluminum. He uses them right to the breaking point, you might say, and this is how he gets those wonderful results that make you stand on end. Your hair is standing up, and you are on the edge of your chair, and it is terrific. You wouldn't think that steel could be so sexy.

To me, *contemporary art is to the art of the past as current events are to history.* The excitement of its happening now is what interests me. Who is going to say whether it is art or not? Are you going to say that the *Mona Lisa* is art? Probably not one square inch of that painting came directly from Leonardo's brush. So what's the difference? Let's say that the way I look at contemporary art is that it should be enjoyed.

2-28. Portrait of Howard Wise in his former New York City gallery, taken by the author.

2-29. Les Levine's booth at the Avant Garde Festival held at the Lexington Avenue Armory, New York City, in November 1971. (Photograph by George Beker.)

2-31. Young exhibitor at the Avant Garde Festival, New York City. His podium is a mound of dirt; his companions are a group of rather frightened white mice. (Photograph by George Beker.)

2-30. Young videotape artists at the Avant Garde Festival, November 1971, New York City. (Photograph by George Beker.)

BOYD
compton

FORMER DIRECTOR, INTERMEDIA PROGRAM, SCHOOL OF THE ARTS, NEW YORK UNIVERSITY

*In Java, art was an internal event. I grew to love
the type of life where life doesn't end and art begin.*

The Intermedia Program, which is one of the four departments of the new School of the Arts at New York University, is an experimental art lab that doesn't have any major students. As far as we can devise it, it's going to be the nearest thing to a commune of experimenting artists that you can get in a bureaucratic structure of a university. . . . Our students are largely undergraduate actors, dancers, scene designers, filmmakers, and television people. . . . It's a place where the direct relationship between the creative artist and the student is allowed to happen, and encouraged. . . . It's a sort of a broker to allow people to come together who should come together so that it's not required that, for example, Mort Subotnick, who is a great music teacher, teach music to all music students who apply.* He could do that anywhere. It's to give the students first exposure before they really know what these guys are all about, and then to give the artists access to apprentices to help them in their work, which almost always involves teamwork of some sort. . . . They work, they labor and the artist teaches them by doing his own work. . . . The *inner* part of Intermedia that interests me is the interconnection between people and their own needs, working in art forms.

The word "intermedia" originally didn't have a great deal of philosophical importance, but that was a time when perhaps critical standards were held in abeyance; it was, you might say, a play time. And, during play time, you do more things. At that time, they started to dance, or combined dance with singing. That's similar to the situation today, when many of the strong artists are playing with new content and new forms. I think it very important that they be permitted to do their *inter* work, and to do it they have to use advanced technology that fascinates them anyhow. For a purpose.

The artists who seem strongest to me are off the easel now. Whether they are incorporating pop or chance elements in the theatrical piece, or in the dance, or in making something more palpable, like a music composition, they are definitely out of the garret, off the easel, not only technically but very often socially.

Anthony Martin's circuitry isn't as fully developed as it will be in two years, but he already has a palette that stretches from here to Dubuque.

*At the date of this interview, Mr. Subotnick was a faculty member of the Intermedia Program.

In Java, art was an internal event. I grew to love this type of life, where life doesn't end and art begin. . . . I became very interested then in the arts that were beginning to connect more with people's natural circumstances . . . happenings, Pop Art. . . ; not because I thought they looked good on the cultural chart. It was fascinating that a whole new dynamic was beginning to make itself felt. . . . It was only later that I discovered that the people working in these arts that involved people were almost without exception interested in very complicated problems in the new technology. So it was very much this great feeling that I got for the communal arts, the intermedia arts of the East Indian islands that opened me up to see what was going on here and feeling that, "Hey! this is a great thing. This needs a lot of involvement by me."

The audience is exposed to these media in such a broad democratic way, egalitarian way. The artists are drawing from social observation of what's going on, and making their materials, and caring about environments, about how our environments are, about what environments they want to make for people to live in. I see the artist drawing close to society.

How beautiful it would be to close up all the museums and get all the objects into homes. The museum simply isn't public enough.

2-32. Boyd Compton, former Director New York University School of Intermedia, photographed in his office at the school. "The *inter* part of Intermedia that interests me is the interconnection between people and their own needs working in art forms."

2-33A

B

C

2-33A, B, C. Len Lye teaching at the New York University School of Intermedia.

2-34. Anthony Martin at the School of Intermedia.

2-35. Martin's Interaction Room.

3 the growing influence of media

Technology, as packaged in its widely experienced forms of television, radio, and motion pictures, is viewed with mixed feelings by the public. One group of social critics looks upon the media as a tastemaker of dubious—even pernicious—value. Television, particularly, is anathema to these critics. To them, the idea of the creative artist using it and other technological media as means of expression is a chilling one.

An equally convinced and articulate group of advocates sees media as an egalitarian force through which the dissemination of information, formerly reserved for the culturally elite, is made available to millions. These protagonists see media as the step toward intellectual emancipation for every segment of society.

I discussed these competing interpretations of that most pervasive medium television with Dr. Frank Stanton, former president of the Columbia Broadcasting System, now chief officer of the American National Red Cross; George Dessart, WCBS-TV's Director of Community Services; Beardsley Graham, a communications consultant, founder of COMSTAT (a publicly held communications-satellite corporation) and former president of Spindletop Research, a firm devoted to research into the impact of technology on a mass society; and Tony Schwartz, a major influence in the science and practice of audio communication. Schwartz taught with Marshall McLuhan at Fordham University during the Reverend John Culkin's remarkable communications symposium.

Dr. Frank Stanton

Dr. Stanton worked in surroundings that reflected his own aesthetic values. He was in many ways responsible for the unified design of the CBS Headquarters "Black Rock" in New York City. Eero Saarinen designed the building, which was completed shortly before his death. It has been hailed as today's concept of total design made visible. The monumental black pillars rising from street level to the uppermost reaches of the building set the tone and give the building its name. Halls, offices, hardware, equipment—down to the last wastebasket and memo pad—carry out the architectural and decorative themes of corporate dignity and efficiency. Employees are surrounded by an environment calculated to create a total experience as surely as one of Len Lye's intermedia environments.

George Dessart

Dessart's documentary film *The Walls Come Tumbling Down*

presented artists who are experimenting in new media. Dessart believes that the artist no longer needs to produce a finished work of art, that his role is fundamentally experimental, much like that of the research scientist. It does not matter that he come up with a good painting, or with any painting at all. All that matters is that he bring his insight, his sensitivity, to a particular problem. And that he shed some light upon it. Once he has done so, he can move on to something else.

Beardsley Graham

Beardsley Graham, a founder of the COMSTAT Communications Satellite Corporation and one of the most brilliant minds on communications theory in the United States, sees the television industry as one of dimly grasped significance. He has no doubt that it will increasingly shape the values of society. He sees the communications complex embracing a full computer storage and retrieval system, which will deliver printouts of material to individual receiving stations. He believes that the things that are known about television, incomplete as our knowledge is, "lead you inevitably to the conclusion that it is slightly sinister."

Tony Schwartz

Tony Schwartz is the Hight Priest of contemporary sound. His studio on West 56th Street, New York City, is appropriately located in a refurbished church building. Schwartz penetrates to the heart of a medium—he has, for example, told the author that radio is essentially "company" for the listener, not information. Schwartz points out that at present, in the United States, there are as many radios as citizens, and that they are usually turned on as background for cooking, driving a car, or making love. In this sense, the medium functions as a "presence" rather than a mirror of reality, as with television.

The premise of this book is that the artist is no more immune to the influences of his society and environment than a taxicab driver, a welder, a stockbroker, or a prostitute. It is quite obvious that every walk of life is modified and changed by the growing influence of media. Stanton, Dessart, Graham, and Schwartz reflect these profound societal forces with penetrating clarity.

Interviews

Interviews with the personalities discussed in this chapter follow. Photographs illustrate the subject matter of the interviews and the theme of the chapter.

DR. FRANK
stanton

RETIRED PRESIDENT OF THE COLUMBIA BROADCASTING SYSTEM; NOW CHIEF OFFICER OF THE AMERICAN NATIONAL RED CROSS

Below are some comments on my interview with Dr. Stanton at CBS, before his retirement:

Dr. Stanton received me in his sumptuous executive suite high up in the CBS corporate headquarters building in New York City. Dr. Stanton and William Paley are both strong champions of contemporary art as they have demonstrated with their very active support of the Museum of Modern Art, New York City. It is perhaps no accident that they located the impressive CBS corporate headquarters "down the block" from the MOMA building on 53rd Street. The CBS headquarters was designed by the late Eero Saarinen and is one of the most elegant of recent New York skyscrapers.

Dr. Stanton worked closely with Louis Dorfsman on the interior design of the building, which was completed after Saarinen's death. Every appointment from the elevator buttons to the fire extinguishers (see Louis Dorfsman interview, figures 5-4 through 5-7, chapter 5) was created under his close scrutiny. Paintings, furnishings, and all interior decorations followed a strong sense of contemporary design.

3-1. Dr. Frank Stanton at his CBS desk, with his Lakeland terrier, "Mr. Crickets." (Photograph taken by the author. Permission to reproduce courtesy CBS.)

My interview with Dr. Stanton focused on television as a medium and how it has influenced contemporary American life. He offered penetrating insights into the nature of the medium. Unfortunately I could not publish this interview but Dr. Stanton kindly allowed me to include an account of remarks he made to the North Carolina Art Society, directly relevant to the theme of this work.

If artists, scientists, and engineers who are working with the advanced technology available to them today are to succeed with their efforts, they will need the help and support of major corporations and the communications industry. Dr. Stanton at CBS has helped set the proper stage for this support and patronage to develop by identifying CBS so closely with communications and contemporary art. Dr. Stanton:

"We are even beginning to see, with the vantage of time, that all the 'isms' we call modern art are the first steps toward an expression of the new scientific thinking of our time. They represent a change from an art of perception to an art of conception. Obviously, no modern artist studied Einstein. But they were all aware of the new thinking that held that the universe was no longer fixed, static entity. They were aware that things are not always what they seem—that matter was energy and energy was matter and everything is in flux. It is not surprising that art and science are close. As a distinguished contemporary sculptor has put it, both art and science are fundamentally ways of arriving at the truth. Because science is a dominant force of our life today, it is even less surprising that in our time art and science should move into a totally new overt relationship.

"The quest of the artist is a quest for perfect freedom to comment upon the realities he perceives. To do this, he needs elbow room; he needs to move around. And to me it seems highly unlikely that the artist who makes a genuine comment on our times, with all their baffling complexities, all their fearsome potentialities, and all their startling promises—that the artist dealing with these realities is going to be content to limit himself to the marble of classical Greece or, in painting, to the qualities of opacity and translucence that the pigments and binders of his time made available to Raphael. The artist wants primarily to speak to his contemporaries and takes his chances on surviving; and is getting a bit more insistent on this point, not because he wants to be difficult, but because he wants to be relevant.

3-2. Portrait of Dr. Stanton. (Courtesy CBS.)

"But what is new in our time is that science has developed new methods of creating and using light and that artists are taking hold of these and making light a vital ingredient in itself. It is no longer something to be represented, no longer a pallid adjunct for illumination. It is a new material. Art has always wanted to have being, not just meaning. The versatility and range of new light techniques is making this a far less elusive goal than in the past—even though the present, and very early, phases of luminism as an art form may still leave us, with our old habits of observation, somewhat bewildered. Until early this month there was in Paris, at the Museum of Modern Art, a truly remarkable exhibition, 'Light and Movement.' When I revisited this unequalled display of light and form and movement and sound last month, interest was so great that it was difficult to move freely among this collection.

"Kinetic art, making free, albeit sometimes uncertain, use of both the moving lights and the moving forms made possible by modern technology, as surely marks the beginning of a new chapter in the history of human expression as did the devising of the chisel in ancient times. And it has already marked, too, the opening of a new chapter in the interrelationship of science and the arts—perhaps in their interdependence.

"In the past year, two significant developments have occurred that can strengthen greatly the relationship of art and science through the agency of business and industry. One was the establishment of the Business Committee for the Arts, which would broaden the base of support of the arts by business. Proposed last fall by David Rockefeller, it now has the beginning of a professional staff and is already launching programs to provide such services as a clearing house of information on the arts for business, counseling to corporate philantropy in the field of the arts, and advice to institutions in the arts that seek such philantropic support. This organization has resulted from a deepened awareness on the part of business of its duty to support the arts better, to understand them better, and to employ them better in its own self-interest. Almost simultaneously another promising organization, called Experiments in Art and Technology, was founded by artists and scientists for, among other things, building an awareness among scientists of the artist's role in contemporary life, 'bringing the artist into an effectve, rapid and permanent contact with technical life, bringing the artist into an effective, rapid and permanent contact with technical processes,' and finding sources of support within industry for advancing these purposes for sponsoring technically realizable projects involving exploratory use of new materials and methods. E.A.T.'s first exhibition at the Museum of Modern Art will take place next fall, with awards for 'the most inventive use of new technology as it evolves through the collaboration of artist and engineer.' Both these organizations will be supported largely by grants from American businesses, and they should be invaluable in giving new impetus to creativity in our time." (Remarks by Dr. Frank Stanton, then president of Columbia Broadcasting System, Incorporated, to the North Carolina State Art Society, November 29, 1967.)

GEORGE
dessart

DIRECTOR OF COMMUNITY SERVICES, WCBS-TV, NEW YORK CITY, EXECUTIVE PRODUCER OF *THE RESPONSIVE EYE* AND *THE WALLS COME TUMBLING DOWN*

The thing that gives television the edge on any other medium is the factor of the expectation of the unexpected.

DESSART. What is it that's unique about television? What distinguishes television, once it is delivered, is that it is the only medium, the only presentational medium, that does not require a specific environment designed primarily for it. It is the only medium we have yet designed in which it is possible for you to sit stark naked in front of someone in evening clothes. And this has profound implications. You are totally stripped of any necessity to react back—to present "the face to meet the faces that you meet." You can be totally free to take in what the person says [or reject it!]. Or reject it, yes. I think that this is what makes television such a very powerful political tool, and this is why it was so effective with the first McCarthy, with Joseph McCarthy. He could charm the pants off a snake in a face-to-face confrontation—but he couldn't do that on television.

3-3. Portrait of George Dessart, taken by the author. (Scene from the film entitled *The Walls Come Tumbling Down*. Written and produced for WCBS-TV by Merrill Brockway. Executive Producer, George Dessart.)

KRANZ. *Do you mean that television allows a certain objectivity and detachment on the part of the observer that a face-to-face encounter does not allow?*

DESSART. It allows the observer to be totally free of the necessity to consider any of the factors that have to do with the way the speaker must regard the observer. You in no wise have to dress up for the occasion. You in no wise have to watch your behavior. You are totally free just to receive.

And the other thing that makes television unique is that the audience does not come to the broadcast, as currently distributed in the home, with any degree of commitment. If you go to the theatre, you stay for the second act because you've got eleven bucks riding on it. . . . Even if you get free seats. You've made arrangements. You ate dinner early. You belted it down and you went off to the theatre and you had already decided that you were going to stay there until 11 o'clock . . . maybe you've got a baby sitter. This is the second part about television. No prior commitments.

We are very unskilled, all of us, in knowing how to read television. We don't really know what our reactions are. And we haven't developed tools for content analysis of the visual and paravisual elements of television. . . . During the [1968] Democratic Convention in Chicago, we sat there—you and I and millions like us—mesmerized by the set. Not quite believing what we saw before our eyes, but alert to what might be coming up next. And we knew that if we wanted to find out what was happening in Chicago, we pushed a particular button on a particular piece of furniture in our houses, and that showed it to us. Now it happens that's the same button that we push to watch *The Wizard of Oz,* or whatever else it happens to be. Certain habits of concentration that we bring with us in moments when we wish information on a particular topic, we carry over to moments when we wish to be entertained. So that we tend to watch it in somewhat the same way. . . .

This is the medium on which we saw Oswald murdered. This is the medium on which we saw Kennedy shot. You can't begin to know what's going to happen there next. Who knows? That's what gives it the edge on any other medium—a certain kind of attention that attaches to whatever it is on that set, even if it is an old Hollywood film made in 1950. The factor of the expectation of the unexpected which attaches itself to the medium.

3-4. Scene from *The Walls Come Tumbling Down*, showing Claes Oldenburg viewing one of his drawings.

Oldenburg: *This monument, for example, which is a set of giant—maybe twelve-story-ten-story-high—balls, rolling down the slope of Park Avenue from Ninety-sixth Street on into some sort of well, some kind of arch, or hole, which would be placed inside Grand Central Terminal. Then they would be carried back up to Ninety-sixth Street via the underground.*
When these things come down the street they go through the intersections without stopping—so that it's part of the adventure and danger of crossing Park Avenue to know when the balls are coming.
This is the adaptation of the balls to Central Park: If you consider Central Park as, say, a pool table, and these balls . . . well, one way would be to have the balls free and rolling. To be more realistic, they could have wheels, like the enormous structures at Cape Kennedy, crawl around the park, changing position. And if you live on the edge of the park, which of course would be painted green all around, you could see things shifting. Every time you looked out, the balls would be in a different arrangement. They could also be used for civic buildings, and housing—the city could purchase them, and they could just creep around.

Some people I know don't see anything funny in my work. Other people see the work as very funny, and think that that's the most important and civilized thing about it. I admire humor—I don't want to put down humor, because I admire it; I think it's one of the things that's going to save us. But this certainly isn't intended to be humorous. It's intended to be—and it's not intended to be—art. in a way. It's just intended to be important. (Taken from the sound track of the film *The Walls Come Tumbling Down*.)

3-5. Scene from *The Walls Come Tumbling Down*. Len Lye in his studio.

Now, this one is Blade. B-L-A-D-E. A blade of steel. It will be about anything from fifty feet to a hundred feet high. It will rotate, and reflect light too. And you'll hear the striker booming out. It's like an Aztec monument to the sun.
My work, I think, is going to be pretty good for the twenty-first century. Why the twenty-first?—this is simply that there won't be the means until then—I don't think there'll be the means before then to have what I want. Which is enlarged versions of my work. And big-scale jobs that will have to be housed in their own temples. For instance, I'll have a temple of lighting, with a sea serpent—150 feet long—raising up—shooting a three-million-volt arc of electricity through a cave goddess to a sun ball.
With me, I end up sometimes with a fancy structure in my work. See? And it could look like a Rube Goldberg. But Rube Goldberg is dealing with fun and games, hokey. I'm not. I'm forever, in my work. I mean it. No messing around.

3-6. Scene from *The Walls Come Tumbling Down* showing Les Levine in his *Star Garden* exhibit at the Museum of Modern Art.

Leonard Harris: *Les Levine's "The Star Garden," at the Museum of Modern Art—four room-sized squares of shaped plexiglass, their convex walls designed to break down the wall between you and the work, between you and your environment.*

Les Levine: *It also has the effect of bringing to you the information immediately surrounding the area, in that, if you look at it as you pass through it, you see the buildings that are the surround here. So what you get is the senation of your own physicality, plus the information around you—and you get a funny sensation, because for the first time in your life you see yourself moving in the environment in which you really move. I mean, you can't get away from the fact that when people see themselves in these reflections, and they see themselves changing from blue to red—well, it turns them on. They just look so beautiful.*

Harris: *Les Levine calls his material for these experiences "disposable art." "Since you can't wall-up experience," he says, "enjoy it, and once you've had it—throw it away."*

Levine: *I'm sort of, like, terribly concerned with getting rid of retentive elements in art—you know, keeping an experience around, because it was a good experience. It's very nice to have good experiences, but it's very bad to want to have the same good experiences forever.*
I don't paint, and I don't draw, and I choose materials that are readily available today. And, in most cases, it's the easiest way to do a thing. In other words, I'd rather take a photograph of something than paint a picture of it. For me, the most exciting artists of today are the ones who make television commercials. I think television commercials are very fine art. (From *The Walls Come Tumbling Down*.)

3-7. Robert Rauschenberg, as seen in *The Walls Come Tumbling Down.*

Rauschenberg: *I tend to make what I would like to see. And I think that's probably the, well, the best excuse. I think I probably wouldn't even make things if other people were busy making things that I would like to see.*
It takes time to see really what you've got—because the combinations are infinite. I think my only tolerance for the present is: I know that I've got to do that in order to do something else. And I feel extremely handicapped, because—technically—it's very difficult. I want to do a piece that's responsive—that is responsive to as many things as a human being would be responsive to. Such as, whether it's raining out, or what time of the year it is, what the temperature is—the total vibrations. And . . . Oh, I'll do it. I mean, I'm sure, I'm sure that it can be done. And I don't even mind if somebody else does it, instead of me. But that's what I would like to see. (From The Walls Come Tumbling Down.*)*

3-8. Spectator at New York City exhibit operating Rauschenberg work entitled *Revolvers*. Scene from *The Walls Come Tumbling Down.*

Rauschenberg: *I'm going to tell you a story. In one of my first shows I had a woman who was looking at a painting—it was a very large painting; it's the one hanging in the Met now. And she said, "If this isn't art, I like it." And what she meant by that was, if she didn't have to bring all those considerations in, if she could just get rid of all those things she was taught to think about, she could have a good time.*
Well, I am trying to do something different, but different in my own range of experience. (From The Walls Come Tumbling Down.*)*

BEARDSLEY
graham
COMMUNICATIONS CONSULTANT

The tools that man gives himself shape the reality which he thinks he observes.

Speaking of man and the machine

I have been much concerned for years about the man/ machine relationship, as it relates to viewers of television. And I modestly admit that I proposed that the Surgeon General perform a study entitled "Television and Health," at least four years ago, and now it's become fashionable. The things that aroused my interest were, first of all, an American Medical Association report that you can hypnotize people more easily over television than you can eyeball to eyeball. And I think that makes sense. It's plausible from your own experience. And the other thing, reported by Gary Steiner in *The People Look at Television,* was that people who watch television behave more like addicts than they do like habitués.

The difference is that if you have a habit and the materials necessary to this habit are withdrawn, you are nervous and unhappy, but you don't get sick—like tobacco. If you can't find your cigarettes, you're nervous and unhappy but you don't die. On the other hand, if you're on morphine and your morphine's withdrawn, you may die. You have gross physiological symptoms, rather than minor psychological symptoms.

The conclusions reported by Steiner were that TV-watching is more like an addiction than a habit. Now, if you couple that with the fact that everyone knows that, from an individual's point of view, from being in a deep hypnotic trance to as bright as you can get is simply a spectrum of awareness. There's no particular place where you can say the person is awake or the person is asleep. There's this spectrum of awareness from being in a deep trance to being as aware of your environment as you can get. And in a deep trance you're subject to post-hypnotic suggestion, which is extremely powerful. This is fully demonstrated. This says, then, to me, that when you're watching television, you're in some form of a light trance. I think this bears out everyone's experience. . . . When you are watching television you are at some level of awareness, probably not the brightest you can get and probably not the sleepiest you can get, but in between. In this condition you're susceptible. This is well established. People in hypnotic trances are susceptible to suggestion. Then, when you couple that with the fact that there are a billion

3-9. Portrait of Beardsley Graham, taken by the author.

For thirty years Graham has been involved in advanced technical planning and management assignments in pioneering phases of new technologies: commercial communications satellites and systems, independent research institute organization, missile systems, information-handling techniques and large-scale computer systems, nuclear weapons and power, radar and television. He is currently a consultant to and member of the board of the Communications Satellite Corporation (COMSAT). His work contributed significantly to the conception and passage of the Communications Satellite Act of 1962. He is also a consultant to the Ford Foundation, and he was a member of the board of the former Videorecord Corporation in Westport, Connecticut.

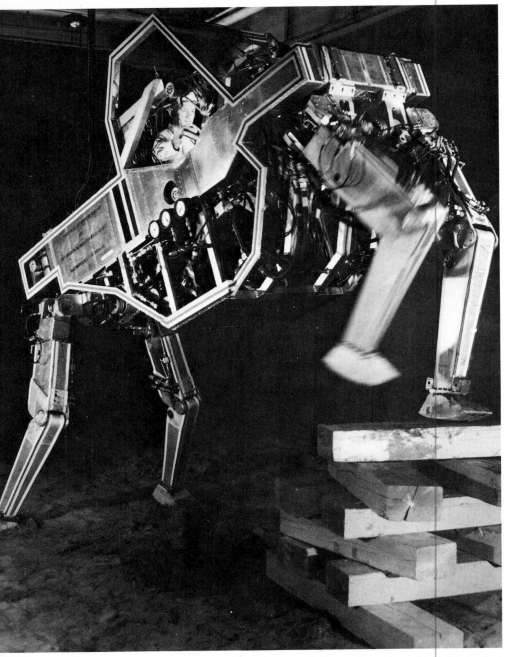

3-10. Research prototype of a Herculean quadruped machine, fabricated by General Electric Company engineers under a U.S. Army contract, was designed to spur development of equipment that will improve the mobility and materials-handling capabilities of the foot soldier under the most severe conditions. By means of an advanced control system, the machine mimics and amplifies the linear movements of its operator. The right front leg of the unit is controlled by the operator's right arm, its left front leg by his left arm, its right rear leg by his right leg, and its left rear leg by his left leg. The research prototype—11 feet high and 3,000 pounds in weight—was built by GE's Specialty Materials Handling Products Operation under a project sponsored jointly by the Advanced Research Projects Agency, Department of Defense, and the Department of the Army. (Courtesy of General Electric Research and Development Center, Schenectady, New York.)

man-hours a day in the U.S. alone spent watching television, you begin to wonder. Here's something that's going on that we need to understand about. And we don't. We haven't the slightest idea.

We talk about man/machine relationship, and human engineering, but the surface hasn't been scratched. We do a little bit about a few men in a very complicated machine. Like a man in a spaceship, or a man and a computer. Very complicated and complex simulators are made to train people to behave properly in given sets of environ-

ments, but has anyone ever produced a true simulation of the man/automobile highway system to understand that better? Killing 50,000 people a year. Nobody cares. And it's the same way with television. There are 65 million TV homes and the average TV set is on six hours and there are three people watching it. Here are tens of millions of people interrelating with a television set and no one has the slightest idea of what's going on.

Furthermore, the overwhelming impact of TV on the public's leisure time has been at the expense of other things. Like reading, going to the movies and the legitimate theatre, thinking, talking. The assertion that TV promotes togetherness is nonsense. You have never seen four people farther apart than when they are all four sitting there looking at a television program, each immersed in his own little world. They all see something different. They all relate to the picture in a different way. So they are completely separate from each other. They are not relating to each other—they are relating to a common thing, but the common thing looks different to each of them, like the blind men and the elephant.

Speaking of art and technology

Technology has always been an inherent part of art. For example: where did the pigments come from? And remember, in the early days the great artists were really great chemists, although they weren't really chemists in that sense, but one of the great problems was learning to make paint. One of the early artists was asked, "With what do you mix your paint?" And he said, "Brains." But there were all kinds of trade secrets in those days. Each of the great artists discovered the necessary pigments and he ground them up in the necessary vehicles and he experimented with ratios and various kinds of oils and various kinds of minerals. When the coal-tar dyes were discovered, this was an enormous step forward. Here was a technology that made possible all kinds of things—new art, costumes in colors, things that were unrealizable before.

The technology is basic to the art form. I guess that it would be fair to say that man cannot conceive of an art form that doesn't require technology to generate it.

I think that the computer is a tool for supplementing man's creative ability. Whether it's technology or art, it's unlimited. To me, the most exciting thing is not the design of new technology in computers, or even new computers, but the creation of synthetic images in computers; and the creation of art, if you wish, therefore, which will inevitably come out of computers. The computer is simply a method of doing things much more rapidly than man can do them—in many cases by the same random technique. You try a million things and one of them is all right, except that with a computer you can do a million things in a second instead of a million things in a million years. So the computer's ability to free man for building better computers, if that's what he ought to be doing, is unlimited.

TONY
schwartz

SOUND DESIGNER AND THEORIST, NEW YORK CITY

I have NO interest in developing an art form. I find when I have communications problems and solve them in their deepest form, they become an art form. Other people marvel at their art, but I'm just trying to solve a problem.

On radio

Radio is our most environmental medium. It's all around us. People not only listen to it, they sit in it. The question of how you use it as a communications medium is a different thing. If you take a frog and throw it in boiling water, it will jump right out. If you take a frog and put it in cold water, and bring it up very slowly to a boil, the frog will be perfectly cooked. How do you affect people with a medium they're sitting in? Change its temperature. Change its character quickly. That's one dimension. Add another sense to it. The young people have brought a tactile sense to it. That's another dimension.

On television

Television is the first visual medium in which the eye is used by the brain in the same way that the ear has always been used by the brain. It heightens our focus on the current instant, because the eye is used as a scanning device. We are always receivers of our auditory input. Until television, we had always been perceivers of our visual data. This is what creates the NOW generation—the fact that our interest in the current instant is heightened. Some interesting effects of this are that we become more volatile, more violence-ridden. We are a less patient society.

On print

The most passive animal in the world is the bookworm. That has nothing to do with what he is reading—murder mysteries or love stories. The medium makes him passive because it lays out the present, the future, and the past— all in front of him. Whereas in sound he has to recall the past, record the current fleeting instant, expect the future. This is how people dealt with communication in the pre-print era, in nonliterate societies and postliterate societies.
    I feel that the concept of the new being an extension of the old has nothing to do with science. It's a thing that 500 years of print has fostered in us. History didn't come

into existence as a meaningful study until print came along. Therefore we begin to think that "historical approach" is meaningful. It's just one aspect that the media foisted upon us, or developed in us.

On videocassettes

The first thing they will do is use the videocassettes for the old purposes. They always fill the new with the content of the old. This happened when they went from the silent film to the sound film. They still used the visual sight gag. Film is basically—the whole Hollywood era was basically —one big bookcase or stage, based on the book or based on the play. It was a word-oriented film world. Radio, basically, was a record jacket. Primarily filled with records. Records were filled with performers. FM is filled with AM. All I can say about everything is: "This is my opinion and it's very true." I feel also that ninety-nine per cent of the people, in all fields around us, are doing everything in "obsoletely the right way."

On the "content" of a medium

The content of each medium changes with each medium. In radio or television we may think that what the person is saying is the content. But I think we have to come to a totally new concept in radio and television as opposed to

3-11. Portrait of Tony Schwartz.

3-12. Tony Schwartz in his sound studio. The shelves on both walls are filled with thousands and thousands of tapes, which he has produced during his years of work with the medium.

3-13. Tony Schwartz at his taperecorder console. In the background is the window to the recording engineer's studio.

print. In print, you find people interested in and focused on what they put into their book or ad. In radio and television, the content is not what you put into it but what the viewer gets out of it, or the listener gets out of it. Or, more important, what the receiver brings to it.

On environmental media

We have to look at electronic media as environmental media,. more than other media. We have an all-at-once world with radio and television, in what they are to the north of us, south of us, east of us, above us, below us, etc. Therefore, just as I put my glasses into this case, with an electronic environment functioning as a surround, or a case, the real content of it is us. More accurately, what was formerly called content is now auditory and visual stimuli, and the content is the effect that that stimuli has upon us.

On multimedia

When people say, "I have seen a multimedia show," I think: Why didn't it work? What was wrong with it? If someone refers to multimedia, it implies that something is not right. It means that they are detached rather than involved, that they can separate the thing into two parts. We don't refer to successful things as multimedia. "Television" is multimedia. "Movies" are multimedia. One word is used when it's successful. I saw a *great* show. I saw a *great* exhibition. I saw a *great* movie, a *great* TV program. But the minute you say, "I saw a multimedia show," it means that it was just media gymnastics.

So multimedia is almost a negative word, like noise. Noise is sound you're not interested in. Sound pollution—noise pollution—is the effect of our electronic technology on our awareness of life today. We've stepped out of the "outside" environment. We are now paying attention to sound from media. We'd rather hear the man coming home from the moon than the neighbor coming home. His coming home is "noise." We'd rather hear Barbara Streisand singing on TV than a drunk singing on the street. That's noise. It used to be information.

I believe that one of the effects of cable TV and cartridges will be our becoming aware of the real pollution today, which is on radio and TV. Because we'll be able to step out of that environment into a new one. And once you step out of it, you are more able to become aware of its nature. We will then not be watching the least objectionable program. We will be watching the shows we want to see.

4 the extension of man's senses through technology

In the last six or seven decades, a series of technological feats has reoriented our conception of reality. First, the gas balloon and then the airplane transported the organism into an alien environment. Later, as aircraft became more sophisticated and powerful, the vantage point for exploring near space moved to the very edge of the earth's atmosphere. As the decade ended, orbital flights were replaced with the most audacious flight in recorded history. Television and photography provided a live, firsthand, vicarious record of this revolutionary view of physical reality.

These achievements have changed our conceptions of time and space. In spite of the fact that they have been primarily engineering and technical accomplishments, the impact on artist, scientist, and layman has been overwhelming. With the advent of satellite photography, man is now capable of exploring the far reaches of the universe with unmanned satellites. These vehicles will record events with startling accuracy and clarity.

Along with the movement into near and far terrestrial space has come a dramatic penetration of the interior space of both organic and inorganic matter. Here the technical surrogates are the electron microscope, the X-ray machine, the stereo fluoricon, and the mysteries of ultrasonics.

Keeping pace with man's widening perception of the physical universe, scientists are studying the processes of perception in man himself. Recent studies have resulted in greater understanding of the way man perceives reality.

As the Newtonian concept of space gave way to the Einsteinian concept, researchers became preoccupied with acquiring a more accurate understanding of the nature of the space-time relationship. Much of the work was done in the field of high-speed and slow-speed photography. The stretching and compressing of time through still and motion-picture techniques has clarified our understanding of natural processes that take place in a continuum of real time.

Finally, scientists have undertaken equally careful inquiries into the nature of our auditory, kinaesthetic, olfactory, and related senses, again to determine the inferences to be drawn about the human being as a perceptor of reality.

The Exploration of Near Space: The Atmosphere

Major S. S. Pike

Major S. S. Pike has been flying airplanes since the legendary days when pilots could recognize one another as they passed in the air. There were so few planes in the sky that everyone knew his neighbor. Shortly after World War II, Pike became a skywriter. These early smoke and vapor calligraphers were artists, using thin lines of smoke to draw pictures on the sky. They had to have a mastery of the ways of the wind—its velocity and direction, and, most of all, a sense of timing, to lay down the letters in a coherent sequence. An awed generation of groundlings looked up and watched the small biplanes, decorated with baroque flourishes, spelling out messages of relative insignificance. Pepsi-Cola inscribed by airplane puffs can hardly be considered an art form, but it did establish a new vantage point for the artist. When these early modest triumphs of technology made it possible to transport man two miles straight up from the earth's surface, startling relationships of scale and volume were experienced. The Abstract Expressionist movement in this country owes some of its unconscious motivation to these magnificent abstracted views of the earth.

The Exploration of Far Space

Dr. Peter Carl Goldmark

With the development of the satellite camera, the exploration of the far universe will depend to a large degree on unmaned satellite systems. Dr. Goldmark, former director of CBS Laboratories, has built a prototype camera that, coupled with other scientific developments, promises to provide ever-expanding reports on the unknown regions of far space. Goldmark's field sequential camera recreates phenomena, in accurate color, at very low-light densities. It has been used successfully in space flights, but an even more valuable potential is in probing the interior of the human body. Organic processes in a live subject may be observed, and medical men will not have to be content with meager findings of cadaver pathology.

Dr. Goldmark is one of the world's leading electronic inventors and innovators. He is responsible for perhaps 150 inventions in the fields of acoustics, television, phonograph recording, and film reproduction. The long-playing record he invented is now in its twentieth year. Another invention, the first practical color television, while not now in general public use, is an important adjunct in closed-circuit television, especially in medical teaching. And his development of electronic video recording (EVR) is described as being to the visual medium what the long-playing record is to sound.

The EVR device will "play" a color video picture through any standard color television. The development of inexpensive videoplayers is proliferating. RCA is developing a device that embosses holographic images on plastic tape; other firms are working on inexpensive videoplayers. In sum, the home videoplayer will eventually destroy the major television networks as we now know them. Video information will one day proliferate just as audio information did in the sixties. Smaller and more selective audiences will provide viable marketing opportunities. Inevitably this development will aid the scientist-artist, the young filmmaker, and the communications iconoclasts in general.

The Exploration of Interior Space

Dr. Vojtech Bystricky

Dr. Vojtech Bystricky of Brooklyn Polytechnic Institute works with what he describes as "a rather new tool of science," the electron microscope. A whole new world of viruses has been made visible in his studies. The electron microscope has opened the way to penetrating the structure of matter as far as minute divisions of the individual cell. Magnifications of more than 100,000 times are commonplace.

Even more promising is the recently developed scanning electron micrograph. Like a motion-picture camera zoom lens, it can change field size while focusing on a particular element of a larger field. Particularly congenial to the subject of art and technology integration is the avocation Bystricky has found in the images that sometimes emerge in his electron micrograph enlargements.

These visual puns drawn from serious scientific studies are a droll footnote to the subject of art and technology. It is refreshing to find that even among scientists, who pride themselves on their detachment, there is room for "found" art objects.

Dr. David G. Bragg

When we couple Bystricky's work with the electron micrograph to that of Dr. Bragg's use of the fluoroscope to watch events as they take place during medical examinations, the potential for exploring interior space through technology is impressive.

Dr. Lajos I. von Micsky

The exploration of the interior of a living organism is very sensitive and often dangerous to the system. In recent years Dr. von Micsky, Assistant Professor of Clinical Obstetrics and Gynecology, College of Physicians and Surgeons, Columbia University, and Chief of the Ultrasonic Division of Radiology, St. Luke's Hospital, New York City, has pioneered in the use of ultrasound diagnosis. Von Micsky has developed methods of recording on a cathode-ray tube ultrasound pulses reflected off interior human tissues. This technique allows live sonograms from de-

veloping fetuses in pregnant women. The sonogram is harmless to the fetus and to the mother. In this way, progress during the entire period of pregnancy can be safely observed and recorded.

The Exploration of the Perceptor (Knowledge of Visual Apparatus)

Dr. Bela Julesz

Dr. Bela Julesz was an electrical engineer in his native Hungary. When he fled to the United States after the unsuccessful revolt against Communist domination, he found himself stepping out of a time capsule that had been projected into the future. Amid the technological electronic progress in this country, he felt personally obsolete. His fundamental brilliance, however, enabled him to completely redirect his professional energies; he concentrated on studies of man's perceptual processes, a subject that had always interested him.

During this period, Julesz noted that the field of perceptual studies had not advanced significantly for over a hundred years, ever since the definitive studies of the German genius Hermann Ludwig Ferdinand von Helmholz. Julesz felt that the science of human perception had floundered on a technical flaw: the basic research tool employed had been simple line drawings shown to research subjects. Line drawings for perceptual study suffered from the fact that the human subject inevitably responded subjectively to the images.

A second disadvantage came from the fact that the visual reality with which we are confronted every day has a rich textural range from dark to light in a continuum of perceptual stimuli.

It was at this juncture that developments in computer programing, coupled with sophisticated graphic plotting devices, enabled Julesz to break the bottleneck in the perceptual field. Julesz used the computer to generate random-dot fields to be used in stereoscopic viewing tests. These computer-generated "fields" appear to the human eye as smudgy textured squares. They conceal within their bland surfaces, however, geometric shapes, which only appear when the subject views the paired fields through stereoscopic glasses. Suddenly the subject "sees" these shapes superimposed against a three-dimensional background. Through the elimination of familiarity clues with these computer-generated fields, Julesz is able to study human perception of depth and texture as they take place, not in the retina of the subject's eye but in the visual cortex of the brain. Thus, the scientist investigates not only the subject perceived but also the perceptor himself—man.

A mature adult's eyes are separated by approximately

three and one-half inches, from center of pupil to center of pupil. This separation enables the human being to perceive space. In attempting to simulate space, it is necessary to generate three-dimensional illusions.

Dr. Dennis Gabor

Convincing three-dimensional illusions using a two-dimensional surface are possible in the photographic technique called holography.

Dr. Gabor, "the father of holography," Nobel prizeman, 1971, made the contribution toward more sophisticated means of visual perception when he discovered how to reconstruct objects from their light-wave interference patterns. The interference principle was used by Gabor to construct the first hologram in 1948. Named after the Greek word *holos* (meaning "whole"), holography is a form of lensless photography. As the observer moves, he can literally see around the object.

The principle of holography is based on the use of a coherent, or columnated, light source. It embraces a unique combination of reflected light from an object and light reflected from a mirror. These two light beams are directed at a holographic negative—essentially a photographic film. Because the light that is used to illuminate the object and the light reflected off the mirror are of the same frequency, they create what is called an interference pattern when they bombard the holographic negative. The interference is obviously the difference between the light reflected from the mirror—which is of a single wave length and has not been distorted by any three-dimensional surface—and the light that is reflected off the interstices of the three-dimensional object being photographed. The amazing hologram itself records this interference pattern in such a way on its surface as to reconstruct in its entirety the optical information that has been sent to it by the object and the mirror.

Dr. Lawrence H. Lin

Holography has many applications in science, technology, and the arts. Dr. Lin, a member of the technical staff at Bell Laboratories and a holography expert, outlined the steps that might be followed in a design research problem. A piece of metal could be photographed holographically before stress, and at significant stages under stress, until fracture. The holograms superimposed one upon the other would present a full three-dimensional image of the entire stress cycle.

Recently, panoramic holography was perfected for producing three-dimensional images with unlimited depth to give large or small structures life-size appearance. Gabor is enthusiastic about its usefulness, particularly with his most recent invention: large-scale, three-dimensional holographic motion pictures.

Faber Birren

If Julesz can bypass the retinal image and measure human perception in the visual cortex of the brain, while Gabor can completely confound our concept of visual reality with a holographically perfect counterfeit, what doubt must we still have about our ability to perceive the "truth" about what we see?

Faber Birren has spent his life seeking to answer these questions. Apparently there is still a large measure of scientific conjecture as to how much our emotional and psychological biases affect our perceptions of reality. Birren has limited his research to only one aspect of human perception—the science of color. He has found that even in this limted factor of perception, the unconscious and the subjective play a very large part. For example, he has discovered that a certain color in a room will elicit significant and measurably consistent reactions on the part of those who inhabit that environment. Birren's work and the interview contained in this chapter have much to contribute to our exploration of man's perceptual apparatus. In the larger context, the work of Julesz, Gabor, and Birren break new ground in the extension of man's senses through technology.

The Exploration of The Space/Time Relationship

Increasing accuracy is possible in the study of natural phenomena through sophisticated photographic techniques. Time can be extended with slow-motion and high-speed methods, or contracted with time-lapse processes. The potential for examining hitherto unobservable time-space relationships is tremendous.

Dr. William M. Harlow

William M. Harlow, Professor Emeritus of The New York State College of Environmental Science and Forestry at Syracuse, New York, is known around the world for his pioneering motion-picture studies, particularly in the field of time-lapse photography. He made the first of more than thirty films, *Time-Lapse Study of Growing Trees,* in 1952. His studies have aesthetic as well as scientific values, with implications for art and technology integration.

R. Wayne Anderson

R. Wayne Anderson, research photographer for the Dow Chemical Company, believes that there is a need for an artist's approach to scientific photographic problems. His work is in the area of ultra-high-speed or extreme-slow-motion photography. Segments of his high-speed photography have approached the range of several million frames per second. Only an infinitesimal fraction of a second is photographed, but, projected over the entire span of a second, the number of potential frames is phennomenal.

Again, modern technology opens windows wide on man's environment and offers new vistas for the scientist-artist.

The Exploration of Auditory Phenomena

Dr. Lawrence G. Kersta

Lawrence G. Kersta studied electrical engineering as an undergraduate, took a master's degree in physics, and worked in communications research for Bell Laboratories before entering into his major and consuming interest: speech and sound analysis. Dr. Kersta spent a major part of his career in experimentation with the spectrograph, a device that enables the scientist to investigate short segments of sound in the form of visual bar and contour spectrograms. This graphlike image of sound is rendered on a revolving drum with a penlike stylus.

Kersta has evolved the theory that the way in which a human being forms words is unique to each individual, in the same manner that his fingerprints are unique. It is not his intention, he says, to substitute the voiceprint for the fingerprint as a means of identification; they are two entirely different means and are used for different purposes.

Still, Kersta's theories have received support from police officials. In several landmark cases, his testimony as an expert witness has been accepted as a new method of positive identification.

More importantly, Kersta has applied his finding to medical research. Teamed with a surgeon, he has investigated the possibility of using the spectrograph to diagnose heart murmurs, with a view to eliminating the necessity for exploratory surgery. He has also worked with psychiatrists in revealing the hidden emotions of schizophrenic patients through the imprinting of speech patterns.

Another sensory faculty that has been extended through technology is that of touch. An anthropomorphic machine created by General Electric amplifies the power and scope of a man's legs and arms. Beardsley Graham points out that the notion of a machine that extends the capability of the human musculature is a very old one, and often has been the subject of science fiction. The device could be extremely small—"an electroscope slide picking a cell apart"—or very large—"charging around the moon"—directed in each case by its human manipulator.

As for the olfactory sense, technology has found ways of detecting a diversity of scents and odors. The United States Army has already made frightening use of these techniques to seek out and destroy military enemies.

Interviews

Interviews with the personalities discussed in this chapter follow. Photographs illustrate the subject matter of the interviews and the theme of the chapter.

MAJOR S. S.
pike

SKYWRITER, NEW YORK CITY

Where has the weather gone to?
What has happened to the clear skies?

KRANZ. *You have been intimately involved with all kinds of graphic devices, using airplanes and signs. What do you think is the future of this field?*

PIKE. That's all my life has consisted of. I've been at it for thirty-four years. The future of skywriting in general is —who knows? Of course, it all depends on the advertiser. I've been peddling sky advertising for thirty-some-odd years, and, of course, in the last six or seven years I've

4-1. Portrait of Major S.S. Pike, a World War II veteran who used his airplane shortly after the war as an instrument to make line drawings in the sky. This activity was as creative as the ancient art of calligraphy, for skywriting depends on the moment of performance. A mistake can never be corrected. (All photographs courtesy Major Pike.)

become a little less active—a lot less active, I should say.

We wait for inquiries now, and when they're interested enough, this is what we follow up. Advertisers today, I find, are buying so many, many mediums of advertising, that you never know. They know we're here; they know we can be used, but they have to have a place and a time for it. Skywriting doesn't lend itself to too many letters of copy. We can't put up names, addresses, and telephone numbers; we can't put up a lot of nonsensical reasons why you should buy the product. The only thing we're good for is trade-name recognition, or for slogan copy, and repetitious trade names. You have got to tie it in with a lot of groundwork. They should buy it over a long period of time and leave it up to our judgment as to coverage, as weather permits. We can do a tremendous job, but they don't want to do that, the majority of them. I gave up on this some time ago because they want to buy it next Saturday afternoon at three o'clock for some particular ball game. And the weather is not going to be right.

KRANZ. *As I understand it, there are only about twenty or thirty optimum days a year that you can—*

PIKE. I'll bear that out. We've got coming up now May, June, July, and August. Four months. I'll repeat that. If we can get two days a week out of those four months, average, that is going to be a good skywriting season.

KRANZ. *Is this true all over the country or just in the Northeast?*

PIKE. Pretty much all over.

KRANZ. *Really, Does it depend on the strength of the winds as well as whether the sky is clear?*

PIKE. Yes. It depends upon winds. Of course we can't work with cloud interference of any kind. But it seems to me that, following the weather as closely as I have for these past ten years, it's insidiously worse. It's gotten insidious over the past ten years. Twenty years ago, when we were working mostly for Pepsi-Cola, we could get fifty to sixty percent weather throughout the country. We would take advantage of weather from sunup to sundown. As time has gone by, I don't think that, if we did the same job today, we'd get fifteen per cent weather.

Where has the weather gone to? I don't know.

4-2. The skywriter's instrument on the ground. The Pepsi-Cola plane anticipated Pop Art.

4-3. A Pepsi-Cola skywriting plane in action. A World War II fighter plane is converted by Pike to the harmless endeavor of making letters in the sky.

4-4. Rigging device used for signs towed behind Pike's skywriting fleet.

4-5. A somber recollection of the past: plane demanding freedom for Morton Sobell.

DR. PETER CARL
goldmark

FORMER DIRECTOR OF CBS LABORATORIES, STAMFORD, CONNECTICUT

Peter Goldmark is as close as we can come in our complex modern society to a universal or Renaissance man. His curiosity has led him into all areas of visual and auditory communication. Formerly with CBS Laboratories, and now with his own communications consultant firm, he explores the frontiers of man's knowledge. At CBS Laboratories, he developed the low-light color television camera used for the first satellite communication of visual material from outer space. The first photograph of the earth taken from the moon, used a camera originally designed by Peter Goldmark.

He deals here with the impact of another development he is associated with: Electronic Video Recording (EVR). Goldmark has chosen the potential of the videocassette medium for the arts, and education, as his focus for this interview. Dr. Goldmark:

Here is where art and technology meet [EVR]. We have merely furnished the technology. The artist takes the information and changes it into an art of entertainment.

The great potential for EVR (Electronic Video Recording) is to become a new, easy, enjoyable form of learning, of finding information, an aid to training, to improving hobbies and sports. Just as the long-playing record provided new dimensions of cultural enrichment, EVR may one day become a new art form. The exploitation of EVR should be in creating something you can't do in any other medium. For example, if you can provide every physician with a way of diagnosing his patients' illnesses in a better way, such as by going to his EVR reference cartridge and locating the latest procedures and finds of his peers, he would become a better informed physician. The same creative extension is true for other professions, such as architecture, mathematics, bookkeeping, tax expertise, and many more.

Perhaps EVR may be the medium to make children look forward to a class. If you had the regular teacher give a class—say in English—twice a week, and, during that class, the children know that there is going to be roughly twenty to twenty-five minutes when the teacher is going to show part of the course from an EVR cartridge, and there we have Bob Hope talk about Shakespeare—he could convey more Shakespeare in those twenty minutes to those kids than any other person. The idea is that you should be able to afford that artist—that you should have a first-class director, the kind of director who directs Bob Hope or Jackie Gleason—and the kids will look forward to it. I think this the way it has to be. Classroom education is only one avenue for EVR. It can also be applied to the home, for correspondence courses, for teaching anything you can mention. Think of the creativity and excitement it can bring to otherwise dull home-correspondence courses.

You have writers and you have a director, and you produce an educational program just like a first-class television show. And it is just as important for those kids to sit on the edges of their chairs as it is for the audience that is going to buy that cereal. Here is where art and technology meet. We have merely furnished the technology through EVR. The artist takes the information and changes it into an art of entertainment. You marry that to the technology, and the two become a team.

4-6. Dr. Peter Carl Goldmark, inventor of the long-playing record, and, more recently, of the tremendously important new visual development electronic video recording, in his home laboratory. (Photographer, Sam Falk, *The New York Times Magazine.* © *The New York Times*.)

"Of the number of people born since the discovery of America, two thirds are alive today. Also, I am happy to say that of the scientists who ever lived, ninety percent are still living.
"I am referring to education in a broader sense: to teach people, in the fastest and most effective way, to get along with each other. I believe that urban, national, and international problems will grow as the density of population increases. The advances in science and technology have outstripped the slow changes in our behavior characteristics. An infant born 5,000 years ago, but raised today, would probably grow up to be indistinguishable from his fellow men. Yet what he has to cope with today is infinitely more complex than in pre-biblical times. What he would have learned then, during a lifetime, would hardly suffice today for a grammar student." (Taken from a presentation by Dr. Goldmark at the Fall Conference for New England Executives, MIT, October 17, 1967.)

4-7. The crater *Copernicus* photographed by NASA's Lunar Orbiter. Space scientists have called this the "Photograph of the Century." CBS Laboratories, under Dr. Goldmark's direction, developed the photographic scanning and imaging system used to achieve this photograph. (Courtesy CBS Laboratories, Stamford, Connecticut.)

4-8. Satellite photograph of the earth as seen from the moon. (Courtesy CBS Laboratories, Stamford, Connecticut.)

"Today, our most powerful tool of communication is television. On the average, television in our homes is watched five and a half hours per day. Why couldn't educational programs be made to attract the audience just as commercial broadcasting does? I am afraid the answer is that most educational television is not entertaining." (Taken from a presentation by Dr. Peter Goldmark at the Fall Conference for New England Executives, MIT, October 17, 1967.)

The important aspect of EVR is that it places a powerful medium—television—under the control of the user. He can select his own programming, play it when he wishes, and, for educational purposes, progress at his own pace. It's natural "do-it-yourself" medium, and there's one area where some day, if I have enough time, I'd like to dabble in what I will call "instant painting"—where you could generate abstract light and color images at home through electronic excitation. You could have large panels where you could, in detail or in large form, change your patterns at will. Conceivably, you could control it by sound, by random effects, or you could control it by yourself. This would be a lot of fun. You could program your painting by moods of the weather outside, or domestic moods. Yes, I think it's going to come, although it may turn out to be the interior decorator's nightmare.

4-9. Historic first picture of the earth taken from the vicinity of the moon. The picture, shot by NASA's Lunar Orbiter, gives a vivid closeup view of the moon's cratered surface, with the earth some 230,000 miles distant. (Courtesy CBS Laboratories, Stamford, Connecticut.)

DR. VOJTECH
bystricky

ASSOCIATE PROFESSOR, BROOKLYN POLYTECHNIC INSTITUTE, BROOKLYN, NEW YORK

BYSTRICKY. The electron microscope uses, instead of light, a beam of electrons. With the electron microscope, we look at our specimen—or, better, we penetrate our specimen with the electron beam, and we treat the beam in the same way that we treat light beams in the light microscope. There we treat them so that they go through ground lenses and this enables us to enlarge the image. Electron beams, of course, cannot penetrate lenses, because they are stopped by matter. But in the electron microscope we have electron lenses, which are essentially electric fields. The electron beam traversing the electric field is deviated in a very similar manner, and according to the same rules of optics, as light in glass lenses, and this enables us, in the electron microscope, to form an image of the specimen upon which we aim our electron beam.

KRANZ. How do you make the electron image visible?

BYSTRICKY. The electron image is projected on a screen coated with a material similar to the material in a TV tube. After selecting the object and focusing, permanent records are made on the photographic plates.

In the last few decades, electron microscopy has opened up a completely new world of ultra structures—for instance, the morphology of bacteria. Bacteria can be studied in the light microscope, but you don't see in the light microscope much more than the overall shape. In the

electron microscope you see details that were unsuspected before, because you can section the bacterium. You can make a hundred sections out of one bacterium. You can look inside. You can see where the inside has been infected by a virus, bacteriophage, which was known, but not seen, with the light microscope. The whole word of viruses was rendered visible only through the electron microscope. So in all fields of science, the electron microscope enables us to discover new worlds. Electron micrographs—or, rather, some parts photographically enlarged—sometimes assume very odd and interesting shapes. Some electron micrographs I have taken during the last few years (figures 4-11, 4-12) illustrate that point.

4-11. Kaolin particles on torn formvar supporting membrane. By chance, under the impact of the electron beam, the particles assumed the shape of a bird. Magnification: 10,000X. Taken with a Czechoslovakian electron microscope, TESLA. (Courtesy Dr. Bystricky.)

4-10. Portrait of Dr. Vojtech Bystricky, taken by the author. Dr. Bystricky is sitting in front of his electron microscope HITACHI IIC at the Polytechnic Institute of Brooklyn, New York.

4-12. Electron Micrograph. This is another enlargement of dirt and suggests the caricatures of Daumier. Particles of dirt of unknown origin stick to supporting grid of electron-microscopical specimen. Magnification: 100,000X. Taken with an ELMISKOPE electron microscope. (Courtesy Dr. Bystricky.)

4-13A. Scanning electron microscope photograph series: photograph 1. Front view of the head of the fruit fly *(Drosophila melanogaster).* Notice the prominence of the eye and the mouth parts *(proboscis).* Magnification: 180X. (Scanning photographs courtesy Lloyd M. Beidler, Professor of Biophysics, Florida State University, Tallahassee.)

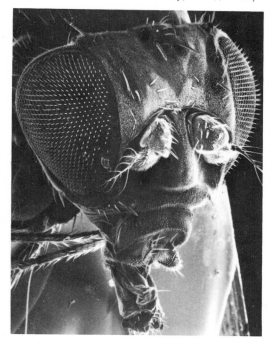

4-13B. Scanning electron microscope photograph series: photograph 2. The eye of the fruit fly contains many simple eyes *(ommatidia)* so that the total image is like a mosaic. Magnification: 350X.

4-13C. Scanning electron microscope photograph series: photograph 3. The facets containing the corneal lenses are grouped close to one another and sometimes setiform hairs appear at the interspaces. Magnification: 2,240X.

4-13D. Scanning electron microscope photograph series: photograph 4. Each facet appears to have a substructure consisting of small humps distributed over its surface. Magnification: 11,200X.

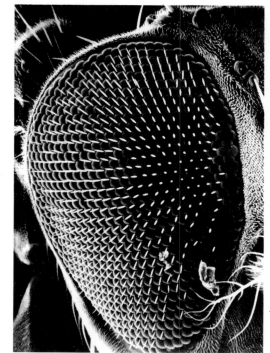

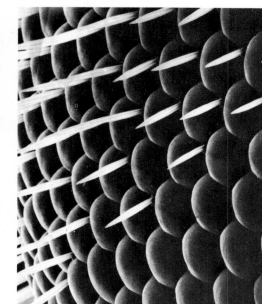

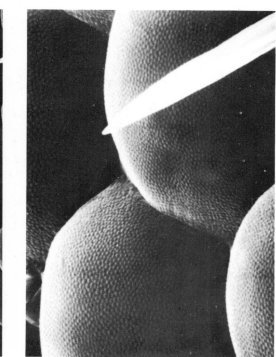

DR. DAVID G.

bragg

PROFESSOR AND CHAIRMAN, DEPARTMENT OF RADIOLOGY, COLLEGE OF MEDICINE, UNIVERSITY OF UTAH, SALT LAKE CITY

The difference between a fluoroscope and the X-ray film is in the image-recording system. With a fluoroscope, we're watching X-rays impinge on a photosensitive screen, watching events occurring as they take place. This is not recorded, except by your retina, whereas with an X-ray film we've replaced that photosensitive screen with a film and we are recording an image—a static event as it occurs.

We use a fluoroscope to watch changes as they are occurring. For instance, when we're watching the stomach work, and we're watching the heart and the lungs work, and we want to record any component, we have devices that allow us to insert a film and take a static event during a fluoroscopic examination. They are complementary, in a sense.

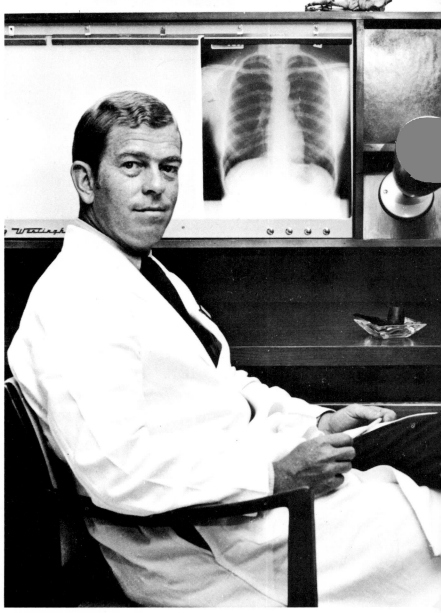

4-14. Portrait of Dr. David G. Bragg.

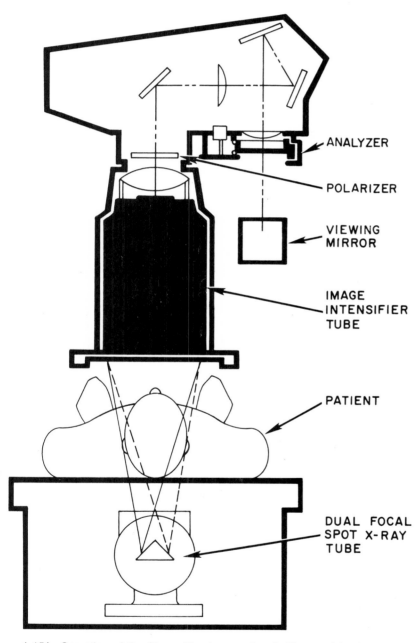

ANALYZER

POLARIZER

VIEWING MIRROR

IMAGE INTENSIFIER TUBE

PATIENT

DUAL FOCAL SPOT X-RAY TUBE

4-15A. Operation of the Stereo Flouricon system is illustrated in the above diagram. (Courtesy General Electric Company.)

The stereo system uses an X-ray tube similar to that used in stereo radiography, with two cathodes approximately two inches apart. Electrical pulses to the tube cause each cathode to fire sequentially, so one X-ray beam passes through the patient every 1/60 second. Because the two beams are slightly separated, each produces an image of the body structure from a slightly different angle, just as eyes do.

These two poralizers separate the alternating right and left images to the left eye and to the right eye of the viewer. At sixty pulses per second, flicker is imperceptible and the viewer sees one continuous 3-D image of the X-rayed area.

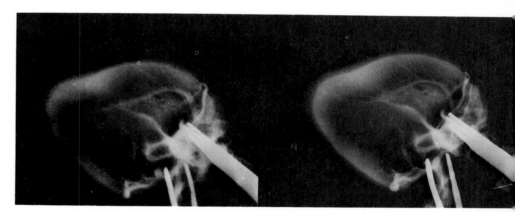

4-15B. The Stereo Fluoricon permits direct 3-D viewing of internal organs in a normally-lighted hospital examination room.

In addition to direct viewing, simultaneous rapid-sequence cinefluorography is possible, and nonstereo images can be projected on a TV monitor while stereo is simultaneously being viewed in the mirror.

This new development in stereo viewing, which can be added to the present Fluoricon system, is expected to be of great value in heart catheterization, and such surgical procedures as pinning of bones, pinpointing the exact location of foreign objects, and examination of the gastrointestinal tract.

DR. LAJOS I.
von micsky

PROFESSOR OF CLINICAL OBSTETRICS AND GYNECOLOGY, COLLEGE OF PHYSICIANS AND SURGEONS, COLUMBIA UNIVERSITY,
AND CHIEF OF THE ULTRASONIC DIVISION OF RADIOLOGY, ST. LUKE'S HOSPITAL, NEW YORK CITY

"I consider the searching sonic beam an extension of my palpatory sense."—Dr. Lajos I. von Micsky, discussing ultrasound as a diagnostic technique.

My involvement with diagnostic ultrasonics grew out of the desire as a gynecologic oncologist to furnish objective reproducible findings in staging the advancement of uterine cancer.

The accurate staging of uterine cancer is of vital therapeutic and prognostic importance: if the cancer is still confined to the organ, we operate, if it spreads outside the limits of the organ, we radiate. An erroneous assessment with a decision in favor of surgery over radiation will thus result in cutting through cancer and could materially contribute to an early demise of the patient. As the problem is further complicated by our almost complete lack of ability of confident palpatory differentiation between

tumor and inflammatory or radiation reaction, it became obvious that we are in need of more objective methods, which, in accordance with a general new trend in medicine, tend to substitute measurable physical quantities for intuition and accuracy for estimation.

Sonography, an imaging application of diagnostic ultrasound, is eminently satisfying those criteria. Since changes in tissue density or acoustical structure of the interior of the body are manifested in the alteration of transmissivity and reflectivity, to which the searching beam is submitted, the energy content of the echos can be utilized as a sonic monitor for a qualitative and quantitative survey of pathologic and physiologic process in soft tissues. The sonic tomogram is a map of the spatial and amplitudinal distribution of the echoes over a cross-sectional area extending into the tissues of the scanned body region.

The utilization of ultrasonic energy, in contradistinction to other imaging diagnostic methods currently at our disposal, is characterized by the complete absence of noxious physical and genetic effects to the ovary and developing embryo and thus can be performed repeatedly without any limits imposed by health hazards. This particular property of the method, together with the built-in acoustical impedance contrast represented by the amniotic fluid surrounding the fetus, established diagnostic ultrasonics as the most valuable tool for the study of the pregnant uterus. Sonography became an integral part of patient evaluation in the High Risk Obstetrical Clinic. The primary information requested includes: 1, determination of fetal maturity; 2, confirmation of post-maturity; 3, elucidation of the causes of discrepancy between actual uterine size and duration of the gestation by date; 4, correlation of the suspected presence of ovarian tumors or fibroids complicating prenancy; 5, plotting the position of the placenta; 6, accurate assessment of the feto-pelvic relations in breech presentation; 7, detection of hydrocephaly or anencephaly; and 8, confirmation of intrauterine fetal demise.

4-16. Portrait of Dr. Lajos I. von Micsky.

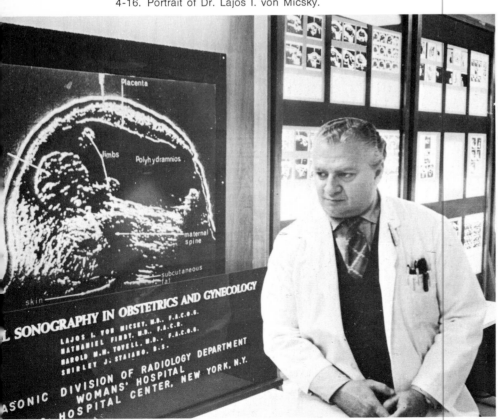

The gynecologic diagnostic problems requiring sonography, besides the oncologic ones already mentioned are: 1, quantative mapping of abdomino-pelvic masses; 2, differentiation of cystic from solid tumors; 3, differentiation between ovarian cysts, hydrosalpinx, and ectopic pregnancy; 4, differentiation of benign from malignant ascites; 5, localization of abdominal wall and intraperitoneal hematomas and abscesses; and 6, establishment of the presence or absence of intrauterine contraceptive devices.

Visualization of the non-functioning kidney, monitoring dimensional changes in the transplanted kidney, recognition of polycystic kidneys, uretero-pelvic obstruction and hydronephrosis, differentiation of renal cysts from solid tumors and quantitative mapping of bladder tumors are the primary indications for urologic symptoms.

Detection of cirrhosis of the liver, liver cysts and abscess, tumor metastases, acute pancreatitis, pancreatic pseudocysts, splenic cysts, and subdiaphragmatic abscesses are just a few of the upper abdominal pathologic conditions amenable to acoustical visualization.

It is apparent from the above, that the imaging applications of ultrasound are vastly expanding our diagnostic potential. As the light and electron microscopes can be looked upon as a means of extension of vision, I consider the searching sonic beam an extension of my palpatory sense. It can provide data not available by any other diagnostic modalities; it is a superb ancillary technique to other imaging laboratory methods and it is a preferable substitute or alternative when radiography with its ionizing radiation is impracticable or inadvisable. More sanguine advocates of sonography like Dr. Joseph Holmes of the University of Colorado Medical Center envision revolutionary future prospects: ''We may visualize the patient of the future systematically scanned by ultrasound while electronic recorders feed the information into computers which process the data and arrive at the diagnosis.''

While such computerized diagnosis is still admittedly in the realm of scientific imagination, sufficient progress in instrumentation and interpretation has taken place to move the basic concept out of the area of science fiction into science fact. With the advent of radiochemical tests for cancer, we will be able to register in the near future that a time bomb is ticking away in the patient's body. I can foresee that in the central biophysical diagnostic unit for the localization of the cancerous processes in the hospital of the future these patients will be studied by x-rays, isotopes, paramagnetic nuclear resonance, thermography, laser techniques, and sonography. I also accept that in order to narrow the diagnostic possibilities, these plethora of data will have to be correlated by and reduced to a manageable quantity by computer processing. The diagnosis, however, will still be reached by the physician for the reason that there is a basic distinction between diagnosis as a mental process and diagnosis as the decision reached. The mental processes involved in arriving at a diagnosis have been analyzed many times and the methods have been judged to be both scientific and artistic. One of these processes involves intution, an important factor in scientific discovery as well as in artistic achievement. Intuition bridges the gap between what is sometimes considered pure scientific technology and pure art.

4-17A. Scan shows fibroid tumor occupying the small pelvis, large fibroid tumor up against the diaphragm, and foetus within the uterus at 19 weeks' gestation. (Photographs courtesy Dr. von Micsky.)

This patient has been in the care of a well-known gynecologist for ten years, with known fibroid, but she refused surgery. Finally, at age 43, she gets married. Within five months, she has very severe pressure syndromes, and on examination, the gynecologist finds that the mass increased considerably. At this age, and with long-standing fibroid, you always have to rule out the possibility of a malignant degeneration, malignant transformation, one of the sarcomas. Under these circumstances, he scheduled her for a hysterectomy. But he did not feel completely right about it. There was the possibility of a pregnancy. He sent the patient down for a scan, and we see on the first picture a fibroid tumor occupying the small pelvis, another large fibroid tumor up against the diaphragm, and here between the two fibroid tumors, within the uterus, there is a gestation sac and a foetal head corresponding to a 19-weeks' gestation. Dr. Lajos I. von Micsky.

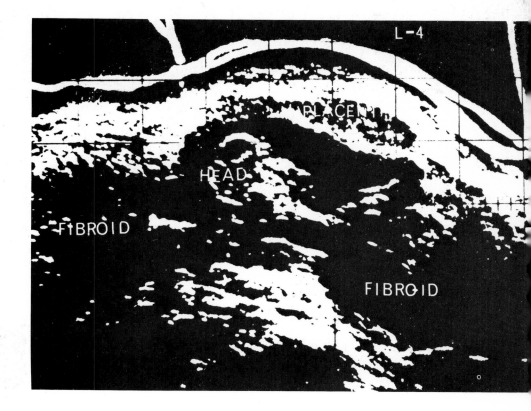

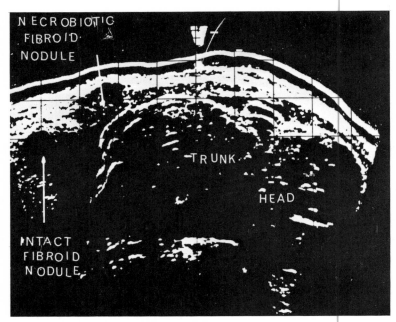

4-17B. Developing foetus showing head and trunk.

Since it was established that she is pregnant, she wanted to have the pregnancy. It was a very grave decision on the part of the obstetrician to agree to this because, first, with all these fibroids, there is little room in the abdomen for a normal pregnancy, and, second, it is a known thing that during the pregnancy, some of the fibroid nodules undergo degeneration and might get infected. She knows in advance that, with these fibroids, she can never have a normal delivery. It will have to be a Caesarian section followed by an immediate hysterectomy. Dr. von Micsky.

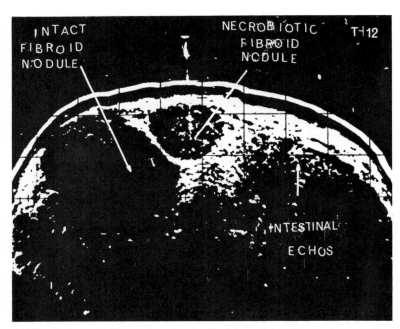

4-17C. Foetus at 26 weeks. Small fibroid nodule shows degeneration. Large fibroid nodule still intact.

On this picture we see the baby at 26 weeks. We can see the head and the trunk. At that time the patient is complaining of feeling pain. We see two fibroid nodules, the small one and the large one. What does it prove. We wanted to show whether the fibroid is still in normal condition, or is it degenerative. The small nodule shows speckling, which is degeneration, but the large nodule is still intact. Since it is just a small area, we convince the patient that it is painful, but to keep on with the pregnancy. Dr. von Micsky.

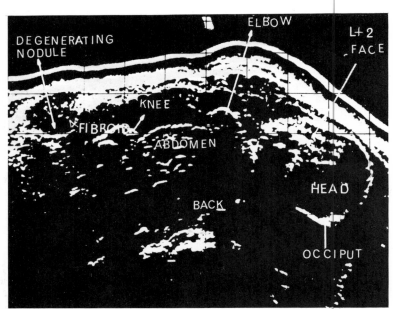

4-17D. Foetus at 28 weeks.

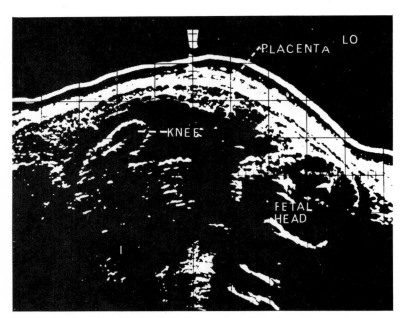

4-17E. Foetus, shortly before patient was delivered of an 11-pound, 8-ounce baby, by Caesarian section.

We go on now at 28 weeks. The black area within the head is the brain. Here we see an elbow, a knee, the abdomen, the back and the fibroids. As you see, some of the tumor nodules are degenerated. At 40 weeks, we delivered an 11-pound, 8-ounce baby, with a Caesarian hysterectomy, which meant that at the time, her uterus was removed. Dr. von Micsky.

DR. BELA

julesz

HEAD OF THE SENSORY AND PERCEPTUAL PROCESSES DEPARTMENT, BELL LABORATORIES, MURRAY HILL, NEW JERSEY

If you have a genie, you can have more creative wishes.

The artist and the computer

The computer, after the artist puts a problem to it, could execute it in seconds. The execution, how you draw it, can really be done in that time. It is a sad thing that people may have wasted a lifetime in the trivial task of execution. Now of course in the artist's case there might be a feedback, and you may change things. But in the scientist's case, he knows more or less in advance what he wants, and also when he has it. He can look at it. If he doesn't like these 10,000 dots on the board, he can change it. So if I had taken a year after I had the idea of how to get rid of the monocular clues, I could have done the demonstration of some of these ideas without the computer. I could have done a stereo image of 10,000 points—that is, 20,000 points by hand—but the mere notion of going into something so terribly complicated had prevented it. I found it ridiculous. Unconsciously I had already rejected it, and it never could reach my consciousness. You see, computers liberate man not only by being able to execute things but the computer liberates the mind unconsciously, too. So computers can do something in a creative sense.

The creative process is more or less unconscious, and there are hundreds and thousands of ideas whirling around in everyone's head. And then there is the censorship, or threshold, which simply rejects most of the things as impossible. If you are a science-fiction writer, of course your threshold is somewhat lower than if you are a scientist. Then you put it up and think, well, it would be nice if I had 10,000 people to help me. The computer is 10,000 people who do it. As a result of working with the computer, I am liberated. I have created ideas that never would have occurred to me because I had suppressed them.

If you have a genie, you can have more creative wishes. That is an important point for people who are so against the computer because they say it is only an imbecile calculator.

Your mind is completely liberated of little details of execution, of computation of subtleties, and you really have the global viewpoint. Now it is only the end result you are seeking.

I want to expand human consciousness, human percep-

tion. I want to create things man has never seen but is able to perceive.

A human brain is the most complex structure in the world and we are still unable to know what the single cell is. A single cell is probably another generation or two away from us.

Leonardo on a deserted island was still a Leonardo. We here, if our data link in the computer gets faulty, are back in the Stone Age. But all is okay—as long as the data link works.

Computers and communication will give access to the best brains in the world, in a sense that was not available before. For instance, how often would you wonder what a Churchill, or a Gandhi, or an Einstein was reading? Or what were their comments about a newspaper item, or some interesting things? Even these great brains could

4-18. Dr. Bela Julesz, demonstrating the method for viewing computer-generated images in three dimensions. "As a result of working with the computer, I am liberated. If you have a genie, you may have more creative wishes." (Photographs courtesy Bell Laboratories, Murray Hill, New Jersey.)

4-19. When the random-dot stereo image pair is viewed stereoscopically, a center square will appear in front of, or behind, the surround, depending on the direction of the mirror. Dr. Julesz and his colleagues have removed the familiarity cues present in monocular vision and are able to study stereoscopic depth perception more precisely, unhampered by the interference of memorized shapes, or previous visual experience on the part of the subject.

4-20. When the random-dot stereo image pair is viewed stereoscopically, a center square will appear in front of, or behind, the surround, depending on the direction of the mirror.

4-21

```
METHODS RECORDS OXIDIZE COLUMNS CERTAIN QUICKLY SDOHTEM SDROCER EZIDIXO SNMULOC NIATREC YLKCIUQ
DEPICTS ENGLISH CERTAIN RECORDS EXAMPLE SCIENCE STCIPED HSILONE NIATREC SDROCER ELPMAXE ECNEICS
SUBJECT PUNCHED GOVERNS MERCURY SPECIFY PRECISE TCEJBUS DEHCNUP SNREVOG YRUCREM YFICEPS ESICERP
EXAMPLE QUICKLY SPECIFY METHODS COLUMNS MERCURY ELPMAXE YLKCIUQ YFICEPS SDOHTEM SNMULOC YRUCREM
SCIENCE PRECISE EXAMPLE CERTAIN DEPICTS ENGLISH ECNEICS ESICERP ELPMAXE NIATREC STCIPED HSILONE
SPECIFY MERCURY PUNCHED QUICKLY METHODS EXAMPLE YFICEPS YRUCREM DEHCNUP YIKCIUQ SDOHTEM ELPMAXE
EXAMPLE GOVERNS OXIDIZE ENGLISH SUBJECT RECORDS ELPMAXE SNREVOG EZIDIXO HSILONE TCEJBUS SDROCER
COLUMNS SUBJECT PRECISE MERCURY PUNCHED CERTAIN SNMULOC TCEJBUS ESICERP YRUCREM DEHCNUP NIATREC
ENGLISH RECORDS EXAMPLE SUBJECT OXIDIZE GOVERNS HSILONE SDROCER ELPMAXE TCEJBUS EZIDIXO SNREVOG
CERTAIN PRECISE PUNCHED METHODS ENGLISH COLUMNS NIATREC ESICIRP DEHCNUP SDOHTEM HSILONE SNMULOC
OXIDIZE QUICKLY SCIENCE DEPICTS SPECIFY PRECISE EZIDIXO YLKCIUQ ECNEICS STCIPED YFICEPS ESICERP
DEPICTS EXAMPLE ENGLISH CERTAIN RECORDS SCIENCE STCIPED ELPMAXE HSILONE NIATREC SDROCER ECNEICS
SPECIFY MERCURY GOVERNS PRECISE QUICKLY METHODS YFICEPS YRUCREM SNREVOG ESICERP YLKCIUQ SDOHTEM
```

4-21. Words and nonsense words. We discriminate between the patterns on the left and the right because those on the left correspond to our memory of similar patterns seen in the past—the patterns make sense to us.

not afford to have a television broadcast every day. But, with computers, now very soon people can have disc files with all their readings and all their recommendations. Then I can just dial and find out what the ten people I respect most in the world recommend.

For me, the interaction between science and art is not through the gimmick. To give little devices—this obviously is what the artist thinks the scientist or engineer means to them. I am not giving them neon lights, and I am not giving them little whirling things and paints that explode, and I don't know what—the gimmick aspect of it. Now that aspect was also given to art when oil painting was developed by chemists . . . that had great impact on art and changed the format. But I think that when Leonardo invented perspective or when Newton had a new color theory, and so on, prisms and so on, this had another kind of influence on art. . . . I am saying that the best brains in every century were furthering the same cause, the artists and the scientists at the same time. The best art and the best science are indivisible. . . .

It is the same with *Homo sapiens.* His activity is the same whether it is a new wallpaper on your wall or a housewife's invention of a new recipe; it is the same process. It is only the goals that differ. The artist's goal is for a certain internal truth; the scientist's goal is for an absolute truth. It is only the goal. The creative process is identical in every *Homo sapiens.*

DR. DENNIS
gabor

INVENTOR OF HOLOGRAPHY, CBS LABORATORIES, STAMFORD, CONNECTICUT. NOBEL PRIZE WINNER, 1972

Dr. Gabor on the delights and uses of panoramic holography.

It is a curious phenomenon how our modern artists reject the gifts of technology. Once upon a time, the artist and the technologist were one and the same person. Jan van Eyck was the inventor of oil paint, and Giovanni Bellini must have had his own secret tricks with tempera. How Rembrandt would have loved the glowing colors of ultra-violet and daylight phosphorescent paints! Leonardo da Vinci dreamt of pictures that surround the viewer like a room. Now we could realize this, too, but would the artists like it?

Panoramic holography is a new offer by technology to artists. They can now create scenes in three dimensions, not just little cabinets or puppet shows, but, for instance, landscapes that extend to the horizon. We cannot create these by photography, because we cannot illuminate a whole landscape with lasers. The artist must build a model that, seen through a special lens, appears in natural size and as deep as he wishes. This is then holographed through the same lens, and the result is a picture that can be hung on the wall and gives the impression of a window, which opens into a real or, if you wish, fantastic landscape. Artists who do not want to imitate Nature slavishly will have a new medium for their imagination.

There are also industrial uses for panoramic holography. Architects often complain that the customer is angry when he sees the house. It looked quite different as a model. Now it would be perfectly possible for the architect to build a small structural model, which will appear to be the exact size of the completed building. The new holographic technique for producing three-dimensional color images with unlimited depth would accomplish this. Automobile designers will be able to produce small models of automobiles that can be looked at through "picture-window" holograms and appear to be the actual size of the finished product.

An interesting property of the hologram is that it imitates the memory process in the human brain. You can destroy a great part of it, but it comes out. You can break the holographic plate in two. You can scratch it. It still comes out. Similarly, you can destroy a great part of the brain, and memory still remains. Another thing: a part of the memory is enough to start the whole thing. You remember a few words of a song—out comes the whole thing. In most general terms, the hologram associates two waves—the object wave and the reference wave. If two waves are sufficiently complicated, you can associate them, so that you put one in and out comes the other, and vice versa. This is the basis of the mind's operation, you can associate things with one another.

It is a characteristic of creative thinking that one jumps a logical gap. For my part, I don't believe in conscious thinking. I have long observed that it's no good to try to solve a problem in waking hours. You think it over, then sleep on it, and it will come out solved. If I start thinking about it logically, I might figure out something on paper, but it's not fun. The fun is when it comes to you already solved.

4-22. Portrait of Dr. Dennis Gabor, taken by the author in Gabor's laboratory at CBS Laboratories, Stamford, Connecticut. Dr. Gabor is the developer of holography and has been called the "father of holography." He was awarded the 1972 Nobel prize for his attainments in the field.

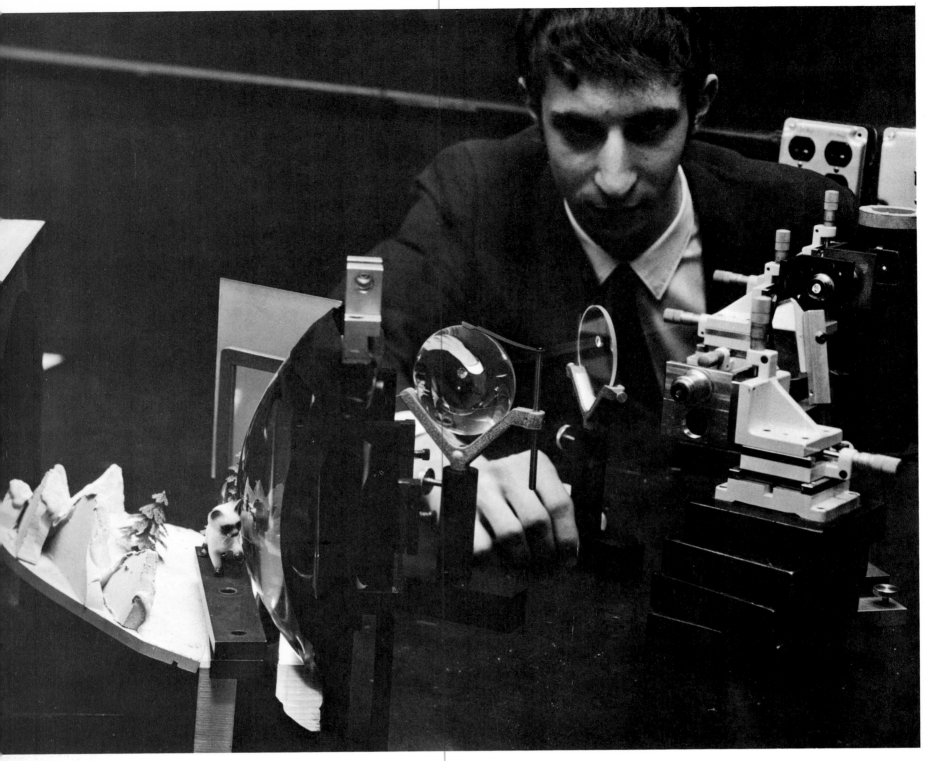

4-23. Gabor's assistant in the laboratory. The photograph shows the setup used for Gabor's experiment in three-dimensional holography. Note the set at the lower left of the photograph. (Courtesy CBS Laboratories, Stamford, Connecticut.)

4-24. One view of holographic image of the setup seen in figure 4-23. (Courtesy CBS Laboratories, Stamford, Connecticut.)

DR. LAWRENCE H.

lin

HOLOGRAPHY SCIENTIST, BELL LABORATORIES, MURRAY HILL, NEW JERSEY

I had the pleasure of interviewing Dr. Lin in his laboratory at Bell Labs. He devoted the better part of an afternoon to leading me through the labyrinth of holography technology. Many experimental applications of the medium were under study by Dr. Lin and his distinguished colleagues.

In the interview Lin stressed the use of holography for sophisticated process analysis. Because the medium offers such an exact replica of the full components of visual reality, it is possible, according to Lin, to use a "before and after" record to document ephemeral events. For example, it is possible to make a holograph of a solid metal form before it is placed under controlled stress conditions. Then, as the specimen is altered by artificial pressure, the changes in its character and configuration can be periodically recorded with a series of still holographs. Finally, when the test is completed, the developed holograph negatives can be superimposed for viewing. This visual "record" would give the scientist an unprecedented opportunity to study an event after the fact in a precise and accurate way. The implications of such holographic study techniques will affect a whole new technology.

During my visit Dr. Lin also demonstrated some of his research with "fly eye" lens systems which can be used in conjunction with holographic systems to recall data stored in microfilm data banks.

It was obvious that, although this new technology is in its infancy, its effect will eventually reach to holographic motion pictures such as Dr. Gabor has developed in the laboratory, and to three-dimensional videocassettes such as RCA has developed in the laboratory before the image is sent to the television receiver. Artists such as Robert Indiana have employed it for creative ends. These early efforts will soon advance to extremely sophisticated graphic imaging systems. With their pioneering work, Dr. Lin and his colleagues have opened the doors for these developments.

4-25. Dr. Lawrence H. Lin (left) with Dr. K. S. Pennington of Bell Laboratories make a multicolor hologram of objects in the left foreground. (Courtesy Bell Laboratories, Murray Hill, New Jersey.)

The hologram is made by combining two or more laser beams of different colors to form a single beam. This beam, in turn, is split into an object beam, which shines on the objects, and a reference beam, which shines on the photoplate. The pattern resulting from the interference of the reference beam with the light reflected from the objects is recorded in the emulsion on the photoplate. When the photoplate is developed, it is called a hologram. The object image is reconstructed in three dimensions by shining the original laser beam, or, under appropriate conditions, ordinary white light, through the hologram. The technique of making multicolor holograms was developed by Doctors Lin and Pennington, who also—in collaboration with Professor G. W. Stroke and A. Laberyie of the University of Michigan—made multicolor holograms that can be viewed with ordinary white light.

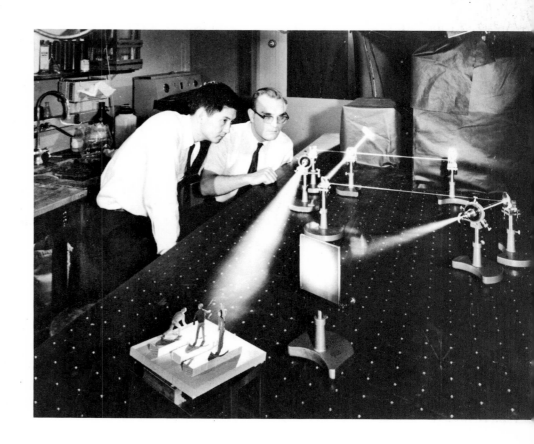

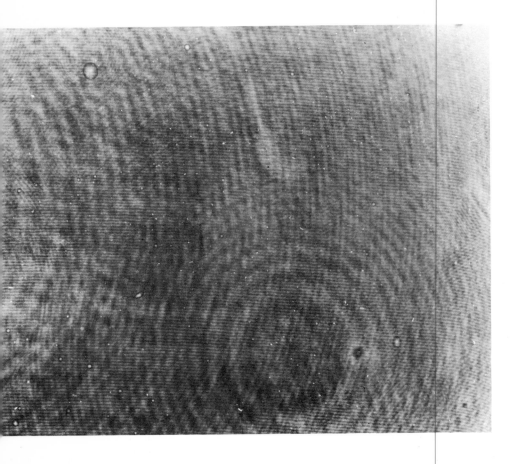

4-26. Photograph of a holographic plate, showing the characteristic circular configurations. If one were to cut one inch out of the negative and illuminate it with a laser beam, or with another light source, depending on the kind of hologram it was, it would still reproduce in three dimensions the entire image photographed on the hologram. (Courtesy Bell Laboratories, Murray Hill, New Jersey.)

4-27A, B, C. This illustrates the unique characteristics of the hologram, in that each of the photographs was made from the same holographic image. The camera or the viewer's eye moves, and, as it moves, you are literally able to see around objects that would be hidden in an ordinary photograph. You not only get a three-dimensional illusion, but the parallax changes as the viewer's position changes. (Courtesy Bell Laboratories, Murray Hill, New Jersey.)

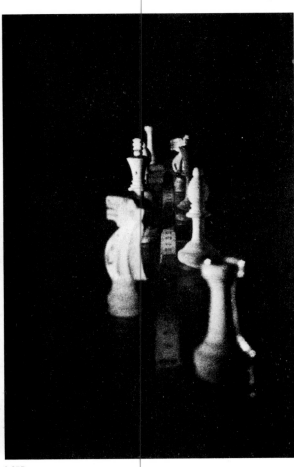

4-27A

4-27B

4-27C

FABER
birren

COLOR CONSULTANT, STAMFORD, CONNECTICUT

James Clark Maxwell wrote years ago that "the science of color must be regarded as essentially a mental science." This has been my interest. It began with a course on color theory that I took years ago as an art student. I decided then that I would like to devote a lifetime to the subject of color. In my middle twenties, I began to write on the subject. I became acquainted through this with a Dr. Flagg, who had done work on the application of color to hospital operating rooms. In those days, operations were frequently performed on the top floor of a hospital, with skylights as the chief light source. When efficient artificial light sources were developed, problems of glare were encountered. Dr. Flagg developed a shade of blue-green which complemented the tint of blood and tissue, and relieved glare from white walls. This was, in my opinion, the beginning of what might be called "the functional art of color," aside from the aesthetic. The use of blue-green in operating rooms had nothing to do with people's likes or dislikes. I began to combine my aesthetic training with functional training and to be concerned with the psychology of perception. On the aesthetic side, I have tried to introduce new principles of color, based on technical and scientific studies of the role of perception.

Things that the Old Masters did by intuition we can now do by actual knowledge of the way the eye and the brain operate. Op art has been concerned largely with the reactions of the eye. Perceptual art takes up at the point that the brain interprets what the eye sees. This then broadens out into physiological reactions to color.

The Atomic Energy Commission and the National Aeronautics and Space Administration are concerned with the influence of light and dark, day and night, on people who travel into space. We have a time clock within our beings, and if this time clock is disturbed, things happen. A lot of what takes place concerns light, a lot of it concerns color.

Psychologists have discovered that the human brain, relaxed, is a human brain in which the senses are constantly and moderately stimulated. You cannot hold any of the senses to a static condition; for instance, if you expose the eye to a white surface that does not vary in brightness, the pupil will open and close anyhow. The latest view is that the best environment is one that flows and ebbs, one in which things fluctuate moderately all the time. This is concerned in great part with the use of color. In a mental institution, for example, you might use applications of bright color on different walls so that, as you circulate through the institution, you would be greeted with constant changes in the visual stimulus.

In the field of art and the psychology of vision, you get farther and farther away from physics. Some very remarkable findings in recent years include the work of Dr. Edward Land of Polaroid, who proved that color can be seen when the light energy that actually enters the eye has no relationship to the perception of the color seen. In other words, he could make you see blue without there being any blue energy in the light source.

People who have taken LSD tell me that the first manifestation is the brillance of color. So we have, within us, a world of color. This changes our theories—we see that the world of color does not necessarily have to be "out there"—it is inside us, too. It is fascinating to me that the big opportunity—the big field of inquiry—is the artist's own mind, his own reactions to color. He doesn't have to study about wave lengths, or anything to do with physics, only his own human reactions, his own perception. He becomes his own laboratory.

4-28. Portrait of Faber Birren. (All photographs courtesy Faber Birren.)

Op art was the beginning of this. The artists began to understand the way their own eyes see things—not only that, but the way the brain interprets what the eye sees.

In Op art, the viewer has to participate. For instance, the conflict of red and green has little to do with the paints themselves. It has to do with the way they are put on the canvas, the relationships they hold when seen by the eye. You interpret these things according to the principles of Michel Eugène Chevreul, the director of dyeing in the tapestry manufactory of the Gobelins in France. His work on perception and on simultaneous contrast is a classic in the field of color literature, and greatly influenced the school of Neo-Impressionism. For many years he was more or less ignored by scientists, who were dealing with the same subject. Suddenly he is recognized as a key figure in simultaneous contrast, which is one of the fundamental interests of the Op Art school.

We know now that man operates best in a moderately changing environment. Forms of art are going to have to change. They cannot remain always static. They must be kinetic. This is particularly true if you are concerned with environmental art. The artist is going to have to learn a lot about control of the environment—and go beyond pictures and frames and sculptures on pedestals.

If an astronaut goes into space for long periods, we are going to have to create artificial day and night and sub-

4-29. What with the steel industry virtually eliminating air and water pollution in the making of steel, "visual pollution" is also being attended. This blast furnace of Jones & Laughlin Steel Corporation in Cleveland (called Susan) was once painted a funereal black throughout. Now it is in rich and appealing tones of green, maroon, gold, with bright yellow accents on piping and orange accents on railings and walkways.

4-30A, B, C. Brightness plus color will influence human behavior. (A) With brightness and warm colors like yellow and orange, attention will go outward and there will be physical stimulation. (B) With the environment reduced in brightness and with colors like green and turquoise, there will be less distraction and hence better mental concentration. (C) A combination of both brightness and darkness will be emotionally exciting—but visually tiring.

4-30A

4-30B

4-30C

4-31A 4-31B 4-31C

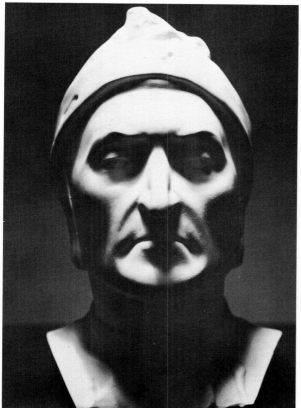 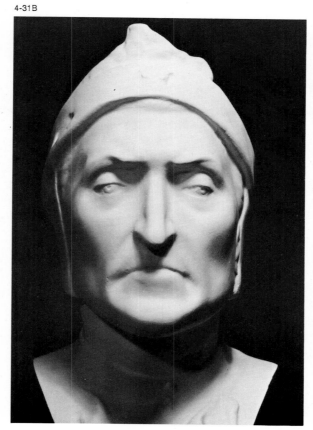 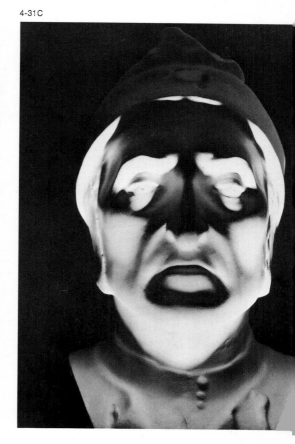

4-31A, B, C. Not light alone but direction of light. Here in 4-31A is Dante in heaven, in 4-31B on earth, and in 4-31C in hell. Experience of conditions that are natural and unnatural will have different interpretation.

4-32. Right side up, there are cups. Reverse top and bottom, and there are mounds. Same things can look different under different situations.

tle changes in light and color to make the body react favorably. Things around us are changing every moment. The light changes. The temperature changes. The air changes. This is the natural environment. It is not static.

As for the future of art, there must be a complete change of viewpoint, a complete change of attitude. Man has to deal with space as never before. He has to deal with things that are intangible, with unfamiliar reactions. The world today is unreal in many respects. The artist must be concerned with things that are not just reproductions, or even abstract forms. He must relate to the way the world may be as times goes on. I am confident that the more understanding there is of the mysteries of human perception, the more art will progress. The artist must be more and more concerned with total environments, the conditions under which men are going to live.

For years and years, artists have looked for secrets in nature. They completely miss the point. There are no secrets—there are no laws—there is no beauty *out there.* If they are there, it is because we, as human beings, put them there. It is all in the individual himself, his own noble perception—and that is where to look.

DR. WILLIAM M.

harlow

PROFESSOR EMERITUS, STATE UNIVERSITY OF NEW YORK, COLLEGE OF FORESTRY, SYRACUSE, NEW YORK

All over the world now, observers are taking time-lapse motion pictures, by the tens of thousands of feet, of such things as cloud formations that move over mountain ranges. By projecting the pictures over and over and studying them, one gets an idea of the air currents and weather. The U.S. Forest Service is taking time-lapse pictures of forest fires. They set up a camera on a high mountain peak and film the fire in the distance as it develops and spreads. They may get a record of what they did to control the fire. They can analyze it afterward.

Recording the opening of a rose, the time-lapse photographer is an artist. You try to get a sequence in which the flower appears to open at a somewhat constant speed. What you see on the screen is not natural as to timing. When filming growing plants, you may speed up the action from 1,000 to 5,000 times or more.

But suppose that you are not looking for something to show for entertainment purposes. You want to study corrosion over a period of time; you are looking for an accurate record. In that case, you set the time-lapse machine at a certain time interval and leave it there.

I used a constant interval with ships going through the Eisenhower Locks on the Saint Lawrence River. I chose a relatively short interval of four seconds. I counted it in my head and operated the shutter manually. I stood there for three hours—but I didn't do it without occasional interruptions from tourists coming and going! It took about half an hour for a ship to go through, and I'd get a rest until the next one came along.

When this footage is projected, the action is speeded up ninety-six times and people see a ship come shooting into the lock, the gates "snap" shut, and the WHOOSH, up it goes; the gates open at the other end, and WHOOSH, the ship darts out and away. So half an hour's time is compressed into about eighteen seconds on the screen. For engineering study, each frame or picture can be enlarged, the pictures arranged in sequence, and then you can see where everything was during each four seconds during the passage.

Another magnificent field for time-lapse photography is the crystallization of chemicals from solution. It may take weeks for the crystals to form. Among other things, you haven't the remotest idea how long it is going to take. And, aside from the entertainment value, it often has

a very important scientific value. More and more, medical and other scientists are using time-lapse photography, making important discoveries not possible by any other means.

(See color photographs of Dr. Harlow's studies reproduced on page 103.)

4-33. Portrait of Dr. William M. Harlow. (Photographs Courtesy Dr. Harlow.)

4-34. Dr. Harlow in his studio with the lighting set-up used in time-lapse photography. At the end of a chosen time interval, set on the timer, the machine turns off the overhead growing lights, switches on the photoflood lamp, and about three seconds later the motor, through a slipping clutch, turns the camera's single-frame shaft 360° thus exposing a single frame on the film. The timer then reverses the lights again until the end of the next time interval.

R. WAYNE
anderson
RESEARCH PHOTOGRAPHER, THE DOW CHEMICAL COMPANY, MIDLAND, MICHIGAN

Some photographic studies have done things to life science that could never have been done any other way.

There is a definite need for an artist's approach to scientific photographic problems, elusive phenomena that cannot be observed by the human eye. There are five basic failures of the human eye, and in all these failures photography can replay the event in a form that the eye can see.

The first failure is in seeing large expanses of land, which aerial photography can record and reduce to a size where the eye can assimilate them. The antithesis, of course, is micrography, where very small things can be photographed through a microscope or an electron microscope and enlarged many, many hundreds, or thousands, of times so that they can be studied.

The next failure is in seeing things that are too fast for the human eye. Anything over twelve images per second the eye sees only as a blur. By the use of high-speed photography, time is magnified and can be magnified up to several million times and played back at slower speeds so the eye can study what is going on. The opposite of the high speed is time lapse, for such things as the growth of plants, corrosion, and so forth, where you minify time by using exposures that are anywhere from eight frames per second to eight one PPM, which could mean one frame per month.

Another failure is that the eye cannot see things that happen outside its range in the electromagnetic spectrum, in the infrared, the ultraviolet, and the gamma regions of

4-35. R. Wayne Anderson with a Beckman Whitley Model 200, a simultaneous streak-and-framing camera used to record time and spatial data regarding detonation velocities. (Courtesy R. Wayne Anderson.)

opposite

C-33—C-39. *Time-lapse Series of Plant Opening.* (Courtesy Dr. William M. Harlow.)

These color illustrations show several stages in the opening of a cottonwood tree leaf bud. Time-lapse photography on motion picture film seeks to show such scenes at a more or less uniform speed so that the viewer can watch the amazing changes as the leaves emerge and expand. However, in nature, growth is usually not uniform. It may start off slowly, then spurt to a speed 10 times or more as fast as at the beginning, and then drop off rapidly as growth ceases.

This makes time-lapse photography of growing things a magnificent gamble, since no two plants develop in the same time, and therefore the only thing to do is to keep watch every few hours, and adjust the time interval as seems best from your experience with this particular sequence (here an opening bud). You may start out with a time interval of one minute just to get a foot or two of film showing the unopened bud, but you will soon change to something between 5 and 10 minutes perhaps. As the bud opens, you look at the footage counter on the camera and say to yourself "how long will this take to project on the screen, and will the action be too slow, too fast or "just right." If too slow, the audience is bored, if too fast, frustration results because there wasn't time to see what happened! This is why time-lapse photography is an art, and why so little good footage results from each 100 ft. roll of film, much of which may not be worth printing, and winds up in the wastebasket. But time and patience do yield exquisite sequences of leaf buds, and flower buds opening, seedlings germinating, and many other fascinating happenings in nature. Dr. William M. Harlow.

C-40. *Falling Drop of Water.* (Courtesy R. Wayne Anderson.)

This high-speed photograph records the oscillations in a drop of water after it emerges from a metal tube. It shows how the oscillations persist until all the energy in the drop is dissipated. Anderson used a water-hammer system to produce the discrete drops as the water flows from the tube.

C-41. Infrared aerial photograph of rolling hills and pasture near Livermore, California. Line pattern is caused by windrowing of cut grass for hay. Taken July 26, 1967 (late afternoon). (Courtesy Mark Systems, Inc., Santa Clara, California.)

TIME-LAPSE PHOTOGRAPHY,
DR. WILLIAM M. HARLOW

HIGH-SPEED PHOTOGRAPHY,
R. WAYNE ANDERSON

INFRARED AERIAL
PHOTOGRAPHY

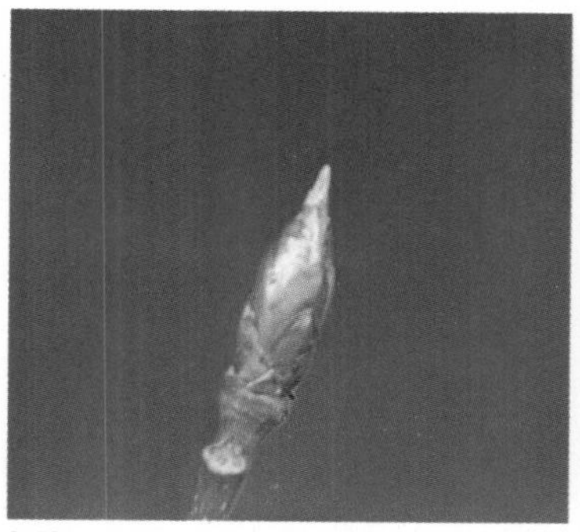

C-33

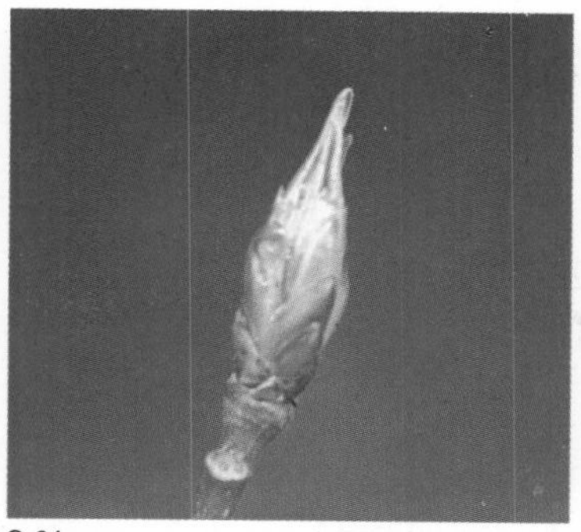

C-34

C-35

C-36

C-37

C-38

C-39

C-40

C-41

4-36A. *St. Jerome in the Wilderness.* Attributed to Angelo Caroselli, Roman, 1585-1652. Radiographs were taken to determine the reason for the recent overpainting in the background of the picture. The X-rays showed that the artist had painted over another picture. (Courtesy The Walters Art Gallery Baltimore, Maryland.)

4-36B. Detail of radiograph. At center one can see the head of a lamb and a book under the present face of St. Jerome. This method of working over other paintings was typical of Caroselli and is one reason why this composition has been attributed to him. (Courtesy The Walters Art Gallery, Baltimore, Maryland.)

the spectrum, which photographic systems are able to record for future study.

There's no question that the human eye is incapable of seeing many, many things that happen. It's been my experience that any time you do a job on a new subject— whether it's time lapse, high speed, ultraviolet or infrared —the job asks more questions than it answers. So you are always asking yourself: What happened? Why did it happen? Let's find out where we go from here. . . . Hopefully, I have completely quit predicting what is going to happen. I've been fooled too many times.

I would like to bring up the story of the four blind men who were asked to describe an elephant. One of them said he is like the trunk of a tree. The next said he looks like a locomotive. The next said that he had to look like a long tapered tube. The fourth said, no, that can't possibly be right. He's got a long tapered flexible hose. So I think that we're all blind when we get into these particular specular regions beyond the human perception. The mind can see things only so far as our eyes will let them. This has, in my opinion, very definite limitations. We're completely blind in many of these regions. We walk around just as the blind men. We preconceive these things because this is the way we feel they ought to be. But we don't know. We don't know until we see them.

Everybody has a preconceived conception of what's going to happen. Engineers, scientists, people of that nature always know beforehand. Well, the human eye and mind work together to disillusion you. You see something happen, so you try to put the two of them together. Nine times out of ten the camera makes a liar out of you. The mind can see things only so far as our eyes will let it.

Some of these photographic studies have done things for life science that could never have been done any other way.

(See color photographs of Anderson's studies reproduced on page 103.)

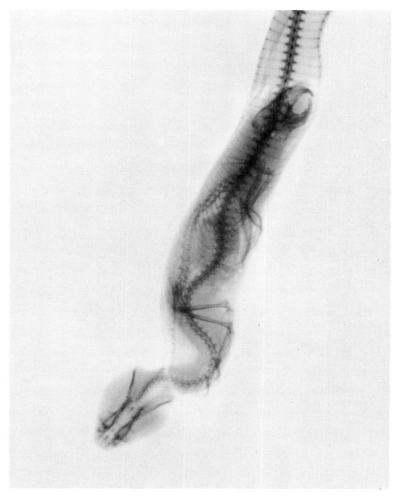

4-37. X-ray of a rattlesnake eating a hamster. (Courtesy The American Museum of Natural History, New York City.)

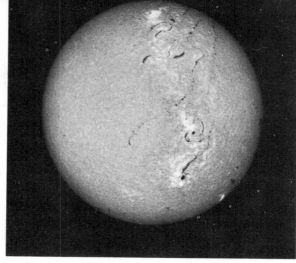

4-38. A photograph of the sun taken in the light of the red hydrogen line with a Zeiss (Oberkochen, West Germany) H-alpha Monochromator. (Courtesy Carl Zeiss, Inc., New York.)

The H-alpha Monochromator is in essence a filter that transmits only the wavelength of the hydrogen line 65630. The filter consists of a number of polarizers (calcite) in various thicknesses. Telescopes equipped with H-alpha Monochromators detect solar flares, which cripple communications and could be hazardous to manned space projects. Taken at the Wendelstein Observatory, West Germany.

4-39. Shadow photography. (Courtesy U.S.A. Aberdeen Research & Development Center, Aberdeen Proving Grounds, Aberdeen, Maryland.)

The shadow of a disturbance in air, such as the air flow about a high-velocity object, is cast upon a large sheet of photographic film by a point-source spark. The spark is set off just as the object is in front of the film. Sharp discontinuities in the flow, such as shock waves, are seen about the silhouette of the object.

4-40. Interferometry. Plane wave fronts from a monochromatic light source are separated into two beams and then reunited at a very small angle. (Courtesy U.S.A. Aberdeen Research & Development Center, Aberdeen Proving Grounds, Aberdeen, Maryland.)

If there is no disturbance in either beam, the plane waves intersect to form straight interference fringes. A disturbance in one beam will distort its wave fronts so that they are no longer plane. Now, when the intersections take place between the distorted wave fronts of the test beam and the undisturbed wave fronts of the reference beam, the resulting fringes will no longer be straight. The displacements of the fringes from their normal straight line positions can be measured and used to calculate the changes in air density around the object.

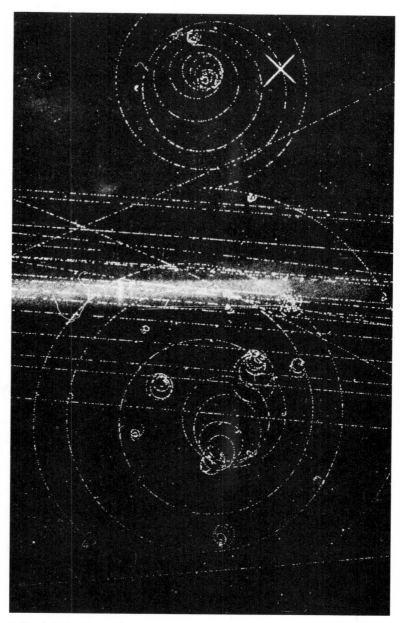

4-41. Bubble chamber photograph. An example of electron-positron pair production in the 80-inch bubble chamber at the 33-BeV Alternating Gradient Synchrotron. (Courtesy Brookhaven National Laboratory, Upton, New York.)

In the experiment in which this event occurred, the incident beam was composed of antiprotons. One of these antiprotons, interacting with a nucleus in the liquid hydrogen in the bubble chamber, has produced a neutral particle. This neutral particle, leaving no track, has decayed into the electron-positron pair, which have left spiral tracks as they give up their initial energy.

DR. LAWRENCE G.
kersta
SPEECH RESEARCH, SOMERVILLE, NEW JERSEY

4-42. Dr. Lawrence G. Kersta at spectrograph.

Dr. Kersta, President, Voiceprint Laboratories, Inc., studied electrical engineering, and later earned a graduate degree in physics from Columbia University. He worked for Bell Laboratories, almost entirely in communications research, except during the war when he worked on radar. Since 1945, his time has been spent in basic research in speech, which he now pursues in his own Voiceprint Laboratories. His tool is the *Spectrograph,* "which has been used in speech and acoustics research for over twenty years." He was one of a group of research scientists who designed it to meet the need for better measuring equipment in speech and acoustic studies. In the following interview he answers critics of the Voiceprint's validity for identification of individuals.

One of the things I have found is that critics of the use of Voiceprints for identification do not understand the legal definition of such an identification.

This is true whether the expert witness is in pathology, medicine, psychiatry, or science. All the expert witness does first is establish his qualifications as an expert in the field. Then his decision is given as his opinion based on his best knowledge and background. His opinion is, in this case, that this voiceprint, this unknown voice on this tape, is the same voice that has been identified on this one, and that, in my opinion, these are exactly the same voice. I have not said that this voice could not possibly be that of anybody else in the universe. I don't know any more than do the fingerprint people today who qualify as experts, get on the stand, and say these are the fingerprints of the same person. If you ask them, "Well is it possible that there could be another person in this world with exactly the same fingerprints?" they would say, yes, it is possible. It is not likely. In fingerprint identification, you do have a large statistical background.

All I can tell you is that I think the same factors in nature that produce the uniqueness in one's fingerprint also produce uniqueness in a person's vocal tract; therefore, it is my opinion that they are as infallible as fingerprints. But we will not know for a long time, until we have made many more applications. You have to realize that there would not be 175 million fingerprints in the FBI Identification Bureau today if it had never been used when there were only a few hundred.

So, you haven't proven that it is infallible, therefore you shouldn't use it? Well, what should we do, fold up and die, or shall we continue using it and build up this backlog? This is the only way to do it. I like to say that we are, in history, where fingerprint identification was sixty years ago.

4-43A

4-43B

4-43A, B. The words, "pictures of sound," are graphically displayed here on both normal wide-band and contour spectrograms. Lower frequencies appear at the bottom and higher frequencies at the top of the spectrograms. Intensity is indicated by light and dark shading. The normal wide-band spectrogram has superior temporal resolution. The contour spectrogram (4-43B) provides more accurate amplitude measurement. The spectrograms shown were made from the author's voice. It reads: "My name is Stewart Kranz."

4-44. Identify a voice: Which "you" has a double? These six voiceprints were made of five different speakers' utterances of the word "you." One of the speakers said it twice. Which two voiceprints are from the same speaker? Answer: The voiceprints at upper left and lower right. (Photographs courtesy Lawrence G. Kersta.)

4-44

A

B

C

D

E

5 the bridge between science and art

The Traditional Bridge: Architecture

Gordon D. Friedlander

Gordon Friedlander, former Associate Curator of the Burndy Library of Science in Norwalk, Connecticut, and currently an editor for the Institute of Electrical and Electronics Engineers, Incorporated, New York City, regards the domain of architecture as the legitimate ground for collaboration between science and art. When the functional relationship of the necessity for shelter is coupled with man's innate desire to embellish his environment, a true synthesis between engineering and art is achieved. Architecture might be termed "the legitimate ordering of space for functional and aesthetic needs." Architectural history is essentially a history of brilliant engineering and aesthetic solutions focusing on the environment. Perhaps this preoccupation with space and environment suggests a legitimate analogy to the intent of the contemporary intermedia and environmental artist; a desire to restructure our perceptions of reality, to make us more aware of our visual, tactile, and aural surroundings.

Louis Dorfsman

During the sixties, the concept of total environmental design was practiced by influential designers such as Louis Dorfsman at Columbia Broadcasting Systems. Working closely with Dr. Frank Stanton, Dorfsman developed one of the most compelling corporate images of the decade. The CBS corporate headquarters building in New York City became the focal point for this concept.

Every detail of the building's interior design was meticulously planned to give an ambience of aesthetic unity. Office layout, location of interior plants and trees, the selection of paintings and sculpture, the design on incidental items such as memo pads and executive cards, and, finally, the color and shape of the lowly ash tray, were all coordinated to create a total environmental unity. The conception was brilliant; its execution broached no compromise with quality; and the result was a personal triumph for the designer. It was hailed as such by its protagonists and damned by its detractors as an Orwellian version of hell. When the new building was opened for use, its reception by some CBS corporate managers was less than enthusiastic; in time, however, the functional beauty of the building and its accoutrements won over the detractors. Ultimately the most satisfying verdict was rendered by competitors: the concept of total design was imitated by many major corporations.

Contrary to this situation in the United States of the forties and fifties, industrial design occupied a vital role in Europe as early as the twenties. The Bauhaus School in Germany marked the return of the artist as a functional designer. Growing almost inadvertently out of the Futurist and Dadaist elevation of the machine-made object to a place of preeminence in art and poetry, the Bauhaus movement invested the utilitarian object with integrity of design and material. The William Morris tradition of hand-crafted artifacts for living, the principles of clean, crisp lines, the importance of function to design, were elevated to a new level of status. In the Scandinavian countries, this tradition was extended: a Spartan quality, coupled with respect for the integrity of materials and workmanship, became a trademark. To a degree, the same design concepts were employed by Italian designers; the product, however, was more colorful in a baroque fashion, warmer and more livable.

The importance and worth of well-designed furniture, appliances, and, in particular, automobiles, eventually penetrated the American consciousness, largely through the influence of television. Functional design successes, such as the little Volkswagen, challenged the American concept of built-in obsolescence. The "bug" worked; it ran; and it sold like hotcakes. The producers of objects for mass consumption had to pay attention. Along with the upgrading of design for functional use came an upgrading of the industrial designer.

An interaction of the design aesthetic and the engineer competence began to take place. The designer was brought into production planning early to advise on appearance as an integral part of the overall function. His role in an advanced technological society was established as an essential one. This climate enabled designers such as John Wistrand, a free-lance industrial designer who has distinguished himself with designs for CBS Laboratories and many other major clients in this country and abroad, to achieve eminence during the decade of the sixties.

The Traditional Bridge: Industrial Design

John Wistrand

The industrial designer is part technologist, part engineer, part artist, and partly mad from the conflicts of his trade. His profession has come into importance only recently. For many years the industrial designer was brought in almost as an afterthought, to make a pretty package of a product. Advertising had not yet succeeded in creating the yawning depths of consumer discontent that characterize the industry's success today.

Scientists as Collaborators with Artists

Dr. Max Mathews

If architecture and industrial design stand more or less as a traditional bridge between science and art, it is not strange that there is today a growing number of scientists and artists working in direct collaboration to create works of science-art.

The history of collaboration is an old one. Leonardo da Vinci was in effect a one-man collaboration, one of the greatest graphic artists of all time, and yet an outstanding architect, sculptor, mathematician, botanist, and poet. Perhaps he approximated in his time what Dr. Michael Noll calls "a new breed of people" in our day.

In Dr. Max Mathews, the scientific and artistic preoccupations are mixed in a measure comparable to today's growing collaboration between art and technology. He has been concerned with computer graphics from a technological standpoint, and with computer music from both technical and artistic standpoints.

With Dr. Lawrence Rosler, he developed a new computer language for composing computer-generated music. Mathews and Rosler found that conventional scores were an insufficient and inconvenient way of describing sound sequences to computers. Together they pioneered a graphic input system using a light pen on a cathode-ray tube. In describing the system, they indicate that this "information is transmitted digitally to a larger computer, which synthesizes the sound and reproduces it immediately with a loudspeaker." The computer program is flexible and enables the composer to alter his composition by simply touching the light pen to the cathode-ray-tube input for the computer.

Dr. Cecil Coker

Dr. Mathews has made these systems available to composers and artists. For many years he has collaborated with the avant-garde composer John Cage. At one time, he built the technical apparatus for a special composition that Cage presented with the New York Philharmonic Orchestra. Dr. Mathews' colleague Dr. Cecil Coker, a synthetic-speech researcher, has also worked with Cage. He directed the technical and electronic aspects of Cage's piece during the *Nine Evenings* performance.

The Artist and the Engineer: Experiments in Art and Technology (E.A.T.) Personnel

Peter Poole/Susan Edgerton/ Ralph Flynn/Claudio Badal

Today Dr. Billy Klüver's E.A.T. group holds forth in the very posh and modern Automation House building in midtown Manhattan. In the early days of the movement, however, things were not so fancy. During the period 1967-68, under Dr. Klüver's paternal guidance, a group of bright,

energetic, and modestly-financed young believers in significant collaboration between the artist and the engineer holed up in a downtown loft. (See figures 5-14, 15, 16, 17.)

At that time the author interviewed some of the early protagonists of the movement, namely, Peter Poole, Susan Edgerton, Ralph Flynn, and Claudio Badal, at the early E.A.T. headquarters. Here the group was busy organizing the Museum of Modern Art and the Brooklyn Museum shows of artist/engineer works.

They had learned from the *Nine Evenings* that engineering is not a spare-time occupation. In speaking of the establishment of Experiments in Art and Technology, Dr. Klüver noted that the conclusion that artists and engineers need to work together has been reached all over the world: in Europe, South America, Japan, and even in Russia.

"We have established a foundation with the purpose of bringing the artists and engineers together and to convince industry that they must open their doors to the artists," he said. "We now have a headquarters in New York where engineers and artists can meet. The ultimate purpose of E.A.T. will be to act as a transducer between the artist and industry, to protect the artist from industry and industry from the artist, to translate the artists' dreams into realistic technical projects. We also hope that we will accumulate enough experience to give help to other institutions who want to set up similar cooperative programs."

The plan is working. Experiments in Art and Technology has chapters in many cities. The E.A.T. organization was originally designed to pair artists who wish to work with advanced electronics and sophisticated imaging systems and with engineers and scientists who could give them technical advice. In time, the cooperating engineers and scientists often found that their interest far surpassed the role of adviser. They found themselves stimulated by the unusual problems they were asked to solve. Furthermore, they discovered that behind the strange facades of their artist friends were innovative and provocative minds. In many cases, the casual initial technical assistance led to genuine involvement with the creative process. This active collaboration was symbolized late in the decade with two landmark exhibitions, one at the Museum of Modern Art, entitled *The Machine as Seen at the End of the Machine Age,* and another at the Brooklyn Museum of Art, entitled *Some More Beginnings.* The entire Brooklyn show consisted of genuine artifacts of collaborative science-art. Each work was created by an artist working directly with an engineer to create a joint work of science-art. The Museum of Modern Art show had a small selection of the best work created for the E.A.T.-sponsored Brooklyn show.

Scientific Theories of Human Visual Perception Employed by the Scientist-Artist and the Artist-Scientist

The crossing of the barrier between art and technology is clearly seen in the work of Richard Anuskiewicz, an artist who uses scientific color data as a basis for his aesthetics, and in Gerald Oster, an optical scientist who nurtured a professional interest in optics into the active creation of optical art.

Richard Anuskiewicz

Anuskiewicz developed a remarkable technical means for creating highly saturated canvases. By juxtaposing very thin parallel and concentric strips of saturated primary colors, he exploited optical characteristics of color. For example, Anuskiewicz frequently employs the juxtaposition of two or more highly saturated colors, such as a red and a blue. The eye is excited where these colors meet—the effect is one of optical mixing which creates a new color mixed on the retina. This preoccupation with optical properties of color reflects the influence of Anuskiewicz's mentor, the great German artist and teacher Josef Albers.

Dr. Gerald Oster

Dr. Oster's training was in mathematics and physics. His doctorate from Cornell University was in theoretical chemistry. He was absorbed in his teaching and research when, in the course of an optical experiment, he was startled at the remarkable patterned effects he was able to achieve when he superimposed moiré screens. He assumed that these optical principles represented a well-established aspect of art literature and criticism. When it developed that there was a limited literature, he became interested in the science of the subject.

During the middle sixties, Oster was approached by Joseph Seitz, who was producing a show for the Museum of Modern Art in New York City. Seitz suggested that Oster enlarge his small moiré-patterned effects and put them in the forthcoming exhibition featuring optical art. Dr. Oster had the moiré patterns enlarged and silk screened on plastic. In some works, he superimposed two of these plastic sheets; as the spectator walked past these works, the interplay of moiré patterns produced a startling visual effect.

The Bridge to the Future: Computer-Generated Design

We have pursued in a rather direct line the areas where a confluence has taken place in art and technology. Perhaps we must now look in the direction of future collaborations—most significantly toward areas in which a new kind of practitioner will emerge, an artist-scientist capable of using the language of the twentieth century.

In this context we cannot ignore the importance of the computer as a tool for creating new art forms. The computer is the preeminent instrument of our time for extending the machine revolution beyond mechanical functions to the realm of storage and retrieval of all cognitive knowledge. It is rapidly approaching the level of synthetic artificial intelligence. "Hal" is with us. A young communications engineer, Dr. Robin Kranz, remarked recently, "The computer is waiting for someone to talk to it."

Dr. Carl Machover

At the present moment, computer-generated design applications have proliferated almost beyond belief. Developments in this field are reflected in the interviews conducted with Dr. Machover of Information Displays, Inc., and with Dr. Gerald Stoodley at the Grumman Aircraft Engineering Corporation.

During the decade of the sixties, a significant breakthrough in computer programming techniques created a remarkable extension for these machines. Most "second-generation" computers were programmed laboriously with individual program punch cards; at the other end of the system, the "readout," or "printout," giving the computer answer to the problem was rendered by a high-speed typewriter. In other words, putting information into the computer and interpreting the computer's response was very time-consuming. In the middle sixties leading savants in computer design, such as Max Mathews, Michael Noll, Frank Sinden, Ivan Sutherland, Steven Coons, and Carl Machover, to mention a few, developed several computer-programming devices, in which the computer input and combined readout could be achieved visually on the face of a television screen or a cathode-ray tube. The most famous of these is Ivan Sutherland's Sketchpad program, which he developed in his doctoral thesis at Massachusetts Institute of Technology in 1963. In Sutherland's system, a computer would accept a drawing, which the user would "render" with a light pen on the face of a cathode-ray tube. This drawing was immediately stored in the computer memory bank; it could also be modified at will with the help of the computer. Each change made by the operator was duly displayed on the same screen as proof that the computer had properly stored the change.

Carl Machover indicated the importance of graphic input and display systems to this writer; in essence, this development has opened the era in which any intelligent layman can use a computer without the need to understand programming techniques. Machover's firm has already designed a visual display computer system in which one operator can control the functioning of an entire oil refinery simply by opening and closing valves with a light pen on the face of a cathode-ray tube. Furthermore, the hundreds of annual development changes in terms of plant and equipment can be added to the computer memory system graphically as they occur. In this manner, the "map" of the system is always accurate and complete.

Dr. Gerald Stoodley

Dr. Stoodley has devoted much of his career to aircraft and engineering applications of computer graphic systems. For example, an entire prototype section of an aircraft can be "constructed" using a computer graphic plotting system. These drawings can be rendered in stereoscopic versions and viewed as three-dimensional forms by the designer.

A leading computer graphics designer reported to this writer the following rather alarming scenario: he suggested that the state of the art of computer graphic design is now sufficiently developed so that one design engineer could design on a computer graphics console an entire three-dimensional object, such as the body of an automobile. When the design was completed, the same computer could be programmed to drive a giant master die-cutting machine. These two steps are the most expensive components of mass production costs; as a result, this computer design expert predicted that if this technique were effectively employed, "it would take the profit motive out of capitalism."

Computer-Generated Art

It is not surprising to realize that with the development of graphic programming-consoles a new generation of artists would emerge. They are quite clearly science-artists: often they have been trained primarily as scientists. With the tools available, these men and women began to explore experimentally the creative potential of computer-generated art.

Dr. Janice R. Lourie

Janice Lourie is a remarkably gifted woman. She has been trained as an artist, with a particular interest in textiles. And yet she is also a skilled mathematician, and a leading expert in computer programming with IBM. This rather unusual duality of ability reached an interesting confluence during the sixties. Several years ago she noted the relationship between input programming for the Jacquard loom and its possible application for computer programming of textile designs. The Jacquard loom was programmed through a rather simple card somewhat similar to a computer punch card. This card progressed through a program device; it informed the loom of the particular operations it was to perform. Dr. Lourie noted this rela-

tionship. It piqued her interest to the degree that she began to develop computer programs to design textiles. She also realized the importance and potential of computer graphic display systems for programming the computer to do a much more sophisticated operation, namely, to store in its memory bank the full information needed to complete the weaving of a textile.

Dr. A. Michael Noll

Dr. A. Michael Noll, a research mathematician at Bell Laboratories, has developed a system for creating and displaying stereoscopic motion pictures using a computer animation system. The computer is used as a facile animation device. In this case the computer is programmed by a punch tape or punch-card input. Information is stored by the computer and, upon command, printed out on a cathode-ray tube. Each frame is photographed by computer command. This animation technique, controlled by computer and recorded on photographic film, obviously opens possibilities for executing extremely complex and laborious concepts on film, without need for human intervention once the program has been designed.

With the method employed by Noll and Sinden at Bell Laboratories, the computer is so versatile that it can simulate objects and movements before they exist!

Noll has used the stereoscopic computer-generated film to explore an interesting phenomenon: namely, that the human being perceives reality in terms of his particular visual apparatus system. In this context Noll recalled a two-dimensional world created by the nineteenth-century mathematician Edwin Abbott, in a remarkable little book entitled *Flatland*. Abbott's people saw only the dimensions of height and width; living in a flatland, they saw without depth. When these strange people were confronted with visitors from a three-dimensional world, they refused to believe in its existence.

To test his theory, Noll created a computer-generated program in which he postulated mathematically a geometric figure that exists in four-dimensional space. This is a difficult concept for a layman, even in an age when Einstein's theory of relativity has facilitated new understanding of time and space relationships. Noll programmed the object in a four-dimensional space. He then had the computer realize the four-dimensional figure in a three-dimensional stereoscopic film. I visited Noll at Bell Laboratories and was privileged to see, through Polaroid glasses, a stereoscopic projection of a four-dimensional object in a three-dimensional film. In due time, a strange linear figure appeared on the screen in full three dimensions. It rotated, jiggled back and forth, and tumbled over itself for several movements. I was able to see a visual reality reserved perhaps for only a few human beings in the millions of years man has existed on earth.

Noll has also created two-dimensional art, using a computer. In one magazine on computer theory, to which he submitted his work, he won a prize for the best piece of computer-generated art in that year. With the computer, he has analyzed aspects of Mondrian's paintings and reviewed some of the mathematical principles implicit in that artist's work. He has exhibited his computer-generated drawings at The Howard Wise Gallery in New York City.

Theodor H. Nelson

The idea of the computer as a willing genie to the creative mind has set the stage for developments that are beginning to emerge: developments that will literally transform the ways in which two- and three-dimensional images are created.

Theodor H. Nelson, a brilliant young computer theorist, self-taught and thus able to come up with ideas for programming outside the established trend, has developed two concepts that have enormous implications for computer-generated art. To these concepts, Nelson gave the rather playful names of *Xanadu, Hypertext,* and *Fantasm.*

Xanadu is a text-handling system, built on a computer, used for storing and shipping information ordinarily contained in printed matter, "putting the information on screens and printing it out very easily." His basic assumption is that in five or ten years we will no longer need typewriters, paper, or cantankerous editors. In their place, he envisions the Xanadu screen for text handling; a light pen to command a graphic display screen to which we may call any written information we desire.

Xanadu is a novel operating system, or monitor program, specially tuned to give sports-car performance on a computer display, allowing the viewer to rove smoothly through multi-dimensional structures, including hypertexts, animated pictures, and much more.

Hypertext is generalized writing, breaking out the forced sequences we have been stuck with for thousands of years. Hypertext intrinsically has nothing to do with computers, except that you can only read and write it with computers (just as flying to the moon has nothing to do with computers intrinsically, but you can't *do* it *without* them).

Nelson's Fantasm system literally staggers the imagination. This system creates on demand a convincing synthetic motion-picture image from representations of scenes stored in the system. With the Fantasm program, the user, who might be a Fellini or a Chaplin, can determine the setting, people it with actors, and then have them perform in precisely the desired fashion. This "performance" would be recorded on videotape or motion-picture film. Every aspect of visual reality—color, lighting, contour, shape, and mass—can be synthetically recreated with the program. In an interview with the author, Nelson postulated a fantasy use for his system: "Imagine if you will a real motion picture of Lyndon Johnson. The beginning of the

scene would show him walking on the White House lawn; this segment would be on actual film. With the Fantasm system, however, it would be possible to show the President suddenly sprouting real wings, flapping them, and then flying off into the distance. Every aspect of his flight would appear as real as the walking sequence; the spectator would not be able to tell that the flying sequence was a completely syntheic scene—it would be real in every visual detail." Nelson estimates that it would presently cost several million dollars to build the Fantasm system, but costs of computer mechanisms are going down fast. Ultimately such a system will be developed; the implications for the future of human-generated art executed by computers are unlimited.

Still, for all this ease and novelty, one questions the use of technology as a tool for works of art. The answer comes back, with increasing vigor, that for the first time in history the creative mind has at its command a reliable, benign, infallible, totally dedicated, energetic servant. In this light, and built into benign systems, which may or may not be the computer, it hardly seems a sinister threat in an Orwellian sense. In its present stage, it is obedient and disciplined. Once the computer is informed correctly of a given task to be performed, it will proceed without variation until the task is done—no matter how laborious, no matter how intricate, no matter how long it takes.

To the artist who wishes to explore projects that require great amounts of time with built-in redundancy of effort, the computer is already a well-proven asset.

Interviews

Interviews with the personalities discussed in this chapter follow. Photographs illustrate the subject matter of the interviews and the theme of the chapter.

GORDON D.
friedlander

FORMER ASSOCIATE CURATOR OF THE BURNDY LIBRARY OF SCIENCE IN NORWALK, CONNECTICUT;
CURRENTLY EDITOR FOR THE INSTITUTE OF ELECTRICAL AND ELECTRONICS ENGINEERS, INC., NEW YORK CITY

An artist should have freedom to experiment, but freedom does not imply license to run hog-wild, to tear down all the accepted criteria, and in a form that is more indicative of anarchy. This is what I object to in much of the so-called collaboration that goes on between, say, electronic engineers and the practitioners of Op and Pop art. I consider this to be a fad, because it plays upon sensory thrills, sensations of sight, sound, touch. These fleeting sensations are not durable things; they are not really tangible, they have no lasting quality.

We refer to the *Nine Evenings,* which took place in the New York 71st Regiment Armory several years ago, and most people today can't even remember what it was about, or what happened. To me, the *Nine Evenings* and other events, in what I call electronic gimmickry, debase the term Art and the definition of an artist, because any kook, apparently, who plugs himself into an electronic circuit,

lights up in all the colors of the rainbow, shoots fireworks out of his ears, and then collapses, is *ipso facto* an artist.

To me, a more proper and sound approach in this collaboration would be for the engineer to learn from the skilled and schooled artist his sense of aesthetics and then work in collaboration. You see, I turn the picture around because I feel that so many of the artists today are adapting their talents (media) to shock effects in these random patterns that lack any cohesiveness in concept and execution. This makes a mockery of art and engineering. Basically they should be for constructive purposes.

I agree that it has had an effect and an influence, but I do not agree with the premise in going along with it. The artists and engineers who continually harp on the sickness in our society are doing nothing to salvage it. They emphasize the waste elements and say that all art should reflect a lousy world. I disagree. I think that their assumption should be to try to reverse this trend, to show that there is some beauty left in this world.

There are many areas for collaboration between the artist and the technologist. Some architects, for example, have a very poor three-dimensional concept of proper site planning and grading. Their concept is to send in bulldozers and clear the land of all obstacles—including many valuable trees and shrubs—to accommodate the architectural design. I have worked with landscape architects on such projects. They have used site grading as a sculptural problem in three dimensions, and the engineers working with them do everything possible to save the natural topography—to make the best use of its valuable trees and shrubs and then to work the building, designs, access roadways, and parking areas around these natural attributes of the site. This is a wonderful example of the proper collaboration between the engineer and the landscape architect—who is really an artist—and the architect.

So many artists and electronic engineers are caught up in the idea that art has to have impact, to leap out and really clobber you, but some of the most beautiful works of art are static, quiet. They don't assault your senses; you come back to look at them again and again. That is why the *Mona Lisa* is timeless.

I think a rotating radar antenna grid has far more beauty than a Calder mobile—because that rotating antenna grid has a function and a purpose. It has power to it. One can get quite mesmerized watching that rotating grid. You realize there is something beautiful about this. It serves a definite technological purpose.

5-1. Portrait of Gordon D. Friedlander, taken in the Burndy Library of Science, Norwalk, Connecticut. Scientific instruments are on display.

5-1

5-2. Through the arch of the high contemporary ceiling, one views the patio. Friedlander stands in the distance.

5-3. Burndy Library, chartered in 1941 as a library devoted to the history and mission of science.

dorfsman

VICE PRESIDENT, ADVERTISING AND DESIGN, CBS/BROADCAST GROUP, COLUMBIA BROADCASTING SYSTEM, NEW YORK

CBS has developed a clear, well-articulated view of practical aesthetics: to maintain a unified posture for both the public and for its own employees. In light of the CBS philosophy, it would be extremely illogical, if not dissembling, to tolerate visual anarchy in matters of the working environment.

The CBS building, sometimes affectionately called "Black Rock," is generally conceded to be a beautiful example of contemporary architecture and technology. The enhancement of the working quarters within that elegant structure involved the simplest of design principles —some as basic as diligent housekeeping—of a different order of magnitude than those of the building itself.

One of our objectives was to bring an appropriately contemporary look to those seemingly endless ribbons of interior walls. The funds allotted for that enterprise were much more limited than is apparent. As I look back at the budgetary limitations, I see them now as something of a blessing because they created a combined challenge of imagination and taste. One route we chose was to purchase lengths of boldly designed fabrics at prices

of $5 to $10 a yard. Sections of the fabric were extracted, then framed and hung or weighted and hung. When placed in appropriate surroundings, these excerpts provided attractively bold decorative splashes of color throughout offices and corridors.

This sort of exercise in judgmental aesthetics is but a modest adjunct to the larger problem of interior design, rather than an act of creative invention. I consider my solutions to the allover problem of architectural graphics more personal and much closer to the graphic designer's contributive capacity. The decisions pertaining to the choice, placement, and arrangement of the architectural typography were particularly interesting to me because they involved a fusion of tradition and innovation. On one hand, CBS has maintained certain traditional letterforms and alphabets. The CBS logo is a case in point. On the other hand, there was the task of incorporating a typographic style consistent with the architectural spirit of a Saarinen-conceived, Roche-executed building.

Less visible to the general public, yet as important in every way, was the design of the day-to-day working materials used by the thousands who toil in the new CBS vineyard, as well as in its myriad annexes. These diverse materials, ranging from all the essential business stationery and business forms to attendant ephemera, were reformed into a coherent whole. Incidentally, the typographic relief mural in the employees' cafeteria has received much favorable critical comment, and I feel it has in some minor way established a mode of design.

To return to the general graphic program, the redesign of the varied printed forms required in the mountainous paper work of a large corporation not only improved their functional appearance but also had the happy perquisite of cutting the cost of many operations and procedures. A logically thought-out design program, it turns out, not only satisfies the eye and mind but also evokes a very salutary response from the more money-minded offices. Disorder, it seems, is a very expensive indulgence.

At the beginning of this interview I directed my comments to the more mandatory interior design requirements of new offices in a new building. There is another area that I think is worthy of some elaboration. I spoke of our objective to spread a forward-looking, contemporary motif throughout the CBS offices. In this regard we chose to add further dimension by the installation of interesting contemporary art—as much as we could acquire within our budget. We could have fallen back on the more ac-

5-4. Entrance to Louis Dorfsman's studio in the CBS Building, New York City. (Photographs countesy CBS.)

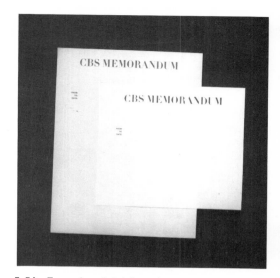

5-5A. Example of total environmental design. Louis Dorfsman's design for the CBS memorandum paper used throughout the various divisions of the corporation.

5-5B. Office door handle, CBS corporate headquarters, New York City. The design of each visual element in this building interior was carefully reviewed with Dorfsman by Dr. Stanton.

5-5C. Elevator push-button, CBS corporate headquarters. Example of unified design concept carried out throughout the entire building.

cepted, conventional forms, but we chose the more challenging course. The first reactions to abstractions or other art forms that were a little outside the popular ken revealed, as you might expect, incredulity or even mild hostility. They led to the usual quota of pithy remarks, the most prevalent being, "What the hell is that?"

Disbelief, dissent, or indifference eventually subsided, not through surrender but mainly through the mute insistence of the drawing or print itself. Human curiosity is a strong countervailing force against initial conservatism. At any rate, what was once considered some sort of ideological assault is now quite well accepted, if not admired.

How would I assess the whole CBS design project as a force in the quality of working life, as a CBS employee experiences it? To be sure, in the beginning we experienced an amount of anguish and strident criticism from employees on many levels. At first, what was thought to be clinical rigidity brought a spate of barbs and minor pranks. Some employees would move desks out of line an infinitesimal amount at a time, just to see how far the desks could be pushed until the provocation might be detected. Eventually this iconoclasm gave way to recognition that the new design environment wasn't so bad after all.

A new frame of reference imposes intellectual pain on some, but I am pleased to report that the present response has become considerably more enthusiastic. The he or she of the CBS work force now can accept a wide range of artistic effort more easily, without feeling uncomfortable. In point of fact, they now like what they see, live, and work with some eight hours a day. It would appear that the CBS design program, conceived to produce a unified environment of a humane dimension, has achieved the positive effect we had intended. Certainly it has made work a little more efficient, a lot more pleasant, and has created an environment that is both aesthetically satisfying and, perhaps, even stimulating.

5-5D. Elevator floor designation in CBS lobby. The type font used for these distinctive numerals is one of the two type styles designed for use on all CBS graphic materials.

5-5E. The employees' lunchroom tableware used in the 51/20 Club, the twentieth-floor lunchroom at the CBS corporate headquarters. Here, again, every detail of the building environment has been considered as a part of a total design.

5-5F. The simple, classic design of the fire-alarm boxes at CBS corporate headquarters. Notice the use of the CBS type face, here incised in brass.

5-5G. Elevator floor numbers for the CBS Building. Notice the two dots in the numeral "eight" as it is illuminated for floor 28. Dr. Stanton requested that Dorfsman design a special letter that would not require the "stencil" effect commonly employed for this letter. This unique solution resulted.

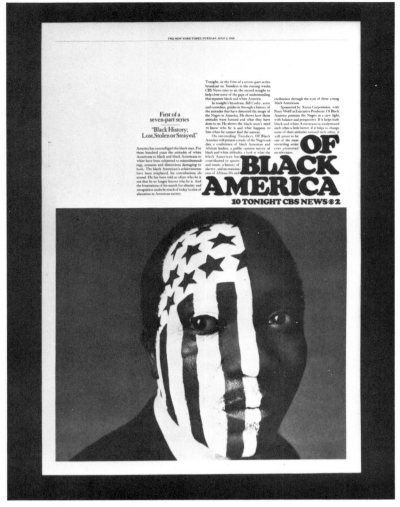

5-6. Louis Dorfsman's design for a *New York Times* ad for a CBS series.

5-7. Louis Dorfsman's book-jacket design for a CBS commemorative book on the Apollo 11 moon flight.

JOHN
wistrand
INDUSTRIAL DESIGNER

I have a fetish for making things simple.

KRANZ. *You are an artist, working in industry. The business demands must be at times considerably different from the aesthetic demands. Have you felt a pull between them?*

WISTRAND. True, at times there is a dilemma, but I find myself in a fortunate position, working as I do in a research laboratory. Designers working for consumer product companies are faced with many more problems. They are influenced by marketing people, by what was sold last year, and by what the competition is doing.

KRANZ. *Then these considerations might dictate aesthetic solutions that are not necessarily the most desirable ones?*

WISTRAND. This is a business, or a field, that came out of the depression. It is fairly young. There is still a lot to be done in the educational end. At one time, the industrial designer was a stylist. He picked the paint or sculpted the shape that he thought would be interesting. This is not enough. It should be total design. We should look at the project or product and try to analyze it thoroughly. We should design it to be a worthwhile device. We can't do this on appearance alone. The first impression is an important one, but we have to consider all the various areas that will make the device better, and make it really worthwhile.

KRANZ. *Then, implicit in the process is the necessity for considerable knowledge of other fields—engineering, possibly as a functional theory for rather diverse and sophisticated machines?*

WISTRAND. True, to some extent. I am not an electrical engineer, certainly not a mechanical engineer, but I think that it is important that we understand the mechanics as they relate to the human being—the man who is going to operate or use this thing. We have to be very much involved with the human factors. We may not be able to solve the mechanical problems, but we certainly could suggest that they be accomplished in a way that will make the machine better from a human engineering standpoint.

KRANZ. *In a sense you are talking about a collaborative effort in which you as a designer have an aesthetic that takes into consideration the ultimate function, and yet you are dependent on the engineer—an entirely different breed —to bring these two things together.*

WISTRAND. We certainly are not a one-man show, by any means. It takes many people to put together a really good product. The designer has to be the architect of this product, but he has to work with all the builders. If he can't work with the builders, he is not going to get the kind of result he's looking for.

KRANZ. *Some architects or designers come into public notice, and become celebrities—a Frank Lloyd Wright, a Buckminster Fuller—because they bring their own subjective aesthetics to a product. They put their stamp on it. The work that you do has a clean high style. Would you discuss briefly your own philosophy of design?*

WISTRAND. I suppose it would be that by eliminating, you can improve. If there is something wrong with the design, I like to try to eliminate something that's there, rather than to add something to it. I have a fetish for making things simple. If we are making a broadcast product that goes into a rack of equipment, I would like to have ours without any knobs, without any lights, without any meters. Just a

5-8. Portrait of John Wistrand in his industrial design office at Stamford, Connecticut.

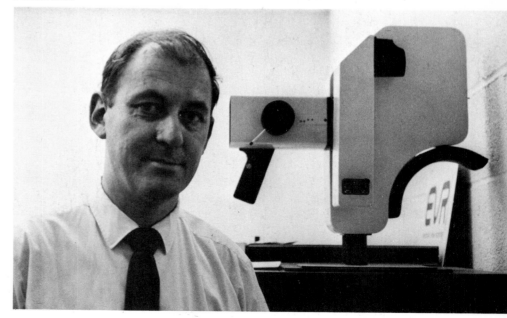

module that goes in there and does the job. In other words, if you have a lot of knobs and dials, someone has to move them. This says that the operator is a slave to this device, instead of having the device slave for him. The other side of it is the aesthetic one. I think that you can live with something simple for a long, long time and not get tired of it.

KRANZ. *Are you suggesting that our lives are cluttered and it is about time that we got back to basic fundamentals?*

WISTRAND. This is very true. I keep looking for a solution. If you take all our gadgets and all our architecture and all our automobiles and everything that we have made, there must be some rule that could be followed to make these things more compatible with one another, and to make them work in greater harmony. I feel that the only way to do this is to lean toward a simple solution to the problem, a clean solution. Then maybe we can get away from this montage of disorganization.

DR. MAX

mathews

DIRECTOR OF BEHAVIORAL AND STATISTICAL RESEARCH CENTER, BELL LABORATORIES, MURRAY HILL, NEW JERSEY

It seems to me that the scientist has the responsibility to make the innovations in technology available to the artist. This is not simple. Because of a difference in training, artists and scientists often have a common problem in talking to each other. So, the scientist has the responsibility to do some education and perhaps some demonstration, showing the artist just what the technology consists of in the field of art. The artist, as an innovator, has the responsibility to strain his brain and learn some things —to devote some time to understanding technology. And he has to have something interesting to inspire the technologists.

On computer and composer

There has been a lot of discussion as to whether computers can compose music. Nobody has answered the question as to whether they can compose by themselves, but they certainly are an effective aid to a human being in composing music. In one possible musical style the composer draws in the general outline of a piece and the computer fills in some of the details. Details may be very time consuming for a man. Suppose you put sixteenth notes in a presto passage. They fill a short time but they occupy a long length of manuscript. There's a great deal of detail on the manuscript. I think there is a correlation between how much a composer is willing to write down and the music's design and style.

5-9. Portrait of Dr. Max Mathews. (Photographs courtesy Bell Laboratories, Murray Hill, New Jersey.)

In addition to programmed instruction, this laboratory does work in the areas of learning, speech communication, vision, psycholinguistics, scaling, sensory physiology, statistics, and economics. Mr. Mathews' previous work at Bell Laboratories was in the Acoustic Research Department and concerned speech analysis as it pertained to both automatic speech-recognition machines and to low-channel capacity speech transmission.

5-10. Dr. Max Mathews (right) and Dr. Laurence Rosler of Bell Laboratories in consultation.

Drs. Rosler and Mathews compose computer music using a new graphic language they developed. The new language enables a composer to draw a musical score directly on a cathode ray tube with a light pen. This graphic score is then fed into a computer which generates the music or orchestration.

The composer denotes each voice in a composition (the music to be played by each simulated instrument) by drawing a separate curve for pitch, loudness, and note duration. A small computer associated with the cathode-ray-tube circuitry converts these curves into a sequence of numbers. This numerical data, representing the musical score, is then fed to another computer, in this case an IBM 7094, which is programmed to synthesize the sound of musical instruments and generates a stereo or monaural type. The composer is, therefore, able to listen to his composition within a few minutes after it is written. By previous methods the composer was required to prepare his musical score on computer cards—as many as twelve numbers on a card being needed to describe one tone.

The study of the reproduction of music, a simpler form of sound than speech, is one part of Bell Laboratories' efforts to better understand speech and its reproduction.

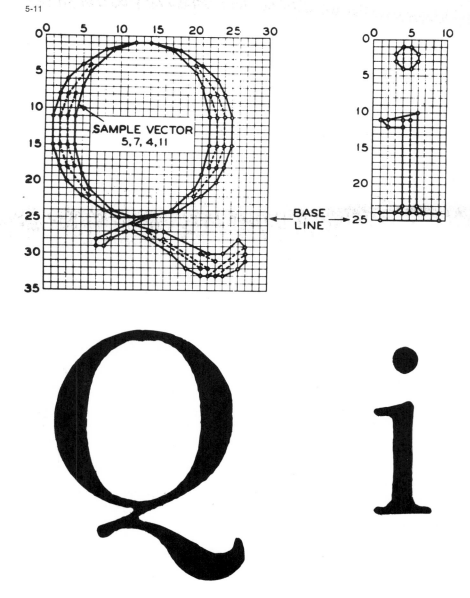

5-11

Of the computer and its future

Computers are very smart devices, yet they are smart in different ways than we are. They multiply much better than we do but have more difficulty in recognizing faces. They have difficulty in understanding human languages; on the other hand, we have difficulty understanding computer languages. This means that they are far more useful in supplementing our kind of intelligence than in duplicating or imitating it.

5-11. Computer-generated type faces. Images of normal type fonts can be drawn on the graphic console at a rate several hundred times faster than with commercial type setting equipment.

DR. CECIL
coker
BELL LABORATORIES, MURRAY HILL, NEW JERSEY

I suspect that technology is going to invade everything, including the arts. John Cage's summation of technology is: "It succeeds."

The surface reason for an engineer to work with an artist is that it's fun. The work is different from his regular work, but something he can handle easily and that others in the group can not.

But there is a deeper reason, too. There is a general mood that an engineering education should be broadened —liberalized—for social reasons as well as purely professional ones. In my field—speech—for example, we get involved in linguistics, physiology, and psychology, as well as acoustics and computers. Almost by definition, the new things don't fit into the old boxes.

5-12. Portrait of Dr. Cecil Coker of Bell Laboratories.

Dr. Coker adjusts a computer-generated model of the vocal tract. Dr. Coker has been engaged in research on analysis and synthesis of speech sounds. The object of his studies is to achieve a better insight into the production of speech and the way speech information is coded in commands to the articulatory system, in movements of the vocal tract, and in characteristics of the sound wave. His approach to the problem is through construction of talking computer programs. (Photographs courtesy Bell Laboratories, Murray Hill, New Jersey.)

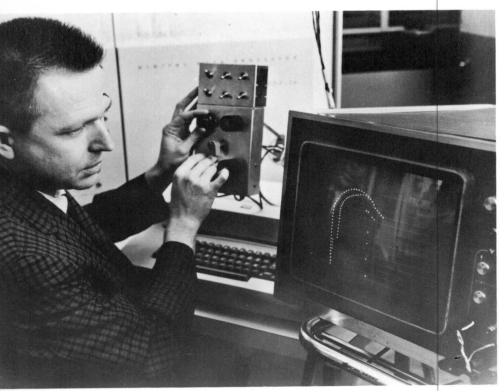

But on a social level, the technically-educated engineer —up from the farm or some other humble beginning— feels inferior to his cultured new friends. He is hungry for the kind of nontechnical broadening experience that the collaboration offers. He is stimulated by interesting new people and surroundings.

At the same time, the engineer, getting his job, and family and house in the suburbs, is pretty well sucked into the establishment. Here is a small way he can break away on his own, without severing any ties or closing any doors. In spite of being committed to mowing the lawn, taking out the garbage, answering the telephone—Monday morning, he can get away and become a seer-artist for a while—a sort of wish-fulfillment.

The project satisfies a curiosity about the non-Establishment world. This may also be an attraction for the artist—to see what's going on on the other side of the fence. Part of my fulfillment in working with artists is being reassured that these guys aren't so different from me after all.

In *Nine Evenings* I got very different impressions from the various projects. In some—especially the smaller ones —there was an attitude of give-and-take, of mutual respect between artist and engineer. Other projects, especially the ones with a large engineering effort, were less successful.

I think these cold, impersonal, big projects require too much commitment for part-time volunteers. In the theatre, we have riggers, electricians, this-and-that specialists. Maybe someday we'll also have electronic and mechanical engineering specialists for the arts. To succeed with big projects with scheduled performances we need a situation where people won't cop out when it gets rough. To stick it out, people have to feel that their careers or part of their personalities are at stake in the project. For big projects, we won't get this with amateurs; we need professionals.

But the smaller projects can succeed with a part-time engineer, if they don't get so big that they jeopardize his career or his home life . . . and if the artist and engineer can reach some kind of rapport. The project can be stimulating for both if they reach the stage of useful discussions about what is interesting for the artist and what is possible, easy or challenging, for the engineer.

The payoff for the engineer is intellectual, social, and psychological. Big, impersonal dogwork projects don't have it. Real collaborations do.

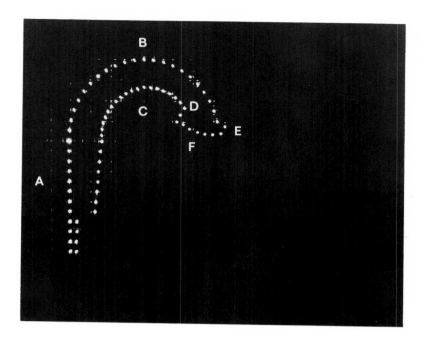

5-13. Computer display of vocal tract. A graphical representation of the vocal tract model appears on the oscilloscope.

The oscilloscope outline of the tract can be adjusted to form shapes that correspond to those formed when making basic sounds. At the same time the sounds are generated by a speech synthesized and heard by the researcher.

Accurate synthetic speech is now being produced with the aid of a controllable, computer-generated model of the vocal tract developed at the Bell Laboratories. The model, stored in a computer, is actually a geometric description of vocal tract areas as they are shaped to produce various sounds. When synthesizing speech, a researcher can see an outline of the vocal tract displayed on an oscilloscope and, at the same time, hear the sound that corresponds to the displayed shape. By flicking switches and turning knobs at a computer console, the researcher can change the shape and sound simultaneously. Thus, synthetic speech can be improved with both visual and aural aids. Shown in the geometric side view is: (A) pharynx, (B) palate, (C) tongue, (D) tongue tip, (E) lips, and (F) lower jaw. The lips, pharynx, and tongue are positioned on the oscilloscope to synthesize basic sounds.

PETER SUSAN CLAUDIO RALPH

poole edgerton badal flynn

EARLY PERSONELL AT EXPERIMENTS IN ART AND TECHNOLOGY LOFT, 1968, NEW YORK CITY

Dr. Billy Klüver has said that "We now have a headquarters in New York City where engineers and artists can meet." He added: "The ultimate purpose of E.A.T. will be to act as a transducer between the artist and industry, to protect the artist from industry and industry from the artist, to translate the artists' dreams into realistic technical projects."

KRANZ. *Peter, how are you going about this, here at the loft? How effective were the open houses that you held this year?*

POOLE. At the first open house, attendance varied from six to eight people at one time, to perhaps twenty to twenty-five during the afternoon. Sometimes there were too many engineers and sometimes there were too many artists. Every now and then it just came off perfectly. People matched themselves. We had nothing to do with matching. We wanted to make that process as impersonal as possible. There was no personal selection. When an artist walked in and said, "I want to speak to an electrical engineer," the electrical engineer got up, and they talked. It was just perfect.

KRANZ. *I understand that you two, Mr. Badal and Mr. Flynn, cooperated in the* Nine Evenings. *When Billy Klüver first discussed doing this, the idea seemed incredible. Artists and engineers to get together! Yet, as it turned out, there was a wonderful sense of comaraderie. What are some of your recollections of the* Nine Evenings?

BADAL. We all knew, during setup time and the actual performances, that things might not go smoothly—in fact, they didn't go smoothly—but to us the fact that we did it all was the important thing. That we actually had something like this in New York City—that kept us moving.

That kept us together. The heavy criticism that the *Nine Evenings* got in the press was for the product. According to those standards, it was a failure, if you like, because there were so many technical faults. And that was due to circumstances, more than anything else. Half the idea of

5-14. The first *E.A.T. News*, Vol. 1, No. 1, January 15, 1967.

Volume 1, No. 1   January 15, 1967

E.A.T. NEWS is designed to reach everyone interested in the activities of Experiments in Art and Technology, Inc. (E.A.T.). As you probably know, E.A.T. was formed out of the collaborative effort between artists, engineers and sponsors that resulted in "9 Evenings of Theater and Engineering" at the Armory last October. During the work for the "9 Evenings" it became clear to everyone that if a useful artist - engineer relationship is to be achieved, a major effort must be made to set up the physical conditions for this to happen. The worlds of the artist and the engineer are simply too different for a working relationship to develop purely out of the artist's desire for contact. We also felt strongly that the collaboration can only be fruitful if the artist's environment is not drastically changed, if the contact with the engineers rapidly results in a practical working situation and if the possibility to work with a professional engineer is open to every artist who wishes to do so. This first issue of E.A.T. NEWS describes what we plan to do with E.A.T. and how we hope it will function. The setting up of a practical organization like E.A.T. will necessarily rely on the experience derived during the formative period. The thought behind E.A.T. is that the organization should be generous, adaptable and helpful.

This first issue of E.A.T. NEWS contains a description of the proposed purpose and function of E.A.T., a list of those who are contributing their time and effort to organize E.A.T., the equipment, built originally for "9 Evenings" and which has a use that far exceeds these performances, will be in part described, a report on the recruiting of engineers from other industries, a report from the meeting at the Central Plaza and a description of our immediate plans for a place in New York.

This issue will necessarily be somewhat crammed with facts. In the future, we hope that E.A.T. NEWS will find a more organic form. For instance, in the next issue Cecil Coker will describe some of the engineering experiences from "9 Evenings" which we believe are of general interest to collaborative efforts elsewhere.

There were four of us who came most of the time. We were doing matchings and trying to drum up some influence and contacts . . .
Matchings are matching an artist's project with an engineer's talent. The finest success would be that E.A.T. had become redundant. When it comes to be a fact of life that engineers want to work with artists and artists can work with engineers—when that happens, then we are not needed any more.

5-15. Peter Poole at his desk.

5-16. Susan Edgerton in E.A.T. meeting room.

5-17. Ralph Flynn in his office at E.A.T.
We are loaning equipment—speakers and amplifiers and various other pieces that we had for Nine Evenings—to artists to do performances.

the Nine Evenings was how it came about, how it was made. Only the people who actually took part were open to that kind of criticism. As far as they were concerned, the collaboration worked; it was a great experience and, to that extent, it was a great success.

FLYNN. Yes, the sophistication of some of these works is one of the motivations for the engineer to get involved. The artist is thinking along lines outside the engineer's working patterns at, for instance, Bell Labs or Xerox Corporation. The engineers have an opportunity to use the knowledge they've gained in school in something that turns into an interesting creative project.

KRANZ. Susan, will you comment on the degree of interest you have had from industry in cooperating with E.A.T.

EDGERTON. The Singer Sewing Machine Company recently approached us with the idea that we would provide them with an artist to work in their computer division. The artist will be given a free hand to play around with the computer to see what can be developed from it. This was a major breakthrough. In one way, that is what E.A.T. is about—to get through to industry that they have a responsibility toward art.

KRANZ. It seems pretty clear that you all agree that the emphasis here is more on the process than the product. Have you any observations on the success of the process, for example, the interaction between the engineer and the artist?

BADAL. The success is in the way that they get along together. An engineer and an artist meeting—something might happen, something might not happen. It really depends on personalities, how people are going to get along with each other. That is my main interest here in E.A.T.

KRANZ. *When you consider that the organization is only a year old, it has had remarkable success.*

POOLE. The finest success would be that E.A.T. had become redundant, no longer necessary. Before, it was difficult for an artist to know how to approach an engineer.

You could presume that there were engineers who were trying to work it out, and artists who wanted to accept technology in the form of equipment as well as knowledge, and they had no channel of communication. We are trying to open up channels. When it is a routine and naturally accepted thing, when it becomes a fact of life that engineers want to work with artists and artists can work with engineers, when that happens—then we are not needed any more.

RICHARD

anuskiewicz

OPTICAL ARTIST, ENGLEWOOD, NEW JERSEY

My work may have a kind of scientific approach, but it still becomes strictly a visual experience. I create various shades of color through a series of lines. It is employing a visual color mixture such as you would find if you enlarged a color photograph and found that the solid colors are a series of dots. It is very different from a physical mixture, where, if you were to mix a violet by using a blue and green, you would get a grayish violet. By using a blue line and a red line, alternating them, you achieve a vibrant intense kind of painting. Since I am interested in a very intense kind of painting and since I use color in full intensity, I like to preserve this quality in the work. . . . In a sense I am a geometric abstractionist.

The paintings are most effective when you can back off to the point where you lose the line and you see the form and the color. The separate line is only important in the context of a network of lines. I use a fine masking tape to make the straight lines. I paint them with a brush, and the lines are actually masked out. The series of lines do not function as lines. The lines create areas of color.

Because of the masking-tape technique, interesting textures are built up. You want to go up and feel them. The Detroit Art Institute purchased one of my paintings, and they actually had it roped off because too many people were going up and feeling it. So this is another kind of sensation, another kind of appreciation that is attained from these works.

I start with an idea in my mind. I visualize the painting. As I start working, it turns out to be a completely different thing. I'm always surprised. In almost all cases, I have to make adjustments and changes. If I want to change an area, I try a color. Rather than actually painting that color, I paint it on a piece of paper or masking tape and try it. If it is not the right color, I just remove it and try something

else. I can try something this way without having to go through the labor of painting it in. These are little time-saving devices that I've worked out for myself.

As calculated as the painting might be, in spite of the predetermined figuring that goes into my work, it still becomes a very creative piece, since I really am not able to visualize the thing as it is. The creative process is continually working in the adjustments that are being made. You start out with an idea, and the idea grows, and the adjustments are made.

(All illustrations for this interview are reproduced in color, overleaf.)

C-42. Richard Anuszkiewicz—a portrait. "My work may have a kind of scientific approach, but it still becomes strictly a visual experience." Richard Anuszkiewicz, during an interview.

C-43. The Anuszkiewicz' ten-story high City Wall at the Eighth Avenue YWCA in New York City, 1972. (A project of City Walls Inc. Photograph by Joel Witkin.)

For his first City Wall, Richard Anuszkiewicz has created a dramatic painting that can be seen for more than a half mile down Eighth Avenue, New York City. The painting adds a new dimension to a normally dull commercial thoroughfare. The artist said that, aside from this painting being the largest he has ever done (75 by 50 feet), the light of day actually determines the colors of the painting: "In sunlight the warm colors brighten and the cool colors darken. At dusk the reverse happens." Mr. Anuszkiewics went on to say, "It pleases me to give a gift to the people of New York and to be able to make this contribution to a city that has done so much for art."

C-44. The large-field scale of Anuskiewicz's work is shown as he stands next to one of his paintings in his studio.

C-45A. The artist removing masking tape used to create the crisp, clean lines of his optical paintings.

C-45B. Close-up of masking tape being removed.

C-46. The artist's palette.

C-47. The artist's home—a Victorian house in Englewood Cliffs, New Jersey.

C-48. Anuszkiewicz in the living room of his home.

C-49. Anuszkiewicz's interest in the optical qualities in sculpture as well as in painting is exemplified by this sculpture on its mirror pedestal.

(All photographs, except C-43, by Michael Fredericks, Jr. Courtesy The Metropolitan Museum of Art, Education Department, Harry S. Parker, Chairman.)

C-42

C-43

RICHARD ANUSKIEWICZ

C-44

C-45A

C-45B
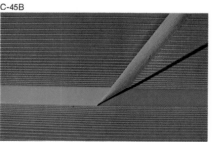

C-46

C-47

C-48

C-49

DR. GERALD

oster

PROFESSOR OF BIOPHYSICS, MOUNT SINAI SCHOOL OF MEDICINE, CITY UNIVERSITY OF NEW YORK

The foundation of science is intuition. It is, let's say, artistic. The flash of genius. The whole thing is the same as in great works of art. The fulfillment of the idea still must come, but if you have nothing to say, it all goes down the drain. It is the same with science as with art. If you know all the works, you're a superb mathematician, but if you haven't got any ideas, then nothing comes of it.

Computers are so inadequate. For example, at the present level of technology there is no device that will read a book for you and digest certain information and codify it for you.

You have the human as the other computer because it can make computers. It can think up the existence of computers in the first place, and it can go to higher levels. I may be wrong in this number, but I think we have something like 100 billion neuron connections in our head . . . and you only need 1,000 neurons to be a normal adult. To have a device that will read with comprehension, line by line, you need a computer that can store all this and then do things with it.

To duplicate what a child does any day, you need a computer the size of the earth. But the human flips a book open and immediately knows what the nature of the book is. If you neglect the human as a fantastic device, you miss the whole point, as far as I am concerned. The way an eye works, for example, its constant scanning, motion, comparing. You wouldn't understand simultaneous contrast if you didn't have a moving eye, a comparing eye.

Op Art is full of visual perceptual devices. People came out of the *Responsive Eye* art show not knowing whether the pieces were stationary or in motion. Fantastic, they thought. I hoped they went away with a feeling that they themselves were fantastic creatures.

I like simple things and I like things that are controlled by the spectator. You go to Times Square; you can see some pretty elaborate lights in orbit. There is something beautiful in just a few elements. A Chinese vase proves that: if you took a green Chinese vase at the Metropolitan Museum and put figures on it, you would kill it. This is the appeal of minimal art.

That's the danger in artists working with technologists, that their work will get too much involved in elaborate timing switches and that sort of thing, and not have much visual meaning.

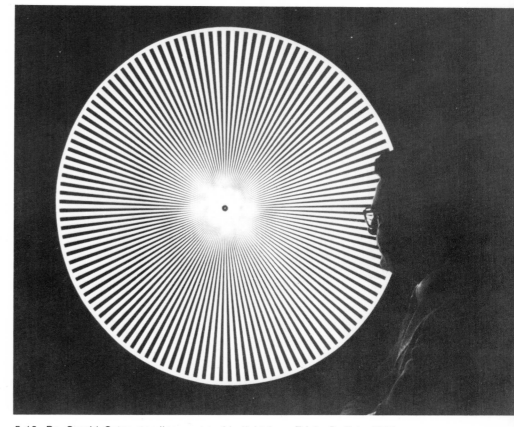

5-18. Dr. Gerald Oster standing next to his light box, *Triple Radial—1964.* (Courtesy The Howard Wise Gallery; photographer, Geoffrey Clements.)

"Optical art is an unfortunate term since all visual art is optical. Whether or not one is able to explain visual impressions in terms of the science of optics, it is usually agreed that all visual phenomena up to the point where they register on the retina fall properly in the domain of optics."—Gerald Oster. ("Optical Art," Applied Optics, *Vol. 4, No. 11 (Nov. 1965), p. 1359.)*

5-19. *Double Equipaced* Circles by Gerald Oster—1964. Silk-screen on plexiglass, 39″ x 39″. (Courtesy The Howard Wise Gallery; photographer, Geoffrey Clements.)

My constructions and paintings are concerned with what would ordinarily be called marginal phenomena of the visual scene, but which for me are the most vivid aspects. Such "useless" information (i.e., not required for our survival) includes the excitement of the edge, the superposition of families of lines to give new patterns (moiré), the hallucinatory figures "seen" with the eyes closed, and the visual aspects of the psychedelic experience. The edge is not a mere geometrical boundary but is a living force produced by the living eye. A well-defined edge consists of rapidly moving moiré patterns produced by the superposition of the diffraction image of the edge and its slightly rotated after-image. . . . Gerald Oster.

5-19

5-20

5-21

5-20. *Triple Log Major,* by Gerald Oster—1964. Silkscreen on plexiglass, 96″ x 30″. (Courtesy The Howard Wise Gallery; photographer, Geoffrey Clements.)

If, then, moiré patterns play such an important role in visual perception, why not be direct and do pure moiré? My constructions are extractions in that I seize those elements of the visual scene and make them an end in themselves.—Gerald Oster.

5-21. *Phosphene Spiral* by Gerald Oster, 1966. Phosphorescent paint. (Courtesy The Howard Wise Gallery; photographer, Geoffrey Clements.)

My phosphenes are suggested by the figures one perceives just before going to sleep. . . . These strange and beautiful pale-colored geometric forms float somewhere there and may be a manifestation of our inner orderliness. . . . In order to create the feeling of flowing in the dark . . . I use phosphorescent pigments. The three colors represent the range of colors I perceive in phosphenes. As the phosphorescent light (stimulated when white light is on) decays with time, various levels of symmetries and textures are revealed. . . .—Gerald Oster.

DR. CARL
machover

VICE PRESIDENT, INFORMATION DISPLAYS, INC., MOUNT KISCO, NEW YORK

KRANZ. *Why would a graphic display be of value to a composer in trying to compose something that's an auditory phenomenon?*

MACHOVER. Well, it's interactive. He can generate his own instrument. As he makes his notations, he can, at the same time, get the exact result. It's as if he were writing music with a symphony orchestra. In effect, he has a full range of instrumentation available to him. Now, in addition to this, people are beginning to do speech synthesis in exactly the same way. Traditionally there have been devices that attempt to analyze the components of speech. One of the older devices is called, I think, the Vocoder, which built the speech up into the frequency bands and then resynthesized it. I guess this was first shown at the World's Fair in 1933. It has found application in recent technology in areas of security communications, where one scrambles and unscrambles a voice by synthesizing it. There are studies now in which people are literally designing new speech by graphically putting wave forms on the face of the cathode.

5-22. Carl Machover working with a light pen on the face of a cathode-ray tube, to be used as a graphic input for a computer program.

5-23A

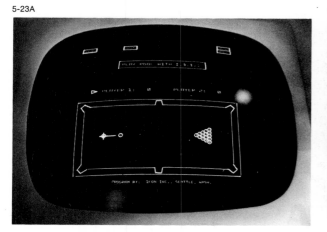

5-23B

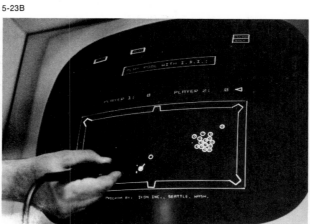

5-23C

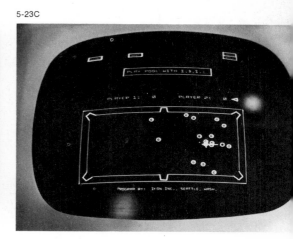

5-23A. A pool game was designed to be played by using a light pen and the graphic image on the face of a cathode-ray tube. In this photograph the game has not yet begun. The cue ball remains stationary.

5-23B. The game was designed as an exhibit to dramatize the I.D.I. computer graphics program, in which the operator interacts with the computer program by using a light pen. Here the operator is about to strike the cue ball opposite the light pen.

5-23C. In this photograph, the cue ball has struck the massed balls and they in turn are moved around the periphery of the table, just as they would have moved had this been a game actually played on a real pool table.

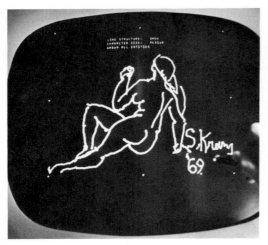

5-24A. The author used a light pen to make this free-form line drawing directly on the face of the cathode-ray tube. The light pen makes a series of very short, straight lines on the tube, and that input is taken into the computer memory bank, where it is retained.

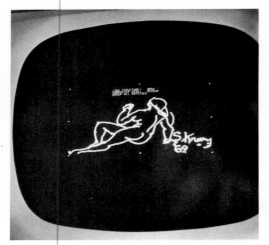

5-24B. The operator has altered the proportions of the drawing to elongate the figure.

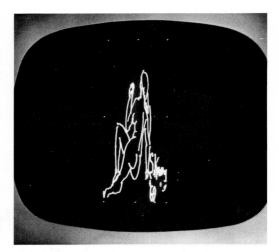

5-24C. Returning the drawing to its normal proportions, the operator has rotated it in space, causing it to be projected out into space and back onto the surface of the cathode-ray tube.

5-24D. The drawing has been enlarged.

5-24E. The drawing in this version has been further enlarged and rotated.

5-24F. The scale of the drawing is diminished to one fourth its original size.

KRANZ. *As I understand it, a main thrust of the computer display system is to make the computer program available to the ordinary man who does not know a computer language such as Fortran.*

MACHOVER. One of the analogies that has been used is that of automobiles: in their early days, they were so extremely complex that one generally had to hire a chauffeur to drive his car—the automobile was a form of transportation and the objective of the individual was to get from one place to the other. But the layman was not sufficiently skillful to operate the machine himself, and he therefore hired an expert to do it. Computers are in a similar situation today. The layman has a problem to be solved. The computer is a device for solving a problem, but he doesn't know how to use it, so he hires a programmer to solve the problem. I'm sure—as in most analogies —there are places where it breaks down. One of the objectives of computer graphics is to give a man with a problem the opportunity to use this powerful computing source to solve his problem without fully understanding how it works.

This tremendous flexibility—the retention of the computer memory system for an input from a graphic image drawn on the face of the tube— is an enormous step forward in computer programming. What it means is that in a very short period of time, anyone who wants to work with a computer, to talk with a computer, will be able to go up to a computer input, like a cathode-ray tube such as this, and draw his input into the computer or, put it in with a typewriter, or by any other of a number of inputs, none of which require that the learner know computer-programming language. He doesn't have to know how to prepare a computer punch card; he merely goes up and puts the information into the computer program that he wants and gets back a transmutation, or a change of this information, based on that simple task. Computer time costs are going to go down. The number of people who can use a computer fruitfully will be multiplied almost infinitely. After all, the telephone system is a very sophisticated information transfer system that does not require any knowledge of how it functions on the part of the person who uses it, with the result that we can communicate with anybody on the face of the earth who can be reached at a receiving terminal.

DR. GERALD
stoodley

RESEARCH SCIENTIST, GRUMMAN AIRCRAFT ENGINEERING CORPORATION, BETHPAGE, NEW YORK

Discussing the uses of computer programming for perspective drawing, Dr. Stoodley was asked:

KRANZ. *How did you people here at Grumman get interested in this kind of stereoscopic image? What practical applications does it have?*

STOODLEY. Many times we want to visualize objects, and in doing this, it is useful to have a three-dimensional image. Once you have the perspective, it is a trivial step to go to the stereo. It's just another picture taken.

KRANZ. *Might we assume that, using computerized design of a three-dimensional object, you could program it directly into master milling machines, which would then mill out a master die, thus eliminating many expensive design processes?*

STOODLEY. It is quite feasible to go straight from the design on the scope to mill output. You eliminate people running back and forth making changes in blueprints, and so forth.

KRANZ. *The use you are making of it here seems to indicate that major industries may use this more and more.*

5-25. Portrait of Dr. Gerald Stoodley.

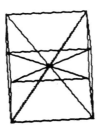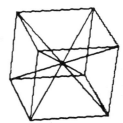

5-26A. Two computer-generated cubes drawn from a computer-driven plotter machine. These two cubes, when viewed with a special stereoscopic viewer, appear to the eye to be one merged three-dimensional cube. (Courtesy Dr. Stoodley.)

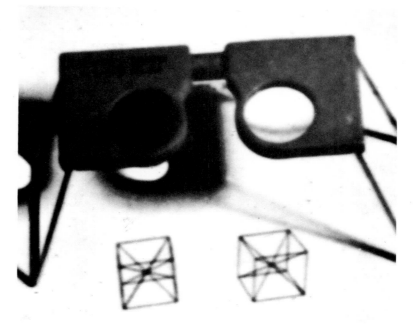

5-26B. Special eyeglass viewer used for stereoscopic viewing. (Courtesy Dr. Stoodley.)

STOODLEY. I would think so. All, or many, analyses are performed on a mathematical model. If you want to, you can crank out a wind-tunnel model, and run it through a wind tunnel test . . .

KRANZ. *On a computer?*

STOODLEY. The computer would be able to convert a mathematical model to the appropriate numerical-control

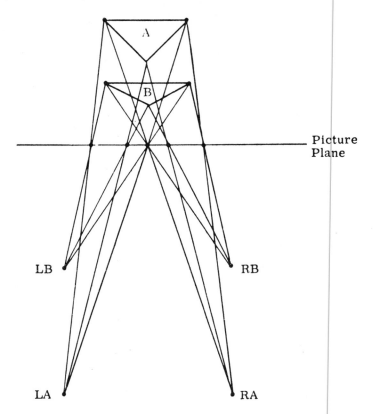

Picture Plane

5-27. This diagram illustrates the differences in the appearance of a stereo view of an object based either on the viewing position or the distance from the object of the observer. (Courtesy Dr. Stoodley.)

tool instructions to get a physical model to be tested against previous mathematical results obtained by relating certain theories to the mathematical model.

KRANZ. *To check out whether it works?*

STOODLEY. Right.

KRANZ. *Will the effects of this research be far-reaching in the aircraft industry?*

STOODLEY. Let's put it this way. Anyone who does not use it will be out of competition. In competitions to get a contract, you must examine so many cases and the only effective way to do this is with a computer. If you are using the design hooked right into the analysis programs, it should be straight ahead to get your design parameters out and checked easily.

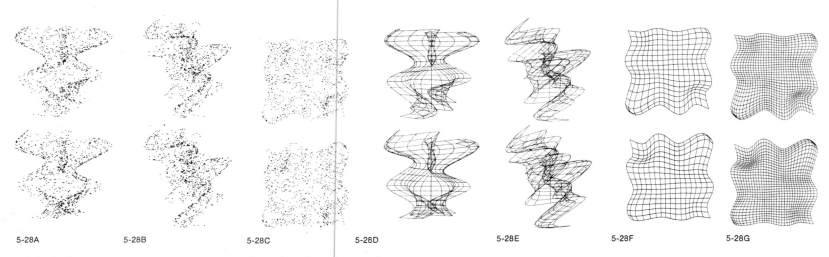

5-28A   5-28B   5-28C   5-28D   5-28E   5-28F   5-28G

5-28A. Each of these versions represents a view of an imaginary surface created by a computer program developed by Dr. Stoodley. The surface of an abstract plane is shown in different views. Each of these diagrams of the same surface illustrates the flexibility of a computer-generated stereoscopic drawing of a three-dimensional surface. (Courtesy Dr. Stoodley.)

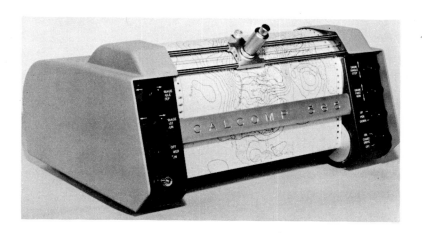

5-29. The applications of this Calcomp plotter are countless. The plotter can move in any direction on the surface of the paper. (Courtesy Calcomp-California Computer Products, Inc., Anaheim, California.)

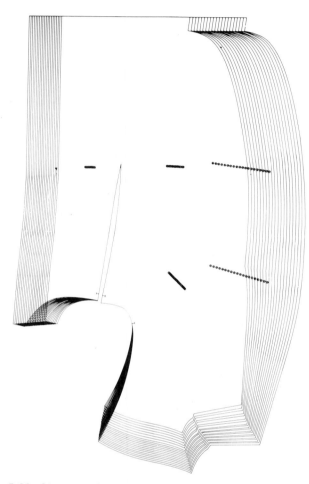

5-30. Given one form-size for a pattern, the plotter produces other sizes for the apparel industry. (Courtesy Calcomp-California Computer Products, Inc., Anaheim, California.)

5-31. Traffic-flow pattern in Rijswijk, Netherlands. (Courtesy Calcomp-California Computer Products, Inc., Anaheim, California.)

Using a 7049 computer program, the IBM Data Center produced the map. Traffic flow in all directions at a given intersection can be plotted, as shown in the smaller diagram. Maps of this type, which formerly required four weeks for production, now can be prepared in up to fifteen minutes at one fourth the cost.

5-32. Computer readout of the *Mona Lisa*. Scanning the surface, the plotter gives a readout based on varying value levels. (Courtesy Calcomp-California Computer Products, Inc., Anaheim, California.)

DR. JANICE R.
lourie

COMPUTER-AIDED GRAPHIC SYSTEMS, IBM NEW YORK CITY

5-33. Dr. Janice R. Lourie sitting in front of a tapestry that she designed. (Courtesy Dr. Lourie; photographer, Robert Sears.)

Janice R. Lourie, a member of IBM's New York Scientific Center, and a tapestry weaver, developed the Textile Graphics technique, which frees the designer from painting in each individual warp and filling end on graph paper. With it, you can build up a library of designs stored within the computer on discs, each of which can hold up to *fifty-seven million* interlacings. The designer can use the graphic screen and a light pen to superimpose his design on the screen, instead of employing graph or point paper. He can erase and improvise to build his design as he goes along. This technique grew out of a "lifelong romance" that Dr. Lourie has had with weaving.

LOURIE. I first became interested in hand weaving when I was a child, and my mother took me to see traveling hand weavers from Kentucky. As soon as I saw them weaving at the loom, I fell in love with it. It has been a lifelong romance. When I got old enough, I got a loom, a big one, which I have in my apartment now. And I've been weaving ever since.

She did her undergraduate work in mathematics at Massachusetts Institute of Technology and got her master's degree in the same

5-34. Dr. Lourie in front of the cathode ray tube before she begins her design. She selects a weave design from a library of hundreds of weaves previously stored in the computer. (Photographs 5-34—5-35F reproduced courtesy IBM Data Processing Division.)

field at Boston University. Simultaneously, she was getting a bachelor's degree in philosophy at Tufts, and studying music. In art she did mainly tapestry weaving. At IBM, she began to think about the connection between the weaving industry and the computer industry.

LOURIE. I wanted to settle this connection. The first thing I did was to go into a professional mill in the industry and ask them to let me look at certain kinds of machinery that I felt had some bearing on computers. I saw the Jacquard loom, which has been in use since 1800 and is actually the forerunner of the computer. It is controlled by punch cards, which look very much like IBM cards. Hanging on top of that loom I saw thousands of those cards, necessary to weave one design. Then I started to work on what tools in the computer industry could be applied to helping in the problem of creating those cards. I wasn't sure at that time. So I did some thinking and I came up with what I considered a legitimate proposal, and I presented it to my management. And it seemed quite reasonable. But of course that's not the only thing necessary. Even if you solve a problem with computers, that's not sufficient justification for doing it, because, in addition, it has to be economically feasible. So the next thing I had to do was to prove economic feasibility. It was a long battle. A fascinating part of the whole application has been the peripheral detail necessary to justify the project itself.

KRANZ. *Will the artist lose his individuality as he becomes chained to technology?*

LOURIE. I am involved in both the computer and the art fields and I consider these to be just the opposite. This technique was originally designed as a tool to help point-paper designers in their work. At first the stylists and the artists, who are also involved in the industry, were afraid of it. But now, look what they can do. Instead of drawing a design and having ten or twenty Xerox copies made, and playing with them—building repeats, trying them, and so forth—they can come to this tool. They can draw on the tablet. They can have the design displayed on the screen. They can enlarge it, contract it, rotate it, repeat it, deform it in various ways, do all kinds of things with it. They can use it as just another tool to expedite their own creative instincts.

In my weaving, even in some writing and in music, it seems to be the same energy, the same kind of insight, the same original impulse, the same excitement. I feel that when I go to those places one goes to in being creative, it is always going to be the same place.

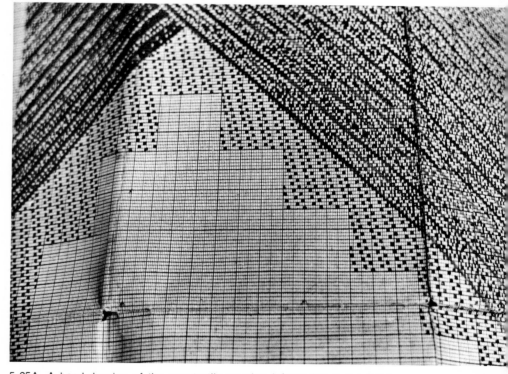

5-35A. A hand drawing of the way textile-weaving information is prepared before the loom can be used. This laborious hand-drawn method is an old fashioned way of doing it, and weaver-designer Lourie has replaced it with her use of the cathode-ray tube.

5-35B. Dr. Lourie working with her light pen on a cathode-ray tube. On her left hand is a device that calls up a particular point in the program. Any segment of the design can be placed inside the window, where it is enlarged.

5-35C. Lourie has drawn images on the face of the tube.

"Artist's sketch is displayed on the IBM 2250 display unit, which is linked to the IBM System/360. Designer uses the 2250's cathode-ray tube (CRT) as a drawing board, drawing on the tube's face with a light-sensing device called a light pen." Reprinted from the May 1967 issue of *Textile World.* Copyright © McGraw-Hill, Inc., 1967.)

5-35D. One image—the image of the bee—has been enlarged through the computer program on the cathode ray tube.

5-35E. A multiple-image photograph that shows the number of different positions that she used to do the bumblebee.

5-35F. Printout of the computer program. Output of the textile graphics technique is a computer printout, which is the equivalent of graph paper. In weaving, the operator punches a card for the loom, working directly from the printout, just as he would from graph paper.

5-36A. Virginia Burton, Associate Curator of Egyptian Art at The Metropolitan Museum of Art, with an IBM graphic display unit for classifying pottery. (Courtesy The Metropolitan Museum of Art.)

"Ancient pottery meets twentieth-century computer: Sketches of ancient Egyptian pottery traced onto the screen of an IBM computer's graphic unit are part of an experimental project devised to help The Metropolitan Museum of Art classify and catalog 2,000 artifacts.

"Virginia Burton, Associate Curator of Egyptian Art at the museum, is shown with an IBM graphic display unit that she will use to classify the pottery by typology—its shape and decoration. She enters information about the pottery by drawing pictures on the TV-like screen with an electronic probe called a 'light pen.' Once the image data is stored in the computer, Miss Burton may enlarge the picture, reduce it, rotate it in three dimensions, or 'blow-up' a section—a handle or a spout, for example—so that it may be studied in greater detail. Other drawings and descriptive data, including measurement statistics, may be displayed on the computer-linked screen for side-by-side comparison." (Courtesy The Metropolitan Museum of Art.)

5-36B. Carl Dauterman, Curator of Western European Decorative Arts at The Metropolitan Museum of Art, using an IBM/360 Model 30 to help classify and catalog Sèvres, an often-faked porcelain art. (Courtesy The Metropolitan Museum of Art.)

"He uses two sets of codes inscribed on each piece of sèvres porcelain as the basis for his investigations. The codes, along with all the other information known about the Sèvres factory and its artisans, are entered into the computer's memory for analysis. The codes can help identify the workers who molded, gilded, and painted a particular vase or dish, and the date of manufacture. By pointing out where the normal patterns of agreement vary between the two codes and the stored background data, the computer will help detect a forgery." (Courtesy The Metropolitan Museum of Art.)

5-36B

DR. A. MICHAEL
noll

ACOUSTICS RESEARCH, BELL LABORATORIES, MURRAY HILL, NEW JERSEY

By training an electrical engineer, by interest a computer scientist, Dr. A. Michael Noll, belongs to what he calls "a new breed of people."

Computer science is itself developing into a new field but included in it are people who have backgrounds in psychology, mathematics, engineering, and all sorts of other

5-37. Portrait of Dr. A. Michael Noll.

Dr. Noll joined Bell Laboratories as a member of the Technical Staff in 1961. He was initially concerned with the assessment of telephone quality and, in particular, the subjective effects of peak clipping and sidetone. In 1965 he was transferred to the Acoustics Research Department, where he was concerned with computer simulations and investigations of short-time spectrum analysis and the method for vocal pitch determination. He is currently in the Speech and Communication Research Department of Bell Laboratories. His interests have included computer-generated three-dimensional displays of data, the application of computer technology to the visual arts, and psychological investigations of human reactions to pseudorandom patterns. He is presently exploring more effective forms of man-machine communication, including real-time three-dimensional computer graphics and tactile communication. He has presented a number of technical papers and has published articles in many different journals.

areas. These people have a tremendous interest in the use of the computer as applied to their own particular fields. But *their* interest in the computer has become so strong that you might as well call them a new breed of people.

Things change so rapidly. You are working on challenging problems in a certain field, and after a while they are to some extent solved. You become slowly bored with the field and go off into something else. A lot of people are doing this. The one thread of interest that usually remains, however, seems to be computer technology.

Communication of man with the machine in the science area is different from the communication of man with the machine in the arts. The basic idea is to try to remove the computer expertise required of the individual for using the computer. That's the whole idea of graphical communication of man with the machine—so that man does not have to know the explicit details of programming. You don't care what the electronics are inside the computer: it's a tool for you. For the arts, however, the communication has to be on an artistic level. This gets into a problem, because most of the people who are developing these new computer systems are scientists. They don't know the communication needs of the artist, or the designer, or the man from the humanities. So until they learn these things, or work with artists and designers, they will not understand what the needs are. Better yet, a new breed will emerge from the design and artistic community, someone with a background in design or art and also a background in computer programming. These people will sit down and write the programs that will enable them to communicate with the machine in terms of their artistic abilities and technological knowledge.

A great power of the computer is that it is a machine that can fill in details. In the field of music, for instance, you have a machine in which you might indicate in a very crude way the overall pattern you want the composition to take, and the computer (by some mathematical algorithms) will fill in all the details. And you might have a way for the machine to calculate some numbers so complicatedly interrelated that they appear random to us. Whenever we say random here, it means pseudorandom. This is a very important concept to get across. The machine is not "tossing a coin." The machine, in a way, completely knows the dynamics of the coin. Before the coin leaves your hand, the machine knows whether it is going to come up heads or tails—but you don't know. As far as you are

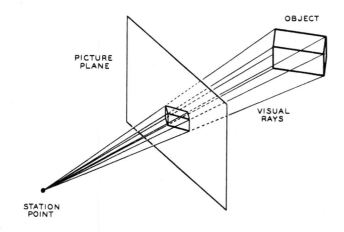

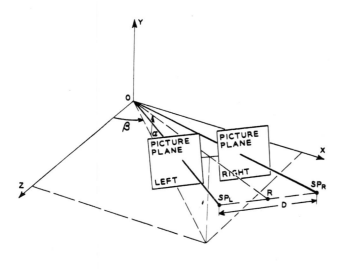

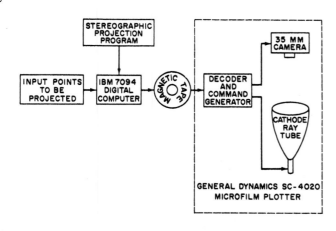

5-38A. Perspective projection of an object. (Taken from *Stereographic Projections by Digital Computer* by A. Michael Noll, Bell Laboratories, Murray Hill, New Jersey © A. Michael Noll, 1965.)

"Stereographic Projection: The basic technique for producing a three-dimensional drawing is the technique of stereographic projection. This technique consists of producing two perspective drawings corresponding to the images seen by the left and right eyes. Usually the drawing of such perspectives is quite tedious, and, in practice, various approximations such as isometric, one vanishing point, and two vanishing point projections are used. (E. G. Paré, R. O. Loving, and I. L. Hill, Descriptive Geometry. The Macmillan Company, New York, 1959.)

"However, the digital computer is so adept at performing 'tedious' calculations that straightforward methods for producing a perspective can be utilized.
To produce a perspective drawing of an object, it is first necessary to choose some point (representing the eye) from which the object is viewed (see Fig. 1). In descriptive geometry terminology, this point is called a station point. A plane, more specifically called a picture plane, is inserted between the object to the station point, and their points of intersection with the picture plane are connected to complete the perspective drawing." (Taken from *Stereographic Projections by Digital Computer* by A. Michael Noll, Bell Laboratories. © A. Michael Noll, 1965.)

5-38B. Pictorial representation of stereographic projection, including rotation and inclination of the station points. (Taken from *Stereographic Projections by Digital Computer* by A. Michael Noll, Bell Laboratories. © A. Michael Noll, 1965.)

"Since two perspectives are required to produce a stereographic drawing, two station points (one for each eye) and two picture planes must be chosen. The object can be viewed from any angle if an angle of inclination and an angle of rotation of the station points are introduced. Assuming that the object is specified in a rectangular coordinate system, the stereographic scheme can be depicted as in Fig. 2. The left and right picture planes, the left and right station points, and the angles of inclination and rotation are shown. If an object were to be projected stereographically, lines would be drawn from it to the station points. The intersections of these lines with the picture planes produce two slightly different perspectives, corresponding to the left and right eye images. When viewed stereoscopically, these two perspectives create the illusion of depth. Of course, the computer does not have the ability to physically draw lines from the object to the station points, and so an analytic treatment of stereographic techniques is required." (Taken from *Stereographic Projections by Digital Computer* by A. Michael Noll, Bell Laboratories. © A. Michael Noll, 1965.)

5-38C. Block diagram of computer technique for producing stereographic projections. (Taken from *Stereographic Projections by Digital Computer* by A. Michael Noll, Bell Laboratories. © A. Michael Noll, 1965.)

"If the rectangular coordinates of some point are known, then the corresponding left and right perspectives can be easily computed. The introduction of angles of inclination and rotation of the viewing point makes the computations only slightly more complex. The projection technique is thus reduced to equations that can be evaluated by a digital computer. It is only necessary to represent the object to be projected by straight lines connecting points. These points are given to the computer, along with parameters, and the computer then computes the corresponding coordinates of the points in the left and right picture planes. The remaining problem is to plot the projected points and to then connect lines between them, thereby producing the left and right perspectives. This is a job far too tedious to do by hand; fortunately, an elaborate device manufactured by the Stromberg-Carlson Division of General Dynamics is available for plotting digital data.
"The Stromberg-Carlson SC-4020 microfilm plotter consists primarily of a cathode ray tube and a 35 mm camera for taking pictures of the information displayed on the face of the tube. Instructions for the SC-4020 are written on magnetic tape; the tape is then decoded by the SC-4020 and used to generate commands for opening and closing the shutter of the camera, for advancing the film, and for deflecting the beam of the cathode-ray tube. Development of the film produces a 35 mm microfilm transparency which consists of lines connecting points, drawn, in effect, directly under the control of a digital computer. In this manner, the perspective points computed by an IBM 7094 digital computer are used as the input to an off-line SC-4020 microfilm plotter through an intermediate magnetic-tape storage. After photographic development, the microfilm can then be viewed directly in a stereoscope, and the final result is an illusion of depth created by a completely computerized technique as diagrammed in Fig. 3." (Taken from *Stereographic Projections by Digital Computer* by A. Michael Noll, Bell Laboratories. © A. Michael Noll, 1965.)

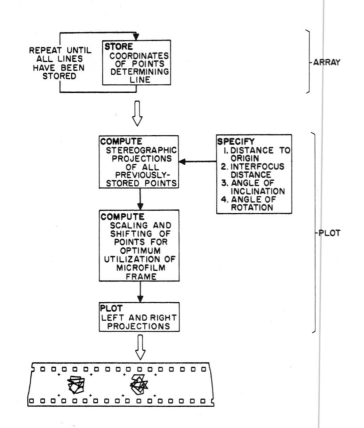

5-38D

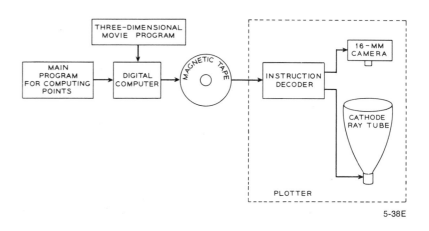

5-38E

5-38D. Basic flow chart of stereographic-projection subroutines. (Taken from *Stereographic Projections by Digital Computer* by A. Michael Noll, Bell Laboratories. © A. Michael Noll, 1965.)

"Stereographic Projection Program: The preceding paragraphs have indicated that the computer requires only the coordinates of the end points of lines to compute the stereographic projections. The projected points are then used as the input to an off-line SC-4020 microfilm plotter, which actually draws lines between them. The command structure of the microfilm plotter has been designed to draw either a single line between two points or a sequence of connected line segments between a set of points. Thus, if all the points are stored in one master array for programming convenience, when they are to be plotted, the proper sets must be unpacked from the projected master array. This can be done conveniently with two subroutines, one to store and pack the coordinates of the points of each set, and a second to actually compute the stereographic projections, unpack them, and instruct the plotter to draw on microfilm the left and right images. Thus, the first subroutine is called repeatedly until all the sets of points to be projected have been packed together. The functions of the stereographic computing subroutines are indicated in Fig. 4. ARRAY is called to store the coordinates of the points of each set. After all the sets of points have been called, a call to PLOT computes the stereographic projections, using the previously derived equations. The argument of PLOT specifies the distance to the origin, the interfocus distance, and the angles of inclination and rotation.

"Since the size of the microfilm frame is restricted, it is important that the perspectives be centered and scaled in size to adequately fill each frame. Accordingly, PLOT searches for the maximum and minimum of the arrays. The maximum and minimum are used to determine the shifting required to center each perspective in its frame. A scaling factor is also computed and used to scale the perspectives in size to assure that they are neither too big nor too little. PLOT then instructs the microfilm plotter to draw lines between the points specified in the shifted and scaled arrays." (Taken from *Stereographic Projections by Digital Computer* by A. Michael Noll, Bell Laboratories. © A. Michael Noll, 1965.)

5-38E. Block diagram of computer technique for producing three-dimensional movies. (Taken from *Computer-Generated Three-Dimensional Movies* by A. Michael Noll, Bell Laboratories. © A. Michael Noll, 1965.)

"Computer Method: The computer method for generating a three-dimensional movie is first to calculate, at some particular instant in time, the three-dimensional coordinates of the points in a line-drawing representation of the desired object. The three-dimensional movie program then calculates the points required for the two perspectives and also generates the instructions for drawing the perspectives with the plotter. The three-dimensional coordinates of the object at a small time increment later are then computed, and the three-dimensional program generates the instructions for another frame of the movie. This procedure is repeated on a frame-by-frame basis until the desired movie sequence is completed. The movie then exists on magnetic tape, which is used as input to the plotter. The plotter decodes the instructions on the tape and repeatedly advances the film and deflects the electron beam until the entire movie is completed. Fig. 1 is a simple block diagram of this process." (Taken from *Computer-Generated Three-Dimensional Movies* by A. Michael Noll, Bell Laboratories. © A. Michael Noll, 1965.)

concerned, tossing the coin is random. As far as the machine is concerned, it knows.

This is not like the brush and the oil, which just flow together. It's like a brush that fills in a line after you have indicated two end points. Sometimes a wavy line, or one with some odd texture to it. It is an active medium. You sit down with this medium. You communicate. There's an interplay back and forth.

The computer supplies the technical ability. Now you are forcing the artist to live by his ideas. You are giving him a powerful medium, but he is going to have to have really good ideas to use it. The little things that some artists exist by being able to do, the machine is going to do. There is going to be a glorification of the artists who have good, new, fresh ideas.

I envision the artist as picking up these tools and using them himself, not relying on the scientist. The artist can learn from the scientist in terms of these new techniques. The artist is going to have to learn programming—at least some will—in order to write these new languages and communication needs, to enable fellow artists to communicate with the machine in terms of their individual artistic needs that involve new devices and the new programming language. It's a joint venture. Each has something to learn from the other.

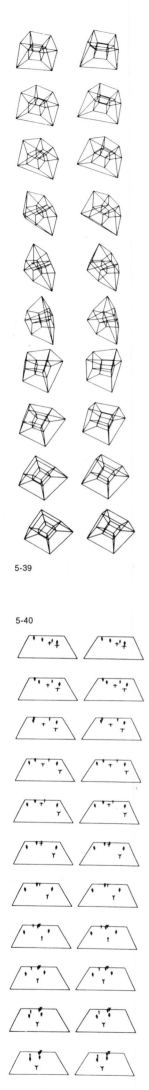

5-39. Selected frames from movie of the three-dimensional projection of a rotating four-dimensional hypercube. (Taken from *Computers and the Visual Arts* by A. Michael Noll, Bell Laboratories. © A. Michael Noll, 1965.)

"This shows a few frames from a computer-generated movie of a rotating hypercube. The rotations, which involve the fourth dimension, result in the object appearing to turn inside out. The motion itself is very intriguing and, although very complicated, immediately implies a sophisticated generating process." (Taken from *Computers and the Visual Arts* by A. Michael Noll, Bell Laboratories. © A. Michael Noll, 1965.)

5-40. Selected frames from a computer-generated three-dimensional movie of stick-figure representation of human motion on a stage, or a form of "computer choreography." (Taken from *Computers and the Visual Arts* by A. Michael Noll, Bell Laboratories. © A. Michael Noll, 1965.)

"Computer Choreography: The results of a very simple attempt at stick figure motion on a stage are shown by a sequence of movie frames. Each stick figure consists of a single line for the body, a single-line shoulder, and single-line arms. The arm positions are completely variable, and the size of each body element can be individually specified. The whole stick figure can be rotated to any specified angle and located at any position on the stage. In the particular example shown, six figures are used. Three move their arms uniformly up and down. The stage motion is random (any position is equally likely), but only one coordinate changes each time so that the motion is always parallel to the edges of the stage. The motion from position to position is at a uniform rate that is individually specified for each figure. At random times all stage motion ceases, and the three figures with the moving arms make one complete turn. The effect is reminiscent of the motion of atoms in a gas. The stage motion then continues. The three-dimensional movie was generated on the computer using the method described in the previous section.
"The above example demonstrates the possibilities for introducing controlled combinations of order and randomness. The stick figures used were quite simple but did, however, require many detailed specifications. The extension to more elaborate stick figures would require new programming techniques in which movement of the limbs is combined into basic movements which might then be combined on an even higher level. In this way the most complicated dance motion could be easily specified as a combination of relatively simple movements. Human movement is extremely complex, and obtaining the equations for as simple a motion as walking would be formidable. A better attack on this problem might be for the computer itself to analyze human motion, using devices that have just become available for converting pictorial data into machine-digestable data. A library of basic movements could be built up within the computer, and particular movements could then be put together at will." (Taken from *Computers and the Visual Arts* by A. Michael Noll, Bell Telephone Laboratories. © A. Michael Noll, 1965.)

5-41

5-41. *Computer Composition with Lines* by A. Michael Noll in association with an IBM digital computer and General Dynamics SC-4020 microfilm plotter. The computer is extremely adept at constructing purely mathematical pictures and hence should be of considerable value to Op artists. The drudgery of drawing or painting complex designs such as those in moiré patterns can be easily done by the machine.

"Since most 'Op' art is definitely mathematical it is not at all surprising that the computer can duplicate 'Op' paintings. However, what could the computer do with more abstract art? The approach to this problem was to attempt a quasi-random duplication with the computer of some abstract painting. The painting chosen for this investigation was Piet Mondrian's Composition With Lines (1917), now in the possession of the Rijksmuseum Kroller-Müller, Otterlo, the Netherlands. This black-and-white painting is from Mondrian's earlier period when he was experimenting with representations of the vertical and horizontal motifs of nature. Mondrian attached symbolic connotations of masculinity and femininity to the vertical and horizontal bars characteristic of these paintings. Composition With Lines was chosen because it was composed entirely of solid black bars which could be drawn very easily by the microfilm plotter.
"A cursory examination of Mondrian's painting reveals that (1) the outline of the painting is nearly circular except for the cropping of the sides, top, and bottom, (2) the bars falling within a region in the upper half of the painting are shortened in length, (3) the length and width of the bars otherwise appear random, and (4) the placement of the bars is not random but seems to follow some scheme so that the entire space is almost uniformly covered.
"A computer program was written utilizing the first three of the observations about Mondrian's painting. The placement of the bars was random with a uniform density. The vertical and horizontal bars were approximated as a series of closely-spaced, and therefore overlapping, parallel line segments. These bars were placed randomly within a circle of radius 450 units. The choice of vertical or horizontal bar was equally likely . . . A trial-and-error approach ensured that the final picture was reasonably similar to the Mondrian painting.

"Since the computer-generated picture looked somewhat like the Mondrian painting, questions now arose as to which picture was preferred. To answer this question, a psychological test was administered in which test subjects were given reproductions of both pictures. The subjects indicated which picture they most strongly liked or preferred. They were then told that one of the pictures was generated by a computer while the other was a picture of a painting by Piet Mondrian. The subjects were requested to indicate which picture was done by the computer. A total of 100 subjects participated in the test, and the majority were artistically naive.
"The test results indicated that 59 per cent of the subjects preferred the computer picture while only 28 per cent were able to correctly identify it as the computer picture." (Taken from *Computers and the Visual Arts* by A. Michael Noll, Bell Laboratories. © A. Michael Noll, 1965.)

THEODORE H.
nelson

COMPUTER THEORIST, NEW YORK CITY

5-42. Portrait of Theodor H. Nelson

Hyper-Tex (Xanadu), *developed by Theodor H. Nelson, is an IBM computer program that enables the operator to go deeper and deeper into the content of a given set of facts—a reference system that would be built into the computer program to give you more and more detail as you request it. Fantasm uses a computer program to create a full readout of visual reality.*

The inventor describes *Fantasm*

In any computer system, the biggest problem is how you organize the data, because on that hinges the question of how you process it, how you're going to look at it, how you will rearrange it. My projected Fantasm system is a complete and comprehensive system of a very large scope. The problems, however, are rather fewer than in certain other very large systems now being built. Fantasm is simple in its overall flow and the arrangement of its parts. You have a central box, the "scene machine," which is going to make the picture: data structures for the characters, sets, animation, and shots. A controlling program, or stage manager looks at the script, decides what sets are needed, sees and gets the sets from the library, goes and gets the character from the library, moves the character according to the script, and keeps on moving in new data as required for each new activity. The purpose is to make movies, television, advertising photographs, and any other realistic or fanciful photographs, without having subjects.

The system allows human creators to make realistic photographs of anything whatever, existent or nonexistent, in the following manner: a sculptor puts in the mountains, the valleys, the people, the houses. An animation puppeteer manipulates them, but the work may be revised; everything can be changed right up to the end. You can look at the thing on videotape and say, "It doesn't look right." Then you make the necessary changes and look at it again. When the work is finished, the system puts out a picture in black-and-white television, or color television, or in any appropriate photographic output: 35mm black and white, 16mm color, Panavision, binocular, even holograms.

To implement this design, you could either use computer software, running on a large time-sharing system, or, to do it very efficiently, you could build a special-purpose machine. I have designed two special-purpose machines: the Scene Machine, which holds representations of surfaces in space and allows their exploration, and a Leaf-and-Texture Machine, which is used for brickwork or clouds or trees. My hope is that these boxes can be made available as general I/O (input-output) devices for regular computers, along with supervisory programs, putting Fantasm capability into universities by 1975.

XANADU:

MOVABLE CROSSROADS OF A VAST TAPE AND DISK FILE,

WHOSE CONTENTS ARE STRUCTURED IN ANY PATTERNS, TO ANY DEGREE OF COMPLEXITY,

AND MAY BE CALLED TO THE SCREEN IN MANY RICH WAYS BASED UPON THEIR STRUCTURE.

5-43. Explanatory sketch by Nelson of his Xanadu text system. (Courtesy Theodor H. Nelson.)

5-44. Drawing by Nelson of his Fantasm system. (Courtesy Theodor H. Nelson.)

The divisible Fantasm array computes in parallel the related parts of a picture. Shown here is a Fantasm array divided in three, with each chamber of the whole containing data for the same curved, three-dimensional figure. An incident sight-line representing a point of the finished picture is presented to the first chamber as an angle vector. That chamber then finds where the sight-line hits the object. Hit-point and hit-angle pass to other sections, which calculate whether the point is in shadow, and, if desired, a hit-point of mirror reflection. The corresponding surface colors are then ascertained and blended to find the color of the picture formed.

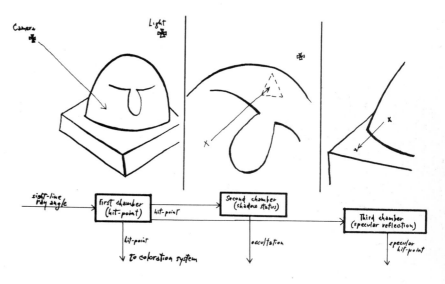

The divisible Fantasm array computes in parallel the related parts of a picture. Here shown is a Fantasm array divided in three, with each chamber of the whole containing data for the same curved three-dimensional figure.

An incident sight-line, representing a point of the finished picture, is presented to the first chamber as an angle vector. That chamber then finds where the sight-line hits the object. Hit-point and hit-angle pass to other sections, which calculate whether the point is in shadow and, if desired, a hit-point of mirror reflection.

The corresponding surface colors are then ascertained and blended to find the color of the picture-point.

6 technology: complete environmental simulation and spectator involvement

NASA (National Aeronautics and Space Agency) Simulation Techniques

Training men to carry on activities in a hostile environment has been dependent on their learning how to react correctly in emergencies. During World War II, pilots were trained in simulated cockpits with the instruments they would be using in flight. The instructor could create emergency situations, such as an abnormal loss of fuel from one of the wing tanks. The trainee was supposed to turn off the flow from this tank so that it would not jeopardize the supply in his other tanks.

The development of computers for simulation techniques has increased the efficiency of training. Astronauts needed to learn how to act when traveling at rates greater than the speed of sound, under conditions of weightlessness, and in the unknown lunar landscape. The simulators had to recreate conditions as they would actually be in flight and on another celestial body. Space views from the windows had to be three-dimensional, in color, and indicate the movement of the spacecraft on the three basic axes, so that it appeared to pitch, roll, and yaw. In some cases the physical environment for the astronaut-trainee had to be recreated. This meant simulating weightlessness, free-fall in space, the diminished gravity of the moon.

The technical term for this kind of simulation is "nonprogrammed real-world simulation." The real world had to be recreated in all its haphazard connotations. In driver-training schools, the student watches a film, and, as situations arise on the screen, he is expected to correct them with the mock wheel in front of him. The film, however, continues on its course, whether the student reacts correctly or not. In the nonprogrammed world of the astronaut, if he were to turn his spacecraft down the visual image would show him plunging to the earth. Without the computer, this simulation would be impossible. The computer can carry out instantaneous calculations, which in turn elicit from the simulation system the correct apparatus, which then changes the visual image the pilot sees.

The imagination of scientists knew no bounds. Environments designed for astronauts who would be walking on the moon's surface were made to look and appear to feel as the men on earth thought the moon would look and appear to feel. A desert in the American Southwest was chosen and the necessary changes were made in the physical features of the topography. The lunar soil and the lunar texture were simulated for a strange new environment.

Why go into computer-aided simulation in a discussion on art and technology? The simulator has achieved the image maker's long, long dream of creating a three-dimensional window into space, a window through which the illusion approximates reality.

Artists are developing environmental art, intent on involving the spectator as a participant in the aesthetic experience. There is a close relationship between participant art and nonprogrammed simulation techniques.

At the *Options* exhibit, held at the Institute of Contemporary Art in Chicago in 1969, a basic requirement demanded from each artist was that the work of art should be sensitive to spectator control. More than fifty artists showed works that depended upon various physical and sensory responses from the spectator in order to be activated. Pressure, movement, voice, and weight on sensitive pads evoked the experiences the artists sought to provide. Most works needed to be physically touched in order to set off optical and aural impressions. The significant aspect of this and other environmental art is the attempt to restructure the spectator's perception of reality, to bring reality to him in a new sensory form.

The simulator is a tool to be used essentially for scientific purposes. And yet, by a totally irrelevant process, the simulations serve as consummate examples of environmental art—in all technical respects superior to anything the artist has created. They represent the ultimate in audience participation, for *they respond directly to human control*. The technological breakthroughs that brought about these nonprogrammed real-world illusions exceed our comprehension. Their very existence seems quite unreal.

At present, the artist cannot expect to use simulation techniques such as those afforded to scientific and military purposes. In simple terms, cost is the only and final barrier. In time, however, as with all technology, what is costly today will be commonplace tomorrow. Such is the inevitable development and genius of technological evolution. These techniques will soon be made available to the artist. When they are, he will be quick, as he always has been, to adapt the new technology to his own creative purposes.

Joseph LaRussa

LaRussa is an engineering genius who developed the simulators for the Mercury, Gemini, and Apollo space programs. Each of these simulators provided the astronauts with complete visual experience before they underwent space flight. The Apollo simulator developed by LaRussa included the ability to place five simulators in the spacecraft windows. Each of the five simulators showed a particular view as the astronauts would look out various spacecraft windows. These illusions, created by the Farrand Optical simulators, included the full effect of the blastoff, penetration of the spacecraft through the cloud cover of the earth, and entry into earth orbit, complete with the star field above, the earth's horizon below. The simulator also recreated the effects of sunrise and sunset, and movement into space orbit. They were so accurate in their designation of the star field that the astronauts could take sextant readings of the star field through the spacecraft window. A unique aspect of LaRussa's simulation was the use of a virtual image system. An image was projected through the window of the spacecraft in such a manner that it had a full three-dimensional look. It was possible with the Apollo simulator developed by LaRussa to interject into this illusion of orbital reality from the spacecraft the approach of another spacecraft from a distance of several hundred miles to docking. Rendezvous and docking were practiced as well by the astronauts in the Apollo simulators.

Michael Collins

In an interview with the author former astronaut Michael Collins commented on the intensive training he underwent in the Kress and LaRussa simulators. He stressed the importance of these devices in preparation for space flight, particularly in anticipating unusual events and planning strategies for handling emergencies. It was apparent from this interview that the visual illusion of space flight in the simulators was less than perfect. It was, however, adequate to create the illusion of conditions in space. Collins indicated that the combined synchronization of the visual simulators with computer-articulation of all in-flight instrumentation comprised a remarkable technological achievement. Reading between the lines of the Collins remarks, it seems that he casts some doubt on NASA's wisdom in emphasizing simulation over other forms of pre-flight training. In sum, the simulator won its place in Collin's estimation in providing a "safe" laboratory to explore the aberant behavior of the astronaut and his spacecraft in the mundane surroundings of the Houston and Cape Kennedy simulation buildings.

Robert Kress

Kress developed a different kind of simulator for NASA at Grumman Aircraft Engineering Corporation. This simulator not only projects a three-dimensional black-and-white image into the cockpit of the lunar landing module, but at the same time it tests the on-board mechanisms of the craft. In other words, the Grumman simulator tests the flight hardware during the same time that it prepares the astronauts for the jobs of lunar landing, lunar takeoff, and lunar rendezvous with the command module.

Military Simulation Techniques

Lt. Commander Leon L. Stine, Jr.

When I interviewed Commander Stine, director of training devices at the New London U. S. Naval Submarine School, nestled in the rolling Connecticut countryside, he introduced me to a remarkable group of training simulators that actually recreate every motion and function of a submarine.

Here, mounted on large hydraulically-operated platforms, was an entire command station for a nuclear submarine. As a sub-commander trainee took the controls, the data that he would see if he were really operating such a ship was fed into the instrument panels and control mechanisms by a huge computer complex. In addition, to increase the sense of reality, huge hydraulic pistons tilted the platforms to the angle of ascent, descent, or horizontal mode called for by the action of the trainee.

Commander Stine invited me to step on the platform while he took the "ship" through a series of maneuvers. We were tilted in space as the entire control mechanism was activated to simulate reality. Stine explained that in training a new sub commander the training director could put into the control system a series of sophisticated malfunctions that might occur in actual operation. The speed with which the trainee responded to an emergency told his superiors how well he would react under operational conditions.

Interviews

Interviews with the personalities discussed in this chapter follow. Photographs illustrate the subject matter of the interviews and the theme of the chapter.

JOSEPH

la russa

VICE-PRESIDENT, ADVANCED ENGINEERING, FARRAND OPTICAL COMPANY, INC., NEW YORK CITY

A conversation with LaRussa leads one to the stars and lands one on the moon.

KRANZ. *In a sense don't you consider yourself to be sort of a magician?*

LaRUSSA. Well, I suppose the whole object of this simulation game is to fool somebody, and, if that is what you mean, I guess yes, that's what we are.

KRANZ. *Why would people simulate something? What is the purpose of simulation?*

LaRUSSA. In the case of aircraft simulation, I think it's not only a matter of safety, where you are not really flying the aircraft, but it's also a matter of economics, where you don't spend as much money as flying with real aircraft. You might say the same thing of space flight. Here, however, something else enters into the picture, and that is the safety of the people involved. We can't afford to send up so many capsules that we could train a host of astronauts. Therefore we have to do the best we can in simulating the environment up there, and we hope that it is faithful and will have some training value for the people who will eventually go up.

KRANZ. *Commander Wally Schirra made the statement that the view from the spacecraft was identical to what he had experienced in the simulator. Would you confirm that statement?*

LaRUSSA. Yes, he did make that statement in a public interview. We certainly tried hard enough to reproduce all the colors of the earth orbital views and an accurate celestial sphere. The infinity display helps, of course.

(Author's Note: The interview with Joseph LaRussa on December 10, 1968, was dramatically substantiated in April 1970, when the trouble-plagued Apollo 13 mission proved the value of the simulator. During the emergency return to earth, each contemplated move by the astronauts was tested in ground simulators. The realigning of the LEM gyro-stabilizer was confirmed by the ground simulator. Visibility of the star field had been distorted by debris from the service module explosion. It is quite likely that the simulator procedures established on the earth saved the ill-fated mission from disaster.)

6-1. Portrait of Joseph LaRussa, taken by the author at the Farrand Optical Company.

6-2. Artist's conception of Apollo mission simulator. Apollo command module, facing upward, at left. Each of five windows has a simulator. The console for monitoring flight is at right, the computer banks are in the rear. (Photograph courtesy Farrand Optical Company, Inc. Original art by Robert C. Sherry, Art Director, Singer-General Precision, Inc., Link Division.)

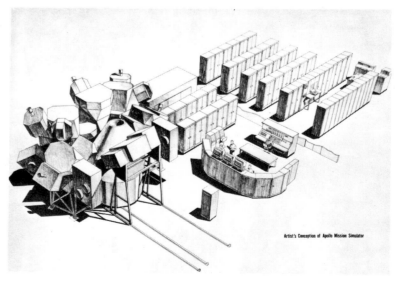

6-3. Astronauts William A. Anders, Michael Collins, and Frank Borman (reading down from top of stairs) are about to enter the Apollo command module mission simulator. Inset shows interior view with the three astronauts in the command module. (Courtesy NASA, Houston, Texas.)

MICHAEL
Collins

ASTRONAUT ON THE COMMAND MODULE PILOT FOR THE APOLLO 11 FLIGHT.
NOW DIRECTOR OF THE NATIONAL AIR AND SPACE MUSEUM, THE SMITHSONIAN INSTITUTION, WASHINGTON, D.C.

KRANZ. *What significance did the simulator have for you in your training for the Apollo 11 space flight?*

COLLINS. As the system is structured, we could not have gotten to the moon without the simulators. The simulators were an integral part of our training. We spent our lives, literally, living inside the simulator. In the last few months before the flight, I spent about 400 hours in the Command Module Simulator. So they were very, very important.

It's a moot point whether it had to be that way, but that's the way it was. That was the way NASA structured the system, and, I think, very intelligently so. Neil Armstrong would not know how to land at all on the surface of the moon had he not practiced time and time again in the simulator. The chain is only as strong as the weakest link. They were a link, and without the simulators we never could have performed the mission.

KRANZ. *Did the visual images that were created in the Command Module Simulator represent effectively what you saw when you were in space? The star field, for example—I understand you were able to take a reading in the simulator, using a sextant?*

COLLINS. The visual was very good in some ways, and very poor in others. It was very good in regard to the star field. A star field is an easy thing to duplicate. Nearly every planetarium has a star field just as good or better than the one we have in the simulator. The star field is essential in performing navigational fixes, so it was important from that point of view. The visual simulation of the earth and of the moon and approaching vehicles was not particularly good, but it did not have to be especially good. It was crude, but good enough. The star field was much more sophisticated, and much more accurate.

KRANZ. *Did the physical simulators, where you actually were moved in space, also add to your appreciation of what you were going to experience?*

COLLINS. Yes. But relatively speaking, those were not nearly so important as the fixed base simulators, the ones that just sat there. The most important ones were the Command Module Simulator and the Lunar Module Simulator. They are really engineering tools hooked onto a huge array of computers, which can be fed equations of motions and other technical parameters, and feed very, very accurate information to the instruments in the cockpit.

KRANZ. *As I understand it, on that one mission that had to abort because of failure in the system of the Command Module, the problems on how to get the mission back were actually figured out on the simulators.*

COLLINS. Yes. Whenever they have problems in flight—relatively long-term ones that can wait several hours, or several days, for solution—it is possible to duplicate on the ground the exact condition that is taking place in flight and to try to map out a strategy for solving it.

Now this is not the ideal way to go. Ideally what you would do is to ask yourself before you ever fly, "What happens if?" And if you ask yourself enough "What happens if?" questions, you compile a complete library on it. Then when some bad thing does happen, you just go

6-4. Portrait of Michael Collins. (Courtesy the Smithsonian Institution Archives.)

6-5. Rendezvous docking simulator at the NASA Langley Research Center. (Courtesy NASA, Houston, Texas.)

Ingenious devices like the rendezvous docking simulator, shown here at the NASA Langley Research Center, are being developed by NASA scientists to explore under controlled laboratory conditions many complex aspects of space flight. The facility will enable scientists to determine man's ability to complete a rendezvous in either earth or lunar orbit using the scale model of the Gemini spacecraft, and by operating its controls bring it into gentle, final contact with a target vehicle. The simulator spacecraft and the target hang on cables from an overhead track. The target can move vertically and laterally, but the spacecraft is capable of all six degrees of freedom of mechanical motion.

6-6. "Look Ma, no wings"—The lunar landing research model (LLRV) is brought to a hover over Rogers Dry Lake, California, by NASA test pilot Donald Mallick prior to making a descent and landing. The wingless machine, built for NASA by Bell Aerosystems, simulated problems of landing a manned spacecraft on the moon in low-gravity conditions. (Courtesy NASA, Houston, Texas.)

to Volume 11, Page 94, Paragraph A, and you get the answer. You have thought of this ahead of time, and you have validated it on the simulator ahead of time, so you know the answer.

Obviously, nobody is that smart—to foresee each and every possibility. So the simulator is a way of filling the chinks, if you will. Those outlandish possibilities for failure, which you did not consider but which nonetheless sometimes happen, can in some limited cases be checked out on the simulator on the ground. Now the simulator certainly is not perfect. It sits in a room, with fifteen pounds per square inch of air pressure. It doesn't work in a vacuum. It doesn't live in weightlessness. Some things the simulator does very well, some very poorly, but within the framework of what it was designed to do, it is a very powerful tool.

6-7. Astronauts practice lunar surface activities at the Manned Spacecraft Center, Houston, Texas. (Courtesy NASA, Houston, Texas.)

6-8. Five-degree manned simulator used to test astronauts' human capabilities during high G forces. (Courtesy NASA, Houston, Texas.)

6-9. Astronaut is instrumented for various physical tests. A gigantic electromagnet will literally shake him in a manner simulating rocket blastoff atmosphere and reentry buffeting. (Courtesy NASA, Houston, Texas.)

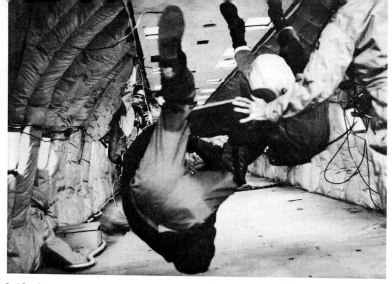

6-10. Astronaut trainees participating in weightless flight. (Courtesy NASA, Houston, Texas.)

6-11. Six degrees of freedom—John B. ("Jack") Slight, project engineer and test subject on the six degrees of operational freedom simulator, demonstrates the capability of the machine in zero-gravity simulations. (Courtesy NASA, Houston, Texas.)

6-12. A technique for simulating zero-gravity performance of a test subject in a pressurized suit by complete immersion in water. (Courtesy NASA, Houston, Texas.)

The technique allows a subject to move in six degrees of freedom without the encumbrance of connecting lines or hoses or other supports and further permits performance simulating of long-duration tasks. The ingress-egress activity characterizes a set of maneuvers in which the weightless subject operates in a pressurized space suit within the constraints of a spacecraft air-lock system.

ROBERT
kress

ENGINEER, GRUMMAN AIRCRAFT ENGINEERING CORPORATION, NEW YORK

Robert Kress, who developed the virtual image simulation system for the lunar landing module manufactured at the Grumman plant, described the system in laymen's terms in an interview with the author.

Basically, the display systems were intended for simulation of the lunar landing mission of the lunar module (LEM) spacecraft. The system that we have consists of a large analogue/digital computer system, which is tied into a cockpit of the lunar vehicle. In the cockpit of the vehicle are all the instruments and controls that the pilot normally uses to fly the mission. One of the primaries that we were working with was the actual final phase of the landing on the moon, which is mainly a manual-piloted flying mission. As the pilot maneuvers the spacecraft, using his thrust

6-13. Portrait of Robert Kress.

control and his attitude controller, the control signals from these two devices are sent up to the computer system; the computer calculates what the motions of the vehicle would be in response to these computer signals, and these motions of the spacecraft are sent back down to his cockpit, where they register on his cockpit instruments. In addition, the motions of the spacecraft are sent to an image-generation system. This image-generation system consists of a set of lunar relief maps, which are three-dimensional, and these maps are scanned by a massive camera transport system. The radar pedestal and the extension boom serve to place this scanning optical head in the right position over the lunar map. Now the scanning optical head simulates the rotational motions of the spacecraft over whatever point it is at above the terrain. This image is then sent over to a television monitor, which is located in close proximity to the front of the cockpit. Basically the way that this image is presented to the pilot is with what we call the virtual image system. We take the monitor face; we put it through a pair of magnifying lenses, which makes a larger image, which is then presented at the focal plane of the parabolic mirror dish. And that means that when you look into that dish, you see every point on the image, and hence every point on the face of the monitor, as if at an infinite distance from you.

KRANZ. *This illusion, then, is virtually what the astronaut would see if he were looking out an actual window?*

KRESS. Yes, but what he's seeing, really, is the monitor face as if it were off in infinity.

KRANZ. *Now the computers are presumably the ones that manage this very complicated series of relationships. I think you mentioned that there are two kinds of information that have to be fed into this image that's projected: one is the image of the surface of the moon. But what if they should have an image that shows the edge of the moon—do you also have a way to simulate the solar system?*

KRESS. Yes, there is a way. We really use a three-camera television system. Now one of the cameras is producing an image of the lunar surface, as I described. It is basically a high-contrast image.

A second camera, looking at the same lunar surface, produces a low-contrast, high-brightness image. That is,

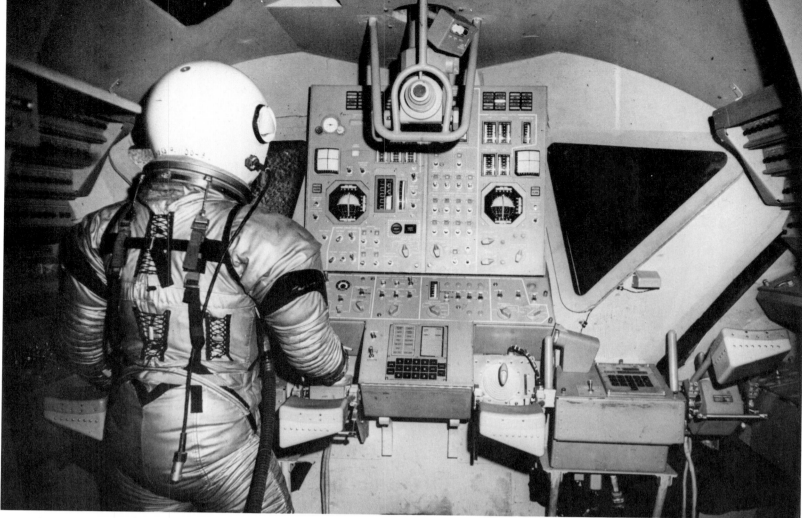

6-14. Astronaut at the control panel of lunar module. (Courtesy Grumman Aircraft Engineering Corporation.)

6-15. The illusion the astronaut sees through the window of the simulator. (Courtesy Grumman Aircraft Engineering Corporation.)

6-16. Circumference of the surface of the moon used in generating a simulated lunar surface. As the TV camera rotates, the astronaut has the impression of flying over the moon's surface. The other simulated (flat) lunar surface, at lower right, is used for obtaining landing simulations (Courtesy Grumman Aircraft Engineering Corporation.)

6-17. Navigation and guidance equipment integration. (Courtesy Grumman Aircraft Engineering Corporation.)

areas appearing as deep shadows on the high-contrast camera, appear as lighter areas on the second camera. This is all done by use of dichroic filters and blue/yellow color on the relief maps. What is the purpose of this second low-contrast image? To explain this we must first refer to the image being generated by a third camera.

The third camera is looking at a sphere studded with steel ball bearings, which, when illuminated by a remote light source, appear as stars in a heaven turned inside-out. Computer signals rotate this ball in correspondence with the spacecraft motions.

Now the first lunar surface camera and the third starfield camera images are electronically mixed to provide the final picture. Stars will shine through the dark heaven area of the lunar surface picture as required, but they would also shine from shadow areas in the surface, were it not for the second camera. The low-contrast lunar surface "keying image," which has some brightness in shadow areas, is used to blank out stars in those regions.

LT. COMMANDER LEON L.
stine, jr.

DIRECTOR OF TRAINING DEVICES, U.S. NAVAL SUBMARINE SCHOOL, NEW LONDON, CONNECTICUT

Commander Leon L. Stine, director of training devices at the U.S. Naval Submarine School, New London, Connecticut, showed me submarine simulators mounted on hydraulic platforms that physically change the altitude, inclination, roll, pitch, and yaw movements of the submarine trainer as the trainee activates the submarine controls.

A sidelight on human reactions to a reality, which is only seeming, comes from Richard Braby, simulation specialist at the U.S. Naval Training Center in Orlando, Florida. In the late fifties, he worked with simulators, using a point light source to project the illusion of flight over low-level ground. As the pilot at the simulator controls called for a particular movement in space, the point light source would automatically respond to computer direction. When these simulators were first used seasoned helicopter pilots became ill while training in them. Psychologists were puzzled. It was finally discovered that the simulator, although it presented an effective visual illusion of movement, did not have the physical vibrations that are integral to the feeling of being in an aircraft. The fact that one signal was present (the moving visual field) and yet an equally important signal was lacking (the shaking of the seat from the plane's vibrations) made the difference that caused the pilots' nausea.

KRANZ. *Commander Stine, would you describe in layman's language some of the conditions that the training officer can put into the simulator?*

STINE. He can create situations that call for a response on the part of the trainee. He can disable the equipment. He can cause the trainee to no longer have the use of the stern planes, or the bow planes, or the rudder. He can cause a leak of almost any size and in any compartment of the ship. This is pretty much the final examination for the casualty training courses—to impose a very large leak at a very deep depth. And I might add that trainees very frequently don't pass, because it's impossible for the ship to survive under these conditions. This is good training

6-18. Lt. Commander Leon L. Stine Jr. at the submarine school in New London, Connecticut.

Students are in a simulator, a device that can tip in any of the physical axes. It can pitch, roll, and yaw, the three basic maneuvers of a submarine. The entire simulator is programmed by computer, and as the trainees call for a certain function, the simulator actually moves into the position that they would physically be in had that function been demanded in an actual submarine.

6-18

if you figure that it reinforces the desire to avoid this kind of situation.

KRANZ. *Could you list the various characteristics of ship performance that you can simulate?*

STINE. Yes. We can simulate the shipboard effects of the attitude of the ship, that is the angle of the control surfaces or planes; the effects of the depth; the effects of the sea state—how rough the seas are, which does have an effect on the ship at fairly deep depths. The propulsion—that is, the speed through the water—and also the acceleration if the propulsion setup is changed. The rudder angle and the weight of the ship, that is, the buoyancy, should be near zero, but sometimes it is negative buoyancy or positive buoyancy, and there is a tendency for the ship in a static condition to rise or go deeper.

KRANZ. *That gives a good review of the diving simulation. Can we now turn our attention to the attack simulators and the situations they can create?*

STINE. Actually, all these computer programs do is tell you what you've got available or make available to you what you want. They simulate the characteristics of our own ship and of the target vehicles, and these target vehicles can range from other submarines to surface ships. They simulate the weapon characteristics, and they simulate the environmental conditions, primarily the sonar conditions. They don't really say, "This ship is doing this at this particular time." They simply say, "We have a vehicle that is capable of doing such and such a speed at such and such a depth," and this type of thing.

KRANZ. *Wartime conditions being rare, would you comment on the value of the attack simulators for training?*

STINE. I think it's fantastic. I'll go even further than that. There's some training that you simply cannot conduct. For example, there are certain weapons that we simply cannot use at sea, even in practice. Perhaps the reason may be less exotic than you might think, such as that they're very expensive and we don't like to lose them. Or perhaps they are of sufficiently high velocity so that our weapon running into another ship would cause it serious damage. These situations have to be done in the simulated attack centers. It simply wouldn't be possible to do out at sea.

7 toward environmental art: precursors of environmental illusions and spectator-activated art

Enlarged Field Painting

The media-based contemporary artist grew out of a relatively recent vintage in American art. The concept of involving the spectator in an environment is not a new one. We need only to recall the great baroque churches. In their elaborate and emotionally charged environments, the Counter Reformation found its full physical expression. The Catholic church, suffering from the inroads of Protestantism, sought to provide the surroundings that would involve the devout, and the wavering, in a compelling emotional and spiritual experience.

The churches of Bernini and the Tiepolo show the uses to which sculpture, paintings, and architecture can be put for an overwhelming environmental effect. Contorted figures of baroque sculpture merge with wall and ceiling paintings to extend the architecture of the churches. Enormous murals cover the walls and ceilings.

Early enlarged-field painting can best be explained through the work of the Baroque painters. Murals were designed to cover both the walls and ceilings of the church. At the point where the physical architecture, with its Baroque pillasters, columns, and decorative sculpture, left off and the mural began, the ingenious muralist would adjust his painting's perspective sight-lines to conform to the actual visual perspective that the spectator, standing below, would perceive for the physical architecture. We must remember that the scale of these Baroque churches was so monumental that children and adults standing hundreds of feet below on the church floor would have a similar perspective view of the painted murals and the upper building architecture. As they looked up, the "boundary" between the physical architectural reality and the painter's mural illusion was cleverly disguised. Often, to increase the deception, the artist inserted painted architectural and sculptural elements at the "boundary" point between mural and reality. As he developed his mural, he could then introduce atmospheric effects until his "space" was pure visual illusion. Then he would introduce fantasy and ethereal regions, complete with flying cherubim and angels far, far above the heads of the adoring congregation.

Sculptural embellishment, painting, structural space, and powerful liturgy were brought together in what surely must have been a moving environmental experience.

During the middle and late nineteenth century, a typically American environmental art movement developed. Entrepreneur painters created huge cycloramas in which great moments in history were depicted. The canvases, some of them hundreds of feet in diameter, were staked out in a circle. Often, sculptural objects were placed in the foreground. Admission was charged and people flocked from miles around to see the spectacle. This kind of painting can be called enlarged-field painting, because the canvas is so large that the spectator is literally enveloped, and the feeling of historic moment is made palpable.

In essence, enlarged-field painting takes into account the size of the human being. The area of the canvas is then scaled large enough to literally enclose him as he gazes. The degree of involvement depends upon his relevant distance from the painting. In usual gallery situations, the scale relationship can be manipulated so that the spectator has the feeling of being in the presence of a monumental work of art.

In the two decades after World War II, enlarged-field painting became almost the order of the day for American abstract painters. Both formal abstractionists and Abstract Expressionists moved toward larger and larger canvases, in which the painting became an impressive aspect of the total space. Helen Frankenthaler and Adolph Gottlieb are leading painters in this genre.

The concept of environmental art in terms of enlarged-field painting extended from the Abstract Expressionist movement into the so-called Pop Art movement. An example of this could be the work by James Rosenquist entitled *F-111*, exhibited at the Metropolitan Museum of Art. (See color illustrations C-4—C-11 on page 26.) In this case, the enlarged-scale painting enveloped the spectator on three sides of an enclosed space.

Adolph Gottlieb

Adolph Gottlieb met me for our first interview at the Whitney Museum of Art where he was having the gratification of seeing his own magnificent retrospective show. His special importance as an American artist was clearly expressed by the huge canvasses that, with great elegance, commanded the Whitney interior space. He also employed a series of multiple related canvasses as modern triptych.

Gottlieb is an intelligent and affable man. After our interview he invited me to his studio where we continued our talk. His studio loft is in the same building as that of Roy Lichtenstein, also interviewed for this book. In the studio, Gottlieb showed me more of his fine works, and then we spent some time in his living room, where his paintings are a backdrop for conversation on the history of contemporary art.

Sensing the theme of this book, he showed me a computer-generated copy of one of his paintings, produced by a special process developed at the Whitney Museum, with the cooperation of a commercial reproduction house. In this process paints are mixed and applied with complete accuracy, including color value, textural elements, and an uncanny sense of the artist's style.

Gottlieb's joy in living is reflected in his painting, his conversation, and his way of life.

Helen Frankenthaler

Helen Frankenthaler is a beautiful, charming, and totally gifted artist. One simply shrinks in her presence, for it seems that the gods went a little overboard in handing out so much to one person. Fortunately, I had the pleasure of visiting her in her pleasant studio in midtown Manhattan.

The studio was filled with her large, elegant, abstract canvasses. She paints them while the canvas is stretched horizontally on the floor of the studio, and the floorboards in themselves create attractive abstractions. During the interview, she bridled a bit when I asked her about being a woman artist. She was correct in her rebuke that the entire concept of sex as related to the artist's creation is a gratuitous belittlement from a male-dominated world.

I found her to be urbane, direct, and much like the clean clarity of her paintings. She has already established herself as one of the important American painters of our time. Her ability to deal with large scale in such a bold way helped to develope the concept of enlarged-field painting.

Environmental Sculpture

George Segal

With the advent of the Pop Art movement and also the environmental enlarged-field painting, it was inevitable that sculptors would turn to the concept of environmental sculpture. A brilliant exponent of this style is George Segal. Segal, in his work, has epitomized many of the most poignant aspects of a highly materialistic culture. His environments draw much of their impact from the use of ordinary objects of daily living. The viewer is shocked into a fresh perception of reality as he moves through the world of George Segal.

Segal's method is to use the human figure as his armature. He covers the model with thinly-layered plaster, then takes various sections of this "cast" and restructures them. The resulting figures, derived directly from a living person, have the nuances of the human model, yet they are transformed in an almost mystical way into something more than human by the genius of the sculptor. The unembellished white figures are placed among and in props from our culture—a kitchen chair and table, a small-town movie ticket office, a motel room. Segal's reconstructed reality becomes a compelling commentary, an inadvertent and disturbing insight into areas of the American environment that we often choose to ignore.

Interviews

Interviews with the personalities discussed in this chapter follow. All illustrations are in color, pages 159, 162.)

ADOLPH

gottlieb

ENLARGED-FIELD PAINTER, NEW YORK CITY

Why I became an artist? It's very simple. I made up my mind not to spend my life in a dull job that would be a waste of time; this was not what I wanted to do in the short span of a lifetime. I wanted to do something that I felt was meaningful and interesting, and I felt that if I had the ability I would be an artist, and so I tried it.

Critics never seem to be able to put me into a category. I thought they held it against me so I decided I'd give them a cubbyhole into which they could put me, and I called my paintings pictographs. Though I had been painting for many years and had had a certain success, people thought these weren't really paintings and that I didn't know how to paint. Well, since they weren't paintings, they were something else. They were pictographs.

It was a form of communication that had to do with my subconscious; a kind of automatic writing, which stemmed from a stream of consciousness. I was trying to arrive at a kind of subject matter that didn't depend on the exterior world—the visual world that painting has always dealt with. When painters painted angels, they always painted them as though they were real girls. I had to find some other way of expressing what I wanted to express, a way that was not in terms of this visual reality around me. Some of the ways were signs and symbols that referred to my experience and certain feelings. A painter is involved in acting out on the canvas what he thinks and feels.

When I started working in my present direction, I gave titles to a couple of paintings. The way I give titles is by looking at the painting, thinking of what it suggests. I want the title to be ambiguous, not too specific. So I used two titles: one was *Burst* and one was *Blast*. People apparently caught on to this *burst* title, and they kept using it indiscriminately, so that now I even find *myself* referring to these paintings as "bursts." The paintings had an explosive quality—blast and burst—I don't make much distinction. All sorts of associations occurred to various people. The atomic bomb. Things like that, which I didn't have in mind at all. Perhaps it was in my subconscious.

The basic concept was the reconciliation of disparate images. It has always been my effort to resolve these differences, to achieve a unity and a oneness. This exists in my work, whether it was in the pictographs or the present bursts and blasts. In many of my paintings I use the disc, which is a very calm contained form, with another form, which is ragged at the edges, not contained at all but trying to break out from its confines.

On his technique of painting

I do everything. I am not doctrinaire. I attack paintings from every direction and I believe in doing what is necessary to express what I want to express. If I can do it with just two brush strokes, then I do it. There is a painting, for example, that is a white ground with a red dot and a black shape like an upside down *E*. There is nothing there but just those two strokes. That's all there is. That's what I wanted. That's all I needed. I didn't need anything more.

continued

opposite

C-50. Artist Adolph Gottlieb and his interviewer are dwarfed before a Gottlieb painting at the Whitney Museum exhibit of his work.

C-51. Artists-in-Residence. AIR$_4$ and AIR$_6$ inform the Fire Department that artists Adolph Gottlieb and Roy Lichtenstein are in residence in this East Village building, New York City.

C-52. Skylight brightens stairway leading to Gottlieb's studio.

C-53. Gottlieb standing next to one of his paintings in his studio.

C-54. Gottlieb beside a rather remarkable example of a collaboration of science and art: the classic computer-painting-reproduction technique inaugurated by the Whitney Museum of Art, New York City, in conjunction with the Slide-a-Chrome Corporation.

C-55. Adolph Gotlieb and his paints.

C-56. The living room adjoining Gottlieb's studio.

C-57. Helen Frankenthaler with one of her large-field paintings. Spectator is diminished.

C-58. Frankenthaler in her studio. "When I'm asked what kind of a painter I am, I say I'm an abstract painter."

C-59. Book-corner in Frankenthaler's studio.

C-60. Long view of the studio.

C-61. "I paint most pictures on the floor."

C-62. Frankenthaler with one of her floor paintings.

C-63. An artist's tools: paints and brushes.

C-64. An artist's tools: rolled-up canvas.

C-65. Helen Frankenthaler in gallery where her work was on exhibit.

(Photographs by Michael Fredericks, Jr. Courtesy Adolf Gottlieb, Helen Frankenthaler.)

C-51

C-52

C-53

C-54

C-50

C-55

C-56

C-57

ADOLPH GOTTLIEB/HELEN FRANKENTHALER

C-58

C-59

C-60

C-61

C-62

C-63

C-64

C-65

On museums

The museum is the free university for the artist or for the art historian or for the layman. The people have to go to the museums. Even though you have organizations, like the American Federation of Arts, sending shows on tour, they cannot send the really great paintings because the museums will not permit these to travel. And rightly so. If one wants to be a writer, he can read all the great books that have ever been written. Through the medium of the printing press it is possible for everyone to have all of literature at his fingertips. You cannot do this with art, and I think that is the whole problem. Most of our art education consists of showing transparencies and color reproductions, which have nothing to do with the actual work. They are wrong in scale. They are wrong in texture. I think there is only one place to study art and that's in the museums. Looking at the original paintings.

The urban center is the key to the whole thing. That's where you have the museums, the congregation of artists, writers, musicians, intellectuals. This is where the proper cultural climate exists for any endeavor in the field of art. Museums have the treasures of the past, and the art galleries have the most interesting things that are happening currently.

(Color reproductions of Gottleib paintings appear on page 159.)

HELEN
frankenthaler
ENLARGED-FIELD ABSTRACTIONIST, NEW YORK CITY

I am an abstract painter. I paint most pictures on the floor. I usually unroll a large roll of unsized, unprimed cotton duck and staple it to the floor so that it is taut. I work on it unstretched, because that gives more flexibility in the final size. I might roll out more canvas than I thought I would originally, or when the picture is completed I may cut it down considerably on one, two, three, or four sides. What was the top of the picture might turn out to be the bottom of the picture. I find if I start out with a preconceived notion about the exact placement of the drawing, or color, and the size of the canvas itself, very often, midway through, the picture dictates something else to me, and I need more space or less space or a different set of limits.

I mix the paint in large pails or pans. I usually pour the paint, or brush it on, or start with a brush or a line or a pool of paint, and proceed from there. I use what is called for at the moment. It might be my hand. It might be a brush. It might be a ruler. It might be pouring the contents of a glass or a pail.

What usually happens over a year, or a year and a half, is that I do many pictures, destroy many, change my mind about whether I like them or don't like them, change the dimensions over the months, add to them, let them cook. Then, to hang a show it's a weeding-out process: deciding which eight or ten pictures of this group present something that is your identity and has your values and is a development for you.

I think that when success is the goal art goes out the window.

It is important to try out and experiment with mediums, because this can force you to develop new problems and motivations for the drawing of the picture itself. Very often, if you don't have enough of a certain color, or if one of your window shades doesn't pull up, or if you are forced to move your studio—suddenly you can get a whole shift in sensibility and result.

It is important for everyone to be true to himself and express what he feels. One should support what he believes in.

(Color reproductions of Frankenthaler paintings appear on page 159.)

GEORGE
segal

ENVIRONMENTAL SCULPTOR, NORTHERN NEW JERSEY

George Segal studied painting under the Abstract Expressionists at New York University. They were at the crest of the wave and had just achieved recognition.

I was interested in art, knew I couldn't make a living at it, and figured I'd take a few education courses so that I could teach it. I graduated pretty confused. All I knew was that I wanted to be a painter but didn't have the tools. I didn't feel comfortable with my teaching, so when I got out of school, I built up my farm. I built the place up to a point where I could sneak upstairs and do my own kind of painting. I painted for about ten years before I went into sculpture. I suppose everybody who wants to be an artist has a rough time coming to his own self in the work. Artist or not, everybody has a problem knowing who he is, becoming defined as a person.

Every generation of artists has to thrash around for a way to state the quality of their particular experience.

In the struggle to find themselves, quite a few artists decided along the line that there was no bad subject matter. The subject matter wasn't crucial because it was more or less a springboard for other responses. Once you decide that anything is subject matter, you are not limited to noble things. You are not limited to portraits of rich men. You are not limited to religious themes to line a church wall. You can deal with the cup and saucer in front of you at the breakfast table. You can deal with the headlights on a car approaching you. You can deal with the woman in bed next to you. You can deal with a toilet. You can deal with a bedroom. You can deal with the highway, the city, streets, cracks in the sidewalk, your dogs, cats. You can deal with anything you encounter physically and visually every day, plus your own sensations. All right, if you start from that point, then the contents of a supermarket are as valid as some beach or romantic natural landscape. People misread Pop paintings. They criticize them in terms of billboards and commercial images. That is not an accurate evaluation of the real attitudes behind the Pop works.

There is the liberation of subject matter, and the liberation of materials. I feel free to use any material in the real world in my work. I can make, build, or incorporate what I find. I can use the expressive qualities of anything that attracts me—the side of a wall, a table, a chair, a person. I can deal with anything in the real world—from heavy to floating. I can deal with it on an intense personal level, historic myth, social content. The choice is mine. It doesn't guarantee good art.

As naturalistic as my work is, I still make a lot of hidden transformations. I am wrenching and twisting qualities that are buried in objects, in their shape and their color and their texture. This is aside from the associations with objects as we use them. We use a chair to sit on, but there are 10,000 kinds of chairs. I am sitting on a kitchen chair. It would be different if I were sitting on a Louis XVI chair with a silk-and-velvet seat.

My first sculptures were traditional. I made the form, and the armature underneath. I was interested in figures —the gesture, movement. I discovered I was interested in something else—some sense of precision, of hard edge, of reportage. I wanted to deal with real form. Every sculptor has his problem: what is the armature going to be? I simply decided that my armature was going to be a person, because a person is capable of infinite variations.

A couple of times I tried combining parts of one figure to make a composite, and that's weird. If you take a whole figure and put somebody else's finger on it, it literally sticks out like a sore thumb. There's an incredible consistency in each of us miserable hunks of human flesh. Our fingers have something to do with the way our ears are shaped. Once you start dealing with a human figure in this way, you find that each person is connected with himself. There are a lot of funny, subtle truths about a human figure. Take manikins, those horrible lifeless creatures in store windows. They start out with a cast of a beautiful knee and perfect breasts or head or neck and put all these dream perfections together and end up with an impossible-looking creature.

(Color reproductions of Segal works are shown overleaf.)

C-66. George Segal's home and workshop—a farmhouse in northern New Jersey.

C-67. George Segal in his studio. Note work in progress.

C-68. "The dentist's office."

C-69. "Theater marquee and lonely ticket-taker."

C-70. "Old woman sewing in a dress shop, by day."

C-71. "Old woman sewing in a dress shop, by night."

C-72. Close-up of old woman sewing in a dress shop.

C-73. Sexual encounter stripped to its lonely essence in a motel room.

C-74. Another view of the motel room.

C-75. Motel room scene.

(Photographs by Michael Fredericks, Jr. Courtesy The Metropolitan Museum of Art, Education Department, Harry S. Parker, Chairman.)

C-66

GEORGE SEGAL

C-67

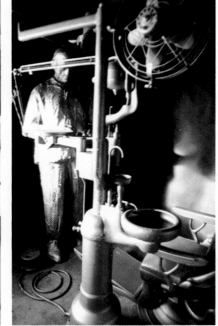

C-68

C-70

C-71

C-72

C-69

C-73

C-74

C-75

8 the language of intermedia, mixed media, environmental art

The artist has always been a craftsman. Each medium he has used has demanded a specific technical proficiency. The earliest potters had to have a knowledge of the location of the clay, the best kinds of clay for various types of pots, and how to shape the clay. One of the earliest solutions for shaping was the potter's wheel, driven by the foot or some mechanical force. He had to learn how to dry the clay so it would not crack, and how to fire it to make it nonporous. Finally, he had to learn how to glaze it or decorate it through a number of firings. In each step of the process, he had to know which tools best manipulated the clay or pot. Throughout history, artists have handled the tools and materials best suited to their time and type of art. The intermedia artist continues this tradition.

The Still Photograph (The Transposed Image)

The still photograph is important in the language of the intermedia artist. One would think this hundred-year-old technique might have been supplanted by kinetic imagery, such as the motion picture and videotape. But the still image has timeless qualities. A still photograph has the power to lodge itself indelibly in the human memory. One can recall single photographs that stand for an idea or an era in history: Chamberlain returning from Czechoslovakia, Franklin Delano Roosevelt meeting with Churchill and Stalin at Yalta; the Hindenburg dirigible burning at Lakehurst, New Jersey; the explosion of the atomic bomb over Hiroshima.

The intermedia artist has discovered the importance of this image, either by itself or mixed with kinetic images of multiple projection.

Recent developments in equipment have extended the possibilities for artistic expression: solarized photographs, high-contrast positive and negative images, black-and-white and colored images, stroboscopic photographs, and photographs in which the still camera is panned during the exposure period. New lenses are also being used—the zoom, the telephoto, the wide-angle, and the fisheye.

Marvin C. Whatmore and Arthur Rothstein

Marvin Whatmore, president of Cowles Communications in New York, has had a profound effect on the development of the still graphic image. Before anyone even imagined that television with its kinetic images would assassinate the picture magazines, Whatmore was experimenting with *Look* to increase its visual impact. He led the movement to color photography in mass magazines but he still sought a method to recreate the full illusion of visual reality. The problem was to develop a three-dimensional photograph that could be mass produced in enormous runs required for magazines such as *Look* and *Life,* then extant. He was very fortunate to have Arthur Roth-

stein, a master still photographer, on his staff. Together they began to explore the concept of "three-dimensional" photography. The stereoptican of the late nineteenth century utilized a divided screen so that each eye would see a slightly altered view of the same photographic scene. This was all well and good if you possessed a stereoptican with independent visual information for the left and right eye. On the other hand, if you wish to achieve separation of images for both eyes on the flat printed page of a mass magazine, the "masking" of both separate images must take a different form. Whatmore and Rothstein developed a camera called a parallax-panoramagram. (See figures 8-1A, B and 8-2). This camera used a unique masking system, which took literally hundreds of dual views of a subject to create a special negative. The camera moved while the subject remained stationary. Then a special plastic sheet was superimposed over the color print made from the negative. When the special print with its plastic "lens" was printed in *Look* magazine, showing a bust of Thomas Edison, the result was the first three-dimensional photograph ever reproduced for a mass magazine.

H. Albert Unger, Jr.

I first met Howard Unger when he joined my art class at Ardsley High School in 1963; there was no indication then that he would become an important creative photographer. Unger studied at Kent State under Beck, a master of exotic darkroom techniques. Unger has done important experimentation with high-contrast photography. He often takes conventional continuous-tone photographs from nature with the idea that he will transpose them through the use of high-contrast positive and negative treatment in the darkroom. His series of transformations of a single subject (see figures 8-6 through 8-8M) indicates the creative range of this technique.

The Animated Film Image

In the nether land between still photography and the full-blown kinetic motion picture stands a medium that takes advantage of the power of articulation possible through the still image and combines this power with the kinetic or moving image. In this form, we find the animated film image is, in essence, a handcrafted sequence of individual still frames, which are photographed successively with an animation camera, to generate, when projected at normal projection speeds, a kinetic or film motion. In a sense, the animated film is a handcrafted film, one in which much attention is given to the structure of each individual frame. This medium has appealed to a number of outstanding graphic film artists, and in many cases these artists have built an entire career using simply the animated film image.

There are many techniques for producing animated

films. Some artists merely scratch on the film with an instrument that cuts through the emulsion. Animation can be achieved through the use of multiple transparent overlays, which allow highly controlled kinetic images to cavort across the screen. One of the outstanding films of this nature is the Beatles' film *The Yellow Submarine.* In this film the animated techniques are subordinated to the lyrical and imaginative story line. There are few full-length films using animation. One second of projection demands twenty-four individual frames from the artist for 16mm film. This means 1,440 frames of original art for one minute of film. An animated film usually runs from three to seven minutes. If this film is the work of a single artist, it may represent a year of his work.

Advanced work in animated film was done by Len Lye in his youth. More recently, Norman McLaren has developed a wide range of techniques for animation. In some cases he films a single frame of an object standing on a surface, then moves the object slightly for the next frame, until the sequence is complete. In other instances he embosses or scratches the film, then colors the scratches in the emulsion with various dyes so that colored shapes appear on the screen. He also has used prepared art work for individual frames.

Carmen D'Avino

Perhaps the most interesting artist working with animated film techniques in America today is Carmen D'Avino. D'Avino has developed a remarkable system whereby he creates an animated film by sequentially hand painting a real object. He places his stop-motion animation camera for a given sequence; then he paints a section of the object, photographs one frame, paints a bit more, photographs the next frame, and so on, until the sequence is completed. In one film, for example, his piano was used as a sort of assemblage star for the entire film. Today, it brightens up a corner of his studio-home on the Lower East Side of New York City. In a recent film, D'Avino used a whole wall of his studio, upon which he constructed an astounding assemblage of two- and three-dimensional shapes. In this film he actually created his shapes from magazine cutouts, discarded objects, and found art. First he would paint them, then mount them on the wall, and finally photograph each object for a single frame. Twenty-four changes in the object, or combined movement of the camera in a zoom or pan, were required for one second of film. Slowly he added to the composition until it covered the entire wall of his studio. The moment the wall was covered, the film was completed.

Cinematography: Wide-Screen, Multiple-Image Projection

The motion picture is a basic tool of the mixed-media

artist. It is flexible: images can be projected on small, wide, curved, and hemispherical screens. It reaches all kinds and sizes of audiences. Technology's impact is most clearly seen and understood in the motion picture. Many acknowledged twentieth-century geniuses have realized themselves uniquely in this medium: Chaplin, Griffith, Eisenstein, Renoir, Carné, Antonioni, Fellini, Polanski, Huston, and Flaherty, to mention a few.

Although the film itself has been such a compelling medium, perhaps the most important development for the intermedia, mixed-media, and environmental artist has been the advent of wide-screen, or multiple-image, projection in film. These developments are necessary for the environmental artist, because he wishes to envelop the spectator in the field. In this case it is necessary, as much as possible, to surround the spectator, so that the full 180 degrees of peripheral vision can be accommodated. Again, the impact of multimedia film projection lies in its ability to totally immerse the spectator-participant in the illusion.

Erik M. Rondum

The concept is not a new one. At the Paris Exposition of 1900 a hemispheric multiple projection was briefly demonstrated. Cinerama was used in training men in World War II. Later, Erik Rondum helped to develop the Cinerama camera technique, and he served as cameraman for the first feature-length productions.

Erik Rondum was part of that epic battle still being waged between Hollywood and network television. As the little black box began to erode movie-theatre-going habits, Hollywood retaliated with the big screen wrapped around its enthralled viewers. Three projectors threw huge images of wild ski runs, stagecoach chases, and Grand Prix crashes into the startled laps of a delighted audience. Simultaneously, an elaborate, independent, multichanneled audio system bombarded the audience with a strategic counterpoint of sounds. When we trace the history of mass multimedia environmental shows, the development of Cinerama in the fifties emerges as a pioneering effort in full sensory involvement.

Francis Thompson and Alexander Hammid

Francis Thompson is one of the great film minds of this century. His consuming interest has been to transpose the visual image through the medium of unique optical systems and multiple projections. Thompson gained the attention of film buffs with a remarkable short film, entitled *N. Y., N. Y.* This masterpiece took more than seven years to produce. He wished to create a surrealist interpretation of New York in which buildings would float in air, change shape as the camera panned, and generally reorient the spectator's view of reality. There was, however, no lens system that could accommodate the filmmaker's vision. So Thompson, craftsman that he was, literally made his own optical devices in order to achieve the remarkable imagery he desired.

For many years now, Thompson collaborated with an outstanding camera director, Alexander Hammid. In the mid sixties Robert Moses proclaimed that New York City would have an impromptu world's fair. The Flushing Meadows burlesque resulted. Hidden among the tin houses, however, the Johnson Wax Company Pavilion exhibited a multiscreened film that would redirect the energies of film makers for years to come. This three-screened jewel was entitled *To Be Alive!* and it won an Academy Award for its two talented creators, Thompson and Hammid. A short three years later, at Expo '67, the multiscreened influence came to full bloom. Thompson and Hammid went to six screens for their Expo '67 film *We Are Young.*

Mel London

The author owes his career in film study to Mel London, who took him on, back in 1956, at a great independent film company called "On Film," located in Princeton, New Jersey. At that time Lenny Hirschfield, Richard Bagley, Tracy Ward, Stan Brakhage, and a group of young artists began their careers. Today, London is a partner in Vision Associates, a successful New York City film company. He has logged many years in the medium, has traveled around the world about twenty times, making films, and speaks with love and affection of the people, places, and things that make film the exciting medium it is.

Videotape Images

Ray Abel/Herb Gardener/Alwin Nikolais

Videotape offers composing and producing ease to the creative intermedia artist. Unlike the long-drawn-out process of filming, processing, and projecting a motion picture, a sequence is recorded directly on the videotape. The recorder can be turned back and replayed at once, allowing the artist to check and alter the work. The self-contained nature of the medium affords greater independence of ideas and subjects, which might suffer censorship under conventional production processes.

The videotape medium offers more than production flexibility; its inherent relationship to television, the most powerful visual image of the century, adds to its significance for the intermedia artist. Ray Abel is a leading exponent of this medium. As a producer-director for WCBS-TV and later for the Videorecord Corporation, he has demonstrated a remarkable talent in coordinating the efforts of creative artists, musicians, cameramen, scenic designers, and the army of technicians that make a videotape show fall into a coherent piece. His collaboration with Herb Gardner, a brilliant electronics engineer, enabled him to explore the potential of Chroma Key switching. With Alwin Nikolais, they created the videotape ballet *Limbo.*

The technique was discussed in an earlier chapter. We note here the importance of collaborative effort between artist, producer, and engineer in order to achieve success with the complex systems currently available to the intermedia artist.

Lumia: the Art of Light

There has always been a classic cause and effect relationship in the history of art between new technical developments and profound changes in the artist's methodology. To a large extent the Impressionist and Post-Impressionist painters owed as much to the discovery of new chemical dyes and substances that vastly increased the range of their palette as they did to the discovery of the physical properties of light expounded by the French physicist Chevreul. After World War II a similar development took place when synthetic plastics began to have widespread application. At first artists used them tentatively, but as the advantages of the fast-drying, water-based paints, capable of producing brilliant color relationships, were explored, artists began to abandon the slower drying and less flexible oil medium.

Thomas Wilfred*

In both above cases, however, the development of a new technical means was explored simultaneously by an entire school of artists. In this limited context alone, we can begin to appreciate the genius of Thomas Wilfred, discussed in chapter 2. He was largely responsible for developing the aesthetic potential of the electric light, He exploited its remarkable characteristics by developing devices such as the Clavilux projector. Not only did he coin the generic term "lumia" but through his hundreds of performances, and the creation of the lumia box for "programmed light shows," he placed his mark on a unique new form of aesthetic expression.

Dr. Tom Douglas Jones

As Faber Birren has noted in his introduction to Dr. Jones' book *The Art of Light and Color,* ". . . Jones has been a pioneer in the art of light and color. His first color projection device, which he called the Symphochrome, was made and demonstrated in 1938. Since then he has continued his creative research. . . . To Jones, light and color represent an art form, not a novelty . . . [Jones notes that]

*Thomas Wilfred is presented fully in chapter 2.

there is a rich tradition dating back to the work of Castel of France, Rimington of Great Britain, and Wilfred of the United States. To the list should be added Tom Douglas Jones." (From the introduction for *The Art of Light and Color* Van Nostrand Reinhold, New York, 1973).

Jones is both a teacher and a lumia artist; his influence has been widespread. He is joined in this section by a group of younger lumia artists: Christian Sidenius, Rudi Stern, Jackie Cassen, and Robert Fisher. Their interviews indicate the range and depth of personal expression possible with this relatively new medium, which exploits the bond between art and technology.

Christian Sidenius

Christian Sidenius is a close follower of Thomas Wilfred's work. He often visited with Wilfred before the artist's death. Sidenius, like Wilfred, believes that Lumia reaches its full potential in a live performance. In the early sixties, he built his own Theatre of Light in Sandy Hook, Connecticut. Using rear-screen projection, he is able to perform lumia pieces during summer weekends for an intimate audience. Behind his large screen he has installed one of the most complete lumia projection systems in the country. He has several Clavilux projectors, remote-control turntables, and a full multichanneled audio system. During his performances Sidenius wears double earphones: in one ear he hears the taped sound track, which is piped into the auditorium; in the other ear he hears his own recorded voice giving instructions as to which piece of equipment should be activated, complete with timing information.

Jackie Cassen and Rudi Stern*

Although these two artists are no longer working together, they established a remarkable collaboration for many years. They both had fine-arts backgrounds and turned to kinetic light as their special medium. Both artists regarded light as a benign and comforting environmental art form. Combining light with sound in a controlled setting, Cassen and Stern attempted to create antimegalopolis environments. They surmised that the constant growth of the cities forced the development of serene and independent environments for living and working. Much of their work in this country and abroad was devoted to this premise.

Recently, Rudi Stern has joined with another intermedia artist, John Reilly, to create a multimedia environment they call "Global Village, The Electronics of Shared Experience." The term "global village" stems from the prophet of electronics Marshall McLuhan; its context is that television has reduced the world community to village proportions—that ethnic, racial, linguistic, and national distinctions are disappearing. Using multiple video-

*Interviews with Jackie Cassen and Rudi Stern appear in chapter 9 under "The Videocassette and the Underground."

tape recorders, Stern and Reilly have created a collage of disparate visual impressions. The effect of the performance is disquieting, primarily because it reflects the confused cacophony of visual and audio segments that bombard us each day of our lives.

Robert Fisher

Robert Fisher was trained in design theory under Gyorgy Kepes at the Massachusetts Institute of Technology. He then studied and taught industrial design at Syracuse University; he turned to light sculpture, however, after his graduation. For a number of years he explored the potential of modular light sculpture, in which small elements of a composition could be combined to create large sculptures. He has recently developed a series of "multiples." Essentially, these multiples are designed for human apparel and for the turned-on spectator of environmental art. Fisher is remarkable for his extraordinary range of expression. He is equally at home with complex architectural design, industrial design, kinetic sculpture, and wild, free-flowing plastic forms. His most ambitious recent statement was as director of a multimedia rock and folk-music festival at the University of Illinois at Urbana.

He and his wife True are my friends as well. Bob and I wrote our first book together, *The Design Continuum: An Approach to Understanding Visual Forms.* Van Nostrand Reinhold: New York, 1966.

Electronic Sound, Audio Synthesizers, Computer-Analyzed Sound

Technology is rampant in today's musical language. Electronic instruments, such as the Moog Synthesizer, the Buchla, and the Putney are used in composition and performance by many artists.

Gershon Kingsley

The Moog has two keyboards, similar to those of an organ or piano, and a sophisticated series of modular sound-generation units. Each of these units can be mixed with the sounds created on the keyboard. Linked with the multihead tape recorder, the synthesizer can be programmed to accompany itself in any number of superimpositions of sound.

The composer of electronic music freely mixes-in sounds of conventional instruments, and either live or recorded sounds of the life around us, from the flushing of a toilet to the warbling of a cardinal.

A further complexity can be created by using the multi-speed tape recorder. Played at different speeds, the music takes on a variety of moods and characteristics.

The most significant aspect of electronic music, as noted

by Gershon Kingsley, is that the composer can realize his intent directly as he composes. He does not have to use a performing group with its natural interpretative biases. He has complete control over the work from the moments of composition to the concert performance.

Discussing electronic music vis-à-vis performed music, the young composer Dr. John V. Gilbert (Chapter 9) said that electronically-conceived music suffers from lack of the nuances of pacing, which are inevitable in human performances. He suggested that a combination of humanly performed and electronically generated sounds is a fruitful area of exploration by the multimedia artists.

The computer is a second major source for generation of sound. Dr. Max Mathews and Dr. Cecil Coker of Bell Laboratories (chapter 5) are synthetic-sound specialists. One of their research goals is to find a system for programming the computer to create synthetic music.

Dr. Jan LaRue

Jan LaRue, New York University musicologist, is using the computer to analyze the structure of musical scores. He has been able to determine relationships heretofore impossible to detect. LaRue is a very deceptive cat. When you walk into his study at New York University the first impression you gather is an ambiance of prodigious academia. Shelves of books, journals, and the usual artifacts of the scholarly world lull one into an impression of staid scholarship combined with that special kind of austerity one associates with musical and mathematical types. And then LaRue starts to talk about computers and the kinds of dialogue scholars can conduct with these machines. Before I knew it, I was ushered into a new world of analysis and critical evaluation. It became apparent that, with the aid of a well-constructed computer program, the advanced musicologist could probe aspects of musical theory that were impossible to the pre-computer generation.

Tactile Impressions

The intermedia artist finds ways and means to stimulate all the senses in the participant beholder. The tactile impressions he creates are perhaps the most intriguing in our "do-not-touch" culture. Unlike the Gallic and southern European people, we tend to hold back from spontaneous embraces, from touching one another.

A Museum of Contemporary Crafts exhibit called *Feel It* attempted to surmount this American inhibition. A tactile environment of hundreds of thousands of plastic streamers, hanging from ceiling to floor, was developed by a group of tactile multimedia artists. As one penetrated the plastic environment, the first reaction was alarm: vision was totally cut off. At first one could not move with confidence. Soon, however, reassurance came in the calls of pleasure and surprise from other visitors also experiencing the environ-

ment for the first time. As one moved on, one was suddenly confronted with another person coming, so to speak, out of the fog. There were from time to time little tactile oases, free-standing sculptures that responded to one's presence with whistles, hoots, bells, and gusts of compressed air. The total impression of this tactile environment was sheer delight.

Olfactory Impressions

Some intermedia artists are including synthetic olfactory impressions in their environments, knowing that the sense of smell affects feelings and responses. We are often unaware of our subconscious associations with the sense of smell. In Paris, shortly after World War II, I learned this lesson at first hand. I found myself troubled by irrational periods of depression. They had no legitimate association with that exciting and gratifying city, and it was several months before I realized that the depressions were associated with an odor, the odor of soft-coal burning. The odor aroused unconscious recollections of Fort Benning, Georgia, a nadir of civilization. The barracks in which I had lived were heated with soft coal in pot-bellied stoves.

Movement, Kinetic Images, and Multimedia Dance

Daniel Nagrin and Eric Salzman*

Intermedia artists have not overlooked the sensory impact of movement. Choreographer and dancer Daniel Nagrin commanded an entire audience for three hours in his solo performance the *The Peloponnesian War,* a tour de force in consciously directed and controlled movement of the body. The effect on the spectators went far beyond the casual observance of a dance.

Nagrin based his dance/theatre collage on a translation of Thucydides' play, while he was artist-in-residence at the State University College at Brockport, New York. Eric Salzman composed the electronic score. The work was made possible by a grant from the New York State Council on the Arts and The National Council on the Arts and Humanities. It was presented by the Cubiculo Theatre of Poetry/Film/Dance in New York City.

The Nagrin and Salzman collaboration points up the basic theme of this book—that intermedia or multimedia artists often reach their highest creative potential in collaborative activity.

Interviews

Interviews with the personalities discussed in this chapter follow.

*Interview with Eric Salzman appears in chapter 9 under "The Videocassette and the Underground."

whatmore

PRESIDENT COWLES COMMUNICATIONS, INC., NEW YORK CITY

8-1. Portrait of Marvin Whatmore. (Photograph by Arnold Newman.)

Marvin C. Whatmore, President of Cowles Communications, Inc., and Arthur Rothstein, Chief Photographer for the now defunct *Look* magazine, discuss Xograph, the three-dimensional photography and printing process they have developed. The name combines *X* for parallax, which is in all photography, and *graph* from the Latin root *graphicus,* meaning "to write."

Whatmore

I think this is important on the philosophical side of the question—that, in our lifetime, we have seen editors and advertisers convert their thinking from black-and-white photography to more and more photography in color. This is in spite of the fact that color comes at a high premium over black and white. The reason for the preference is not just that color photography is pretty. It transmits information. That is the reason it is used at a premium. If we do our job right, improve quality (which we are doing all the time), and get the economics down, we have, with the Xograph, a superior form of communication over color.

ARTHUR
rothstein

PHOTOGRAPHER, NEW YORK CITY

Rothstein

The Xograph is produced by interposing a screen between the lens and the film while the photograph is being taken. The screen divides the picture into thousands of vertical parallel strips. A 3-D effect is produced when each of the viewer's eyes sees a different image simultaneously, just as in normal binocular vision. When you put the plastic material over the finished print, it is in register with the vertical strips. This is where extreme accuracy is necessary. The lenses made from the plastic material focus

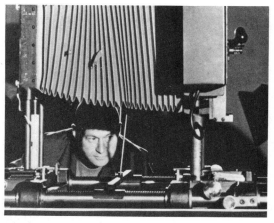

8-2. Portrait of Arthur Rothstein standing behind the bellows of his three-dimensional parallax-panorama-gram camera. (Courtesy Arthur Rothstein.)

your eyes onto the vertical strips—more than 100 to the inch. You see a different picture with your left eye than you see with your right eye at any given time, no matter where you put your head, thus satisfying the requirements of stereoscopic vision. At present we are producing pictures in multimillion quantities with basically the same techniques that other people have used, except for the very important consideration of extreme accuracy. This is where all the others have failed. In order to achieve this extreme accuracy, our cameras are engineered with great precision. They are very complicated and highly sophisticated pieces of equipment, which enable us to maintain accuracy both in the production of the picture and the consequent separation of the transparencies for printing.

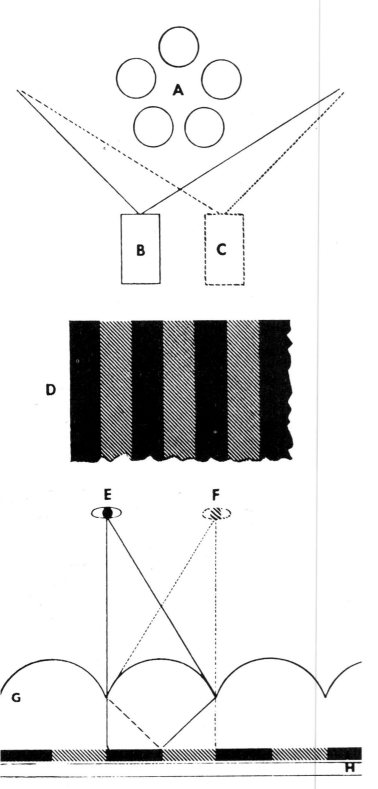

8-3. Diagram of the process for producing a parallax-panoramagram.

"Xograph 3-D printing is nothing more or less than an effective and practical method of three-dimensional reproduction.
"The Xograph is produced by a screen being interposed between the camera lens and the film while the photograph is being taken. This screen divides the picture into thousands of vertical parallel strips. The screen also blocks out some images while acting as a lens for other images, and thus the 3-D effect is produced, because each of the viewer's eyes sees a different image simultaneously, just as you do in normal binocular vision" (from Arthur Rothstein's "Visual Photographics" address at the Sixteenth Annual Conference, Research and Engineering Council of the Graphic Arts Industry, Pittsburgh, May 16-18, 1966.)

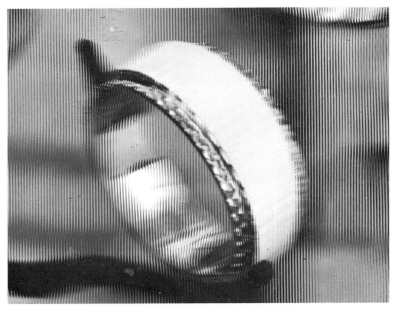

8-4. Photograph of parallax-panoramagram negative (wedding ring).

8-5. Standard photograph of ring shown in figure 8-4.

H. ALBERT
unger, jr.

PHOTOGRAPHER-DESIGNER, DOBBS FERRY, NEW YORK

The artist is inevitably influenced by science and technology. He has to be if he is going to represent the time in which he lives.

Here I am taking photography out of its traditional realm. I am bending it to an expressive kind of medium for the designer to create certain patterns of form, which become art. I am taking something that was once used to record fact—a given scene, a given picture of someone—and I am beginning to use it to express something, in this particular case, the beauty of the female form. I am doing it in such a way that the medium becomes abstract. It is my means of exploration, my attempt to further explore the photographic design and continue a tradition of experimentation. The photograph no longer records the actual female figure as we would see it. It becomes abstract because of the various processes through which I have run the image. We see things that are not inherent in our everyday world. Here, the female form is pure black and white. The average person sees it in full color. Beyond that, I have taken it and reduced it to pure line and texture through photographic technique.

I have used one study to achieve a variety of different effects. The artist Monet takes a railroad station or a pond of lilies, and, working all day to study light changing on objects, creates a variety of very intense personal studies, an analysis of change of light, texture, and composition. In the processes with which I am working I have begun to study the patterns of light on the surface of a model's skin.

Photography has been around about a hundred years. We can expect a great deal more from it. With certain new developments in technology—I'm speaking here of the laser—new vistas will open up. The artist is inevitably influenced by science and technology. He has to be if he is going to represent the time in which he lives.

8-7. Mattbox photograph of a dancer taken by H. Albert Unger, Jr. (Courtesy H. Albert Unger, Jr.)

8-6. Portrait of H. Albert Unger, Jr.

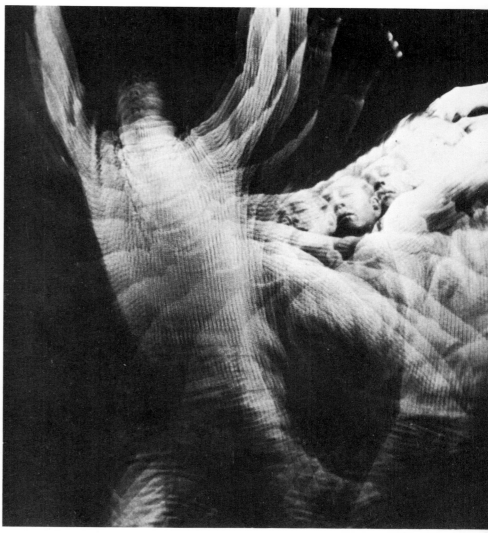

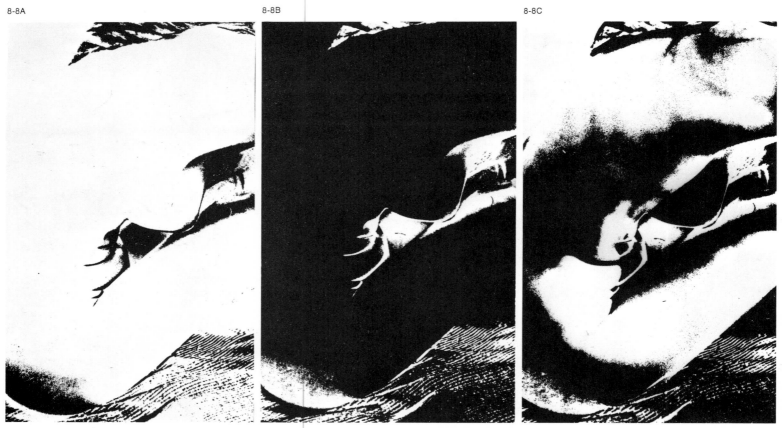

8-8A 8-8B 8-8C

8-8A—M. A continuous-tone negative placed on a high-contrast film creates images that range from a recognizable human form to a highly abstracted form. The first two images, figures 8-4A and 8-4B, become studies in light and shade and overall massive form. Progressing with the experiment, Unger gets into linear and textural studies (Courtesy H. Albert Unger Jr.)

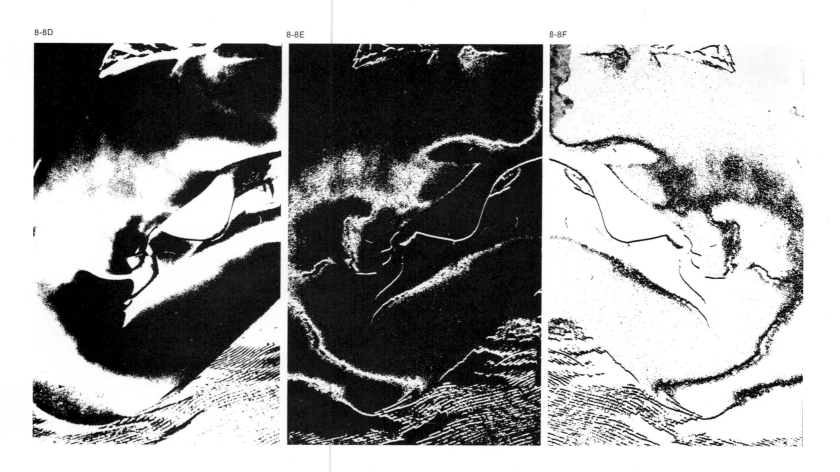

8-8D 8-8E 8-8F

8-8G   8-8H   8-8I

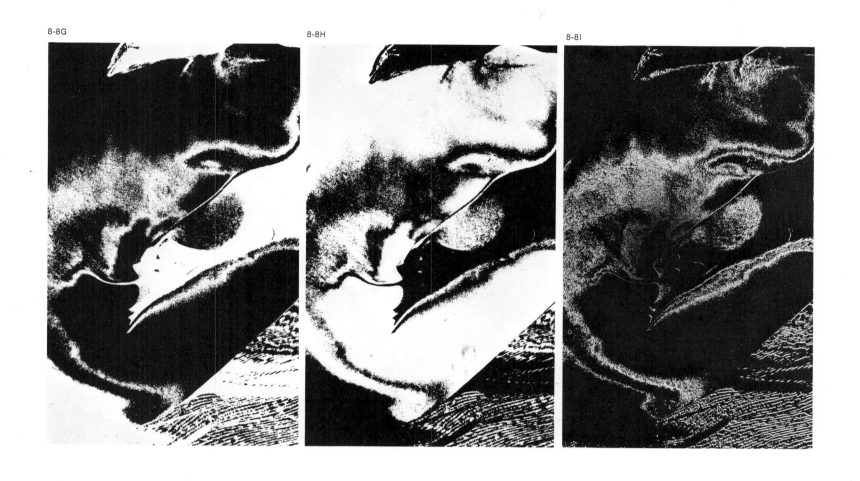

8-8J   8-8K   8-8L   8-8M

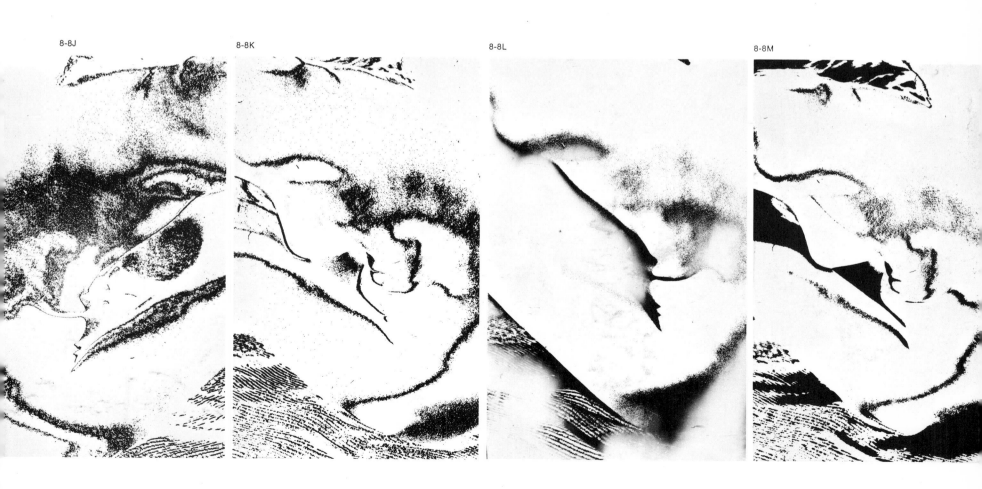

CARMEN
d'avino

ANIMATED FILM ARTIST, NEW YORK CITY

Conversation with an artist who animates pianos, walls, rooms.

I had an idea that one could animate over solid objects, and out of that came a dream of going out to an abandoned hotel—out West in a ghost town, possibly—a great old, ornate hotel that was abandoned, deteriorating. I would go in there and paint that whole damn furniture, using a sort of animated technique, the outside, the inside, the staircase. . . . So, in order to test the possibilities, I did the film *The Room.* I couldn't get out of the hotel. I couldn't get out even to get the film, but in my room—which was a dilapidated room, falling apart—I did it. I painted the whole room, and I realized that here was something that had never been done before. Animation of a three-dimensional object in space. I thought: Why not? What the hell have they been doing? Why haven't they seen this possibility?

The reason that I remained so close to animation was that I realized that the field was absolutely unexplored. It was only through the process of animation that I could grasp this thing. The moment you start doing animation

8-10. D'Avino seated at his dining table; the piano at right is decorated with paintings with which the artist animates three-dimensional objects.

8-9. Carmen D'Avino, standing beside one of his sculptures, peers through bouquet of flowers.

you become aware of the single frame. You begin to think of the single frame as a single brush stroke on canvas. The ultimate painting before our eyes is made up of thousands of brush strokes, each one put down with some thought or in some instinctive manner. The regular running film never does this. When you press a button on a camera, twenty-four pictures are running through that thing in a second, and it just goes on and on—camera men shoot millions of feet of film and cutters have to cut it. But in animation, every single frame becomes a specific thing. One frame is a frame. You have total control.

I always tell young painters who drift into the film medium that they must learn rapidly that film, as a medium, has its own laws and its own beauty and its own form.

It's all magic. It's all illusion. But it must be understood on a frame-to-frame basis. Really, we are at the threshold of art. The great discovery in film is when one discovers the single frame. It brings film into the area of art, where all you need is a piece of paper or a pencil or a canvas.

8-11. Wall in Carmen D'Avino's home studio. Little by little, under the artist's technique of animation, it grew into a film.

Film becomes the same thing because you can do a direct-on-film thing.

One can go to some of these film houses, get film that has been put in the waste can, and create masterpieces by just dabbling on it, by scraping and scratching. Anything you want. If you have the visual capacity, you can come up with some brilliant stuff.

When I lecture, I tell the students: "Don't make excuses about how you need money. You want to make films? You can make them as cheaply as you could write a novel. It's not a question of a million dollars. You bring your imagination to it."

This is my big fight. I've read it time and time again—that cinema is a form that requires big money, many talents. Nonsense. It requires one man, like all arts. If one man wants to bring another form into it, that's his business. But essentially the film is a singular form, as much so as literature, or theatre, or painting, or anything else.

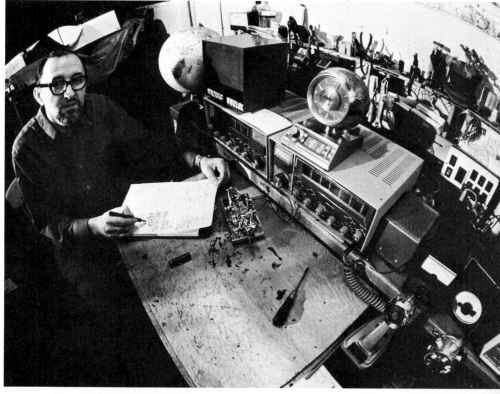

8-12. D'Avino's second passion is his ham radio equipment.

ERIK M.

rondum

OPTICAL SCIENTIST, DESIGNER OF CINERAMA CAMERA SYSTEM

KRANZ. *Cinerama was one of the first efforts to integrate sight with sound and motion, and thus create a total environmental illusion. What was your work with Cinerama?*

RONDUM. I became chief engineer. I went there to build the cameras. There was a bread board. But I built the first cameras that we could calibrate so that we could intercut the films. Each camera had three films in it, and they had to be made so that we could intercut from them. There were three films and three lenses grouped in one camera. A unique configuration, in that there was a cross-over point for the three axes of the three lenses. Very close in front of them is where the shutter cut through. It was so designed that we focused the lenses for whatever distance we needed; we also got parallax correction, which made our images match at that plane in the field in front of us.

KRANZ. *That was an exceptional feat optically.*

8-13. Erik M. Rondum photographed at home.

Rondum, developer of the Cinerama camera system, was chief cameraman for many of the early Cinerama films.

RONDUM. It was a lucky situation, it was also worked into and used. But it happened to be there.

KRANZ. *In designing the cameras, what was your goal—to be able to project a full 180 degrees so that you could take in peripheral vision?*

RONDUM. We found that it wasn't necessary to take a full 180 degrees to get the effect of peripheral vision. We ended up with about 150 degrees. And this was a more practical solution for theatre installations. It made it easier to seat people, and also to fit those monster screens into existing motion-picture houses.

KRANZ. *Well, tell me, what was the reason? Why did the Cinerama artists try to get the environmental effect?*

RONDUM. To create a new form of entertainment, which it really did become. And it came at a very important time because the motion-picture business was at a low point. We were startled at the success we had with it. We had no idea how our opening on Broadway would be taken. And of course it was a colossal success. . . . The Cinerama function set a big scene, and the action within the scene took in the viewer. It became more natural and real-looking. People found themselves in a situation that was normal to them, one that they were accustomed to.

Three things were important to the system. First, the peripheral field of view; second, the use of color film. We tried it with black-and-white film and it left us flat. We didn't get the depth perception. And the third thing was sound, with proper perspective pitting the pictures that were surrounding us. Seven separate sound systems had to run together in synchronization and be properly positioned to hold that relationship.

The first film we made was *This is Cinerama.* It had the Grand-Canyon-flight sequence in the second half.

KRANZ. *Was that done with a helicopter?*

RONDUM. It was done with a big B-25 North American Mitchell, which Doolittle used to fly. We mounted the camera in the nose. We rebuilt the nose on it. We went down into the canyon at 300 miles and hour. We couldn't slow down enough.

CINERAMA

<u>27 MM LENS</u>

Angular Field Coverage - Camera Aperture

Horizontal 146°   Vertical 55½°

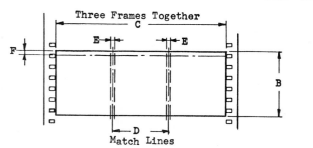

C 2.895" To Perforations
D 0.9478" Between Match Lines
E 0.051" Overlap From Perforations
F 0.062" Keep Important Composition Below This Line.

CAMERA ASPECT RATIO 2.59 to 1

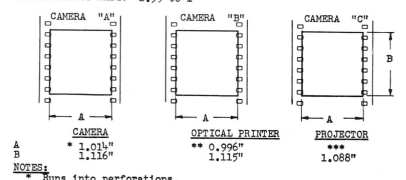

	CAMERA	OPTICAL PRINTER	PROJECTOR
A	* 1.014"	** 0.996"	***
B	1.116"	1.115"	1.088"

NOTES:
* Runs into perforations.
** Special Acme Head 0.985"
*** Because of vignetting "gigolos" projector aperture width is meaningless. There is no specification.

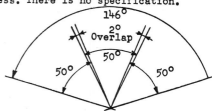

8-14. Three strips of film for Camera A, Camera B, and Camera C are shown in this Cinerama diagram.

Stereophonic sound was recorded on a separate magnetic tape. When the three frames were drawn together, the result was a screen nine times greater than ordinary 35 mm film. This led to the high resolution that the system was able to achieve.

KRANZ. *I would say that this Cinerama film is a landmark in the entertainment industry. In many ways it had as much impact as the change from silent films to sound films, or from black-and-white to color films.*

RONDUM. Yes, I agree that it is one of the significant stages in environmental arts—a wonderful thing was created, for all its technical difficulties. It was a useful thing. It was like the Model-T Ford.

8-15. Blueprint of the early Cinerama system.

The curved screen at the top is the object field for the cameras. The camera at far right photographs the left-hand segment of the object field. The center camera photographs the central segment. The far-left camera photographs the right-hand segment. The object is to create the illusion of peripheral vision, essentially 146 degrees of the images projected on the curved screen. Each camera photographs 50 degrees of the 146 degrees. Each of the camera fields overlaps 2 degrees, to make a total of 150 degrees for the entire scope of the field. At the bottom of the diagram, three projectors project the film exactly on the portion of the screen that was the object field designated for each camera.

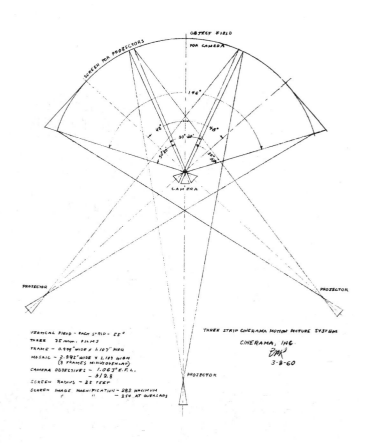

FRANCIS
thompson

FILMMAKER, NEW YORK CITY

Notes on an interview conducted with Francis Thompson. (The artist requested that no tape recording be made.)

Origins of Francis Thompson's aesthetics

Thompson was influenced by the painters Van Gogh and Leger, and the film *The Cabinet of Dr. Caligari*. He liked particularly Van Gogh's ability to get below the surface to the feeling of things. The Caligari film used stylized abstract sets and tilted planes to create bizarre images. Thompson sought, in his own work, to distort the visual image in a way more convincing to the viewer.

The development of Kodachrome film early in the thirties found a willing disciple in Thompson. He felt that, with the use of color, film was far more powerful as a medium.

He began to use color film in a series of shots of New York City. To get the desired distortions, he relied at first on surfaces—buildings reflected in windows, and so on. Then he began, in his own words, "to fool around with the prism." He mounted a prism in front of his camera before the lens and began his experiments with multiple images. The experimentation lasted for eight years and led to the techniques employed in his film *N. Y., N. Y.*

Image control

Thompson says that he was seeking "a grammar and syntax" of image distortion for film. As a painter evolves a personal style, Thompson looked for his own language, his own idiom. He referred to his films as painting in mo-

8-16. Francis Thompson, seated, and Alexander Hammid, at left, producers of *We Are Young* for the Canadian Pacific—Cominco Pavilion at Expo '67, editing their film. (Photograph courtesy Canadian Pacific.)

With six screens, six visual images must be edited simultaneously. "It takes several months to edit a multi-screen film, even if it is only twenty minutes long," Hammid said. "Creatively it is a very satisfying and challenging period."

opposite
C-76–C-82. A series of photographs from Francis Thompson's film, *N.Y., N.Y.* (Courtesy Francis Thompson, Inc.)

This work was a culmination of Thompson's long research into color optics and new methods of controlling and using the filmed image. The N.Y., N.Y. film won prizes at Cannes, London, Edinburgh, and the American Film Festival in New York. Shown are seven different scenes. Through specially created lenses and optical systems, Thompson was able to create these highly surrealistic and abstract shapes with the motion-picture camera.

C-76

C-77

C-78

C-79

C-80

C-81

FRANCIS THOMPSON'S *N.Y., N.Y.*

C-82

8-17. *To Be Alive!*, three-screen film by Francis Thompson and Alexander Hammid. (Courtesy Mrs. Hella Hammid, New York City.)

Witnessing the finished film To Be Alive!, the viewer is invited to regain his sense of life's mystery, joy, and wonder, even while surrounded by the pressures of contemporary living. To Be Alive! received the award from the National Conference of Christians and Jews for the outstanding contribution by a motion picture to the cause of better human relations. It also received the New York Film Critics' Special Citation for Outstanding Achievement in the Creative Use of the Motion Picture.

"As film makers we try to direct our work toward matters of human concern. We believe the motion picture is the most potent and widely appealing of all communications media, and that its possibilities have hardly begun to be explored. We are all familiar with its long-demonstrated ability to speak directly to the universal audience with visual images, transcending language barriers and other cultural differences. We know the cinema's special capacity to produce intensely emotional responses, to move people and cause them to act. But today there appear new and startling extensions of the medium's power through the use of such techniques as a heightened control over the photographic image and the use of the multiple screen in a variety of configurations.

The first of these—control over the image—opens up the possibility of inducing responses in ways formerly restricted to painting and sculpture. The second—the multiple screen—operates in two basic ways: (1) enlargement of a single panoramic picture area to more nearly envelop the audience, thereby causing them to share almost physically the world through which the film moves and unfolds its story; (2) projecting different images side by side in carefully worked-out juxtapositions to produce a variety of results, such as revealing human universality beneath superficial cultural differences, simultaneous picturing of different moments in time, different aspects of the same personality or event, and so on.
Image control and multiple-screen techniques have already revealed themselves to be possessed of startling power, but their full development still lies ahead. It is our hope that they and other emerging film methods may be used for humane purposes now in such urgent need of our best efforts."
—Francis Thompson

In 1962 Francis Thompson and his co-director, Alexander Hammid, were commissioned by the Johnson Wax Company to make a motion picture for their New York World's Fair pavilion. They felt that the film should contribute to the World's Fair theme of "Peace Through Understanding," and the year and a half that followed found them traveling in Europe and Africa, as well as across the United States, to photograph vignettes that point out the universality of various human experiences.

tion. He wanted to get a dense color image that would approach, in film, the texture of paint. His own knowledge of painting was a strong base for his aesthetic. In discussing his work, he frequently uses painting terms, such as "a great solidity" in image, or "sharpness" of the image. Specific effects were used to convey specific feelings.

N. Y., N. Y.

Thompson pointed to the flexibility of the image in N. Y., N. Y. He used unequal multiplication of an image. He varied other parts of the frame, while holding one image in one section of the frame.

Influence of "Cineorama"

In 1926 Abel Gance, a producer and director, made a six-hour film, Napoleon. At its first showing in the Paris Opera House, the French Opera Orchestra played a musical ac-companiment to go with the multiple-screen images.

The first known use of multiple cameras and multiple screens, Thompson said, was in 1896, in a process called "Cineorama." Ten cameras were mounted in a balloon. As the balloon ascended over the Paris rooftops, the cameras photographed a 360-degree image simultaneously. Synchronization was accomplished by a shaft running vertically upward from a platform where two men stood. The shaft had an eccentric in it so that each man could hold a section as he turned it manually. A huge cogwheel at the top operated the cameras in unison. Needless to say, the speed of the cameras was not constant. An attempt was made (the film was shown, I believe) to show this film at the Paris Exposition of 1896. To give the maximum illusion of reality, the audience was asked to stand in a basket similar to the gondola of the balloon. An alarmed and aroused fire department terminated the performance. Like all motion-picture film of that time, the stock had a nitrate base. When heated, it could have blown up and literally dispatched the entire audience.

continued

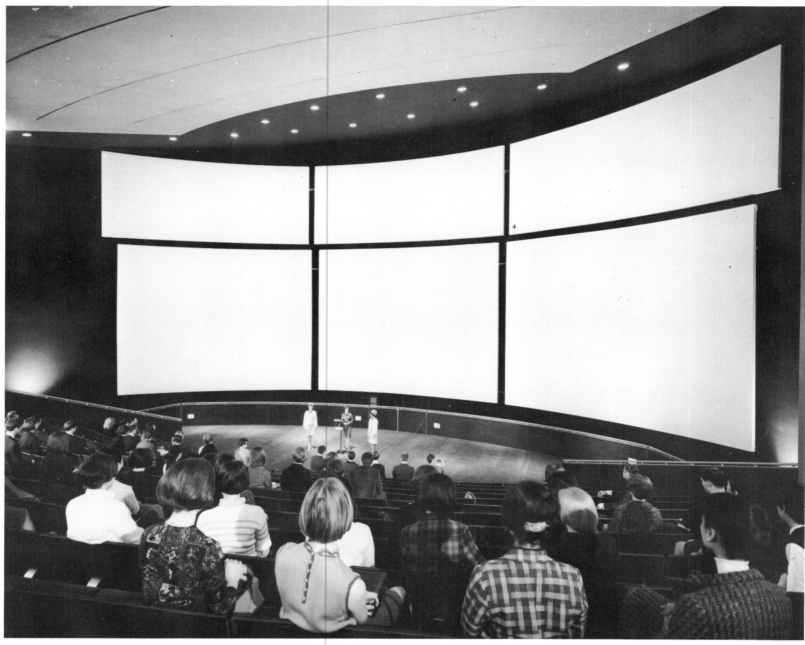

8-18. The scale of the auditorium and the size of the screens used to project *We Are Young* at Expo '67. (Courtesy Canadian Pacific.)

The use of three screens

Thompson's use of three cameras, mounted and synchronized mechanically, enables him to achieve one large, continuous image. Or, using separate cameras, he can build a counterpoint of three different images. These must, of course, be carefully related visually and in terms of content; otherwise they will have no meaning for the viewer.

8-19. This shows the capability of multi-screen projection to give multiple simultaneous views of the same object (Courtesy Francis Thompson, Inc., New York City.)

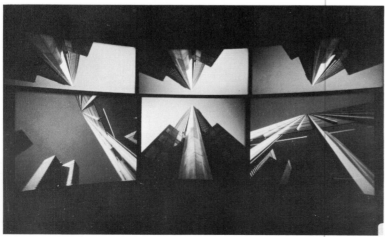

The Cinemasphere: ultimate aim of filmmakers

Thompson feels that one ultimate development in motion pictures will be the cinemasphere—a nearly 360-degree spherical screen surface inside which the audience can literally be suspended. The aim is to simulate visual reality or to construct a new visual ambience with all the impact of peripheral vision. The audience would be almost completely surrounded. A spherical theatre is needed to achieve this total absorption, to bombard all the senses of the audience. The very thought of such a medium stirs up the megalomania in him, laughs Thompson.

Nature of screen for Expo '67

Thompson's use of a six-screen format for Expo '67 was a step in the development toward the cinemasphere. Though the illusion of envelopment was increased in his films *We Are Young* and *To Be Alive!,* Thompson pointed out that he made no attempt to imply that the viewers were seeing anything other than the six individual images. The six screens were kept quite separate from one another. Each stage of the development toward the 360-degree image should have its own discipline and a completeness within itself. His present six-screen technique has its own aesthetics, its own limitations, its special virtues.

Audience participation in multi-image projections

The audience, in Thompson's observation, thoroughly enjoys—possibly unconsciously—the technical problems involved in moving an image from one screen to the next. A caterpillar traveling across the screen in *To Be Alive!* is introduced in the right-hand screen. As it comes to the edge of the frame, the audience begins to laugh. Suddenly the little creature pops up in the proper position in the middle frame—to the delight of the audience. They seem to share in the feeling of technical triumph with the filmmaker.

Film compared to other media

Thompson believes that the motion-picture image is the most powerful image of the twentieth century. Television is too limited in size and scale. Painting is static, lacking the advantages of time and motion. The motion picture offers great control of each phase of the process, from shooting to editing. Yes, Francis Thompson says, the motion picture is the pre-eminent art form of this century.

ALEXANDER

hammid

CINEMATOGRAPHER, FRANCIS THOMPSON, INC., NEW YORK CITY

Alexander Hammid's interest in filmmaking goes back to 1927 to his student years in his native Czechoslovakia. He met Francis Thompson when they worked together in the Office of War Information during World War II. They later collaborated on the multiple screen films *To Be Alive! We Are Young,* and *US.*

Hammid compares the single and multiple screens

The difference is similar to one between a small painting that you hang on the wall and a large fresco. They are two different things and serve different purposes. About films, one type is more capable of providing intimacy between itself and the spectator, the other has a more grand effect and lends itself to large impressions. But still one doesn't eliminate the other. You can have a very grand small painting, and you can have something very intimate on a huge screen. So there is nothing clear about this division.

The multiscreen form is something new, and therefore it has the appeal of novelty. Beyond that, it has more psychological involvement with the spectator. You are confronted with a large screen with one or several huge images. You become a part of the world. You forget more easily the fact that you are sitting in a theatre and seem to be right in the middle of the action. You are wrapped around in the images.

The multiple screen gives a more vivid, overwhelming interpretation of visual reality because you enrich the view, you simultaneously present several different angles. You create new reality. You create something that you can't experience when you confront the actual architecture. Of course, a single camera can do a lot in that direction, too, by showing a succession of different angles. But there you put them side by side. They are not simultaneous.

Hammid speaks of his collaboration with Francis Thompson

There isn't a division of roles. We are completely flexible in accepting each other's ideas. Francis would do the photography sometimes, and I would do it, and he would do it, and I would do it. It is really a fifty-fifty collaboration. I think it can be said that I do more of the actual photography and carry out the technical problems, and Francis is more on the ideological side of deciding what should be done.

A hemispherical screen that completely envelops the spectator—this is something both Francis and I are talking about a lot. There are very great problems in designing the right kind of projectors, projection lamps, and screens. The problems are almost insoluble—such as light bouncing back from screen to screen, or from one side of the screen to the other; washing out the image; getting enough light on the screen from the tiny hole of a projector.

A desirable goal, one that we certainly hope we'll be able to try out in our lifetimes.

(See *N. Y., N. Y.* color photographs shown on page 179.)

MEL
london

VICE PRESIDENT, VISION ASSOCIATES, INC., NEW YORK CITY

Mel London, a pioneer in television and film, talks about developments that have brought film to its present versatility.

When you talk about change in the medium, you are looking over only 23 years. It isn't that far back to the beginnings. Television has developed in the same way that aviation has developed. You can *see* the change.

When you say "the early days of television," I think about the days when we used electric light bulbs to light sets. When the airconditioning went out, children in the audience fainted, and we had to revive them, fanning them with cue cards so that the parents at home could see that their darlings were OK. This actually happened several times on hot days. So not the least of the important developments would be a combination of improved airconditioning and lighter equipment.

At the same time in motion pictures we were using very slow speed films, in color, 16 mm Kodachrome II. In sound cameras it was the Mitchell, a camera totally impossible to carry around. You had to have two to three sound men working on the sound equipment with the mixers. And we had to light the studios with tremendous

8-21. Chinese Tea Dancers (Hong Kong). From *Celebration*.

amounts of light. On exteriors, if it became fairly dark late in the afternoon, we couldn't shoot.

The first big change came about, therefore, because of the technical developments that helped move equipment and crews out of the studios. And the second change came because of the first. As people began to be more familiar with film, they began to accept film more. They began to accept the film maker. They became interested in film as a medium. Today we consider it the art form of the young. Why do we have 60,000 film students in the schools? It is because film became the art form, through the dissemination of film crews, so to speak, through the world.

As the film speeds became faster and you needed less light for better quality, and as you began to get the Ektochromes and what we have now—7252 and even the high speed film (7242) post flashing and things like that —what began to happen? Where we formerly had to move out of the studio with eight or ten men, we now have a sound recorder that *one* man can operate while doing three other things. The *Nagra* is an ingenious piece of equipment. The sound man carries it around his shoulder, has a microphone, and, while he is walking or moving around, he can interview people.

We now have radio microphones. Because of crystals, we no longer need what we used to call the umbilical cord tied from recorder to camera. The cameraman can be 30 feet from the sound man. We can hide a microphone,

8-20. Portrait of Mel London, on location for his 1972 film *Celebration*. (Courtesy Vision Associates, Inc., New York City.)

which means we can take an interview without disturbing people.

From the Mitchell camera we went to—probably the work horse—the Arriflex. That is still one of the best cameras for documentary photography, a very strongly made German camera. We now had a camera that could be hand-held. We had a camera that could be loaded quickly. We had a camera that could be, in essence, carried. Taken anywhere in the world! There is also the Eclair, a light-weight camera, quickly loadable, totally noiseless—and the new Eclair Acl, weighing only eight pounds!! And the CP-16 for newsreel work.

We are now using quartz lights, which are so intense that with a combination of four double-quartzes—each about the size of three cigarette packs—a few months ago we lit an entire Turkish club in Istanbul.

Because of the quartz light, because of the high speed film, because of post-fogging, which is a technique that gives you quality with no grain, because of this light equipment, suddenly film crews moved out. Now I travel throughout the world with a cameraman, and an assistant cameraman who doubles in sound. We have in the last year travelled 150,000 miles to places like Africa, Turkey, Australia, where power is at a premium. The film we are doing now, *Celebration,* is on the celebration of life in 15 cultures. We were remote in villages and we found the power where we needed light. And this by carrying only a case of lights and a couple of cables.

So those two things—the development of film equipment and the flexibility it has allowed us—have brought the kind of acceptance from people that means you don't have to explain that you are making a film, only what kind of film you are making.

The film medium has also changed enormously because of the young. They have grown up with film. They make us see new techniques. One example is quick cutting. We know for a fact that an eight- or nine-year-old can look at a quick-cut commercial or a quick-cut sequence in a documentary and tell you more of the content than those of us who have been trained for a long time. They see it. They are faster. So they, in turn, have made us look more carefully at the techniques they accept.

There is a second factor. No doubt about it, they're the ones who are going to have our jobs. They are the ones who are going to be film makers. So I think we have to listen to them.

Film is a NOW medium that is growing because so many young people have been exposed to it. One of the most joyous things I've done was to organize a contest for some Autumn and Christmas spots for the National Broadcasting Company among the students in film schools in England. Out of 40 entries, I had 20 potential first-prize winners. Most of the series was presented at the Museum of Modern Art. I had the rest presented on NBC. Interestingly enough, the first-prize winner took the money and went into business. Now he is in competition with me.

8-22. Mel London on the set at On Film Inc., Princeton, New Jersey, during the fall of 1958. (Courtesy Vision Associates, Inc., New York City.)

8-23. Arnold Stang and Howard Da Silva in Mel London's documentary film *Her Office Hero.* (Courtesy Vision Associates, Inc., New York City.)

8-24. On set scene from Mel London's *Indoor World,* 1972, a film on decorating, for Armstrong Cork. Decorator Louisa Cowan is shown on set with London and his crew. (Courtesy Vision Associates, Inc., New York City.)

8-25. Scene from the Mel London film *To Live Again,* chosen as a 1963 Academy Award nominee for documentary films. Surgeon Dr. Irving Cooper of St. Barnabas Hospital is shown during an operation for Parkinson's disease. In the scene, the patient's hand stops shaking while he is still on the table. (Courtesy Vision Associates, Inc., New York City.)

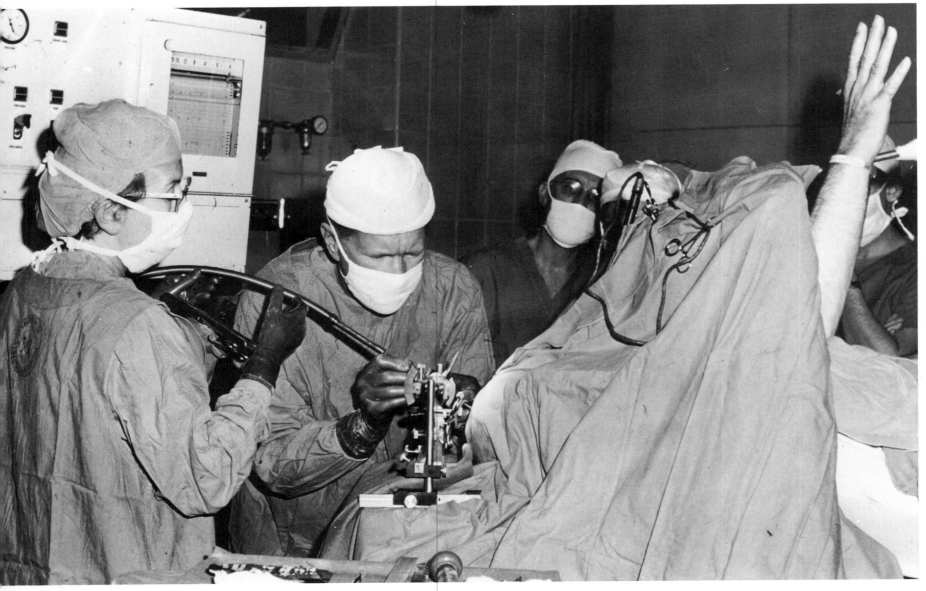

RAY
abel

EXECUTIVE PRODUCER, RAY ABEL PRODUCTIONS

HERB
gardener

STUDIO OPERATIONS ENGINEER, CBS-TV

A producer-director, an operations engineer, and a choreographer—how they worked together on *Limbo*.

RAY ABEL. I approached Alwin Nikolais* and asked him to do a planned electronic piece. He's such a very fine choreographer to work with in the first place, and so imaginative. We had a meeting and talked about this and that, and what could be done. Nikolais went home and did some sketching and planning. He did this many times. Each time I would follow it up with a meeting with the technical department, and we would determine whether or not it could be done, or how it could be done. Herb would tell us that. . .

HERB GARDENER. Yes, when Ray came to me, he had specific ideas in mind. He said, "How do we accomplish this, if we want to stage it this way, and what do we do to get an effect like this?" And so I went to work with a few pencils and paper and came up with some method. We got a studio; we got special effects involved in it—that is, staging special effects. To differentiate between special effects and electronic effects—they do the physical things like the art work that goes by, and the fire, and the bubbles. But the mating of these things into a surrealistic, or realistic, picture was my part of it. . . . Chroma Key has been around a long time. It's a fairly simple device. What it requires is imagination, and that's where Ray and Alwin come in.

RAY ABEL. One of the most interesting aspects of art of the twentieth century is that so much of it is a result of collaborative effort. If you look at motion pictures, for example, there's a tremendous range of personnel involved in making a fine film. Somewhat the same thing happened here, in *Limbo*. . . . A philosophic observation —this trend makes people work more closely together. . . . We're thinking today of violence and separation, but actually, in business, unless you work together, you "ain't gonna have nothing!" I just wonder if, in terms of war and the whole mess, this might have some application. You know, Russia is interested in space. So are we. It's too much for one person or one country.

Although it's always in the back of your mind, actually *Limbo* turned out, unexpectedly, to be a director's dream. You always want to come up with something no one else

*See also "Alwin Nikolais" in chapter 2.

8-26. Portrait of Ray Abel.

8-27. Interior of the CBS studio, with Ray Abel directing early shooting procedures.

has done, and *Limbo* probably achieved that more closely in television than anything so far. It's a good feeling. Because it's a dream, you know. You've got to have the right people, not only the artists but the technicians. The kind of people who are not concerned with the time of the next meal break—everybody gets hungry, but the show comes first. And these were the kind of people we had.

ALWIN NIKOLAIS. My experience has been that the finer the artist, the easier it is to work with him. One excites the other by his capacities, aesthetic focus, and professionalism. The more experienced and highly gifted artist is sure of his identity. This is already established, so it doesn't have to become part of the collaborative effort.

(See *Limbo* color photographs shown on page 190.)

8-28. Portrait of Herb Gardener.

8-29. Herb Gardener in control room of CBS-TV.

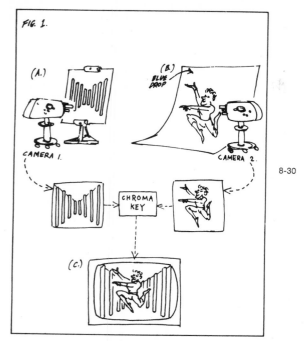

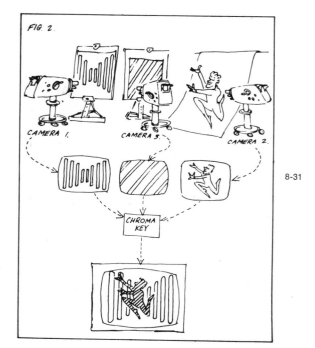

8-30. Chroma Key switching (See diagram Figs. 1A, B, C). Diagram of a man walking down a passageway lined with a series of tall pillars. (Ray Abel production of *Limbo*.)

"The Chroma Key is a device that will allow any color foreground, such as a person, to be matted on any color background, be it film, tape, slides, or live camera. Suppose the effect wanted is a man walking down a passageway that is lined with a series of tall pillars. To do this would normally mean constructing a set large enough to contain the pillars and the man. Using the Chroma Key, the same effect can be achieved using an art card of suitable size (15" x 20") with the columns and corridor drawn on it. Camera 1 shoots the art card and it becomes the background (Fig. 1A). Camera 2 shoots the man walking across a blue floor against a blue backdrop (Fig. 1B). When these two cameras are combined in the Chroma Key, everywhere blue appears on Camera 2; the Chroma Key allows the art work from Camera 1 to show on the screen. Wherever there is no blue, or where the person gets in the way of the blue, the Chroma Key allows the person on Camera 2 to appear on the screen instead of the art card. The final effect, then, is a person walking down the passageway between the columns (Fig. 1C)." (Taken from *How We Did It* by Herb Gardener. Courtesy WCBS-TV Repertoire Workshop.)

8-31. Series of complex visual effects may be arranged. (See diagram Fig. 2.)

"What has happened is that wherever blue is present on the foreground camera (Camera 2), the background picture shows through. Wherever something gets in the way of the blue (the person), a "hole" is cut in the background (art work). This "hole" is then filled up with the object that created it, in this case, a person. The end result is a person walking in this artificial scenery. The fact that a "hole" has been cut in the background means it can be filled up with either the same thing that created it (the person) or any other video signal, perhaps another camera shooting a striped pattern (Fig. 2). The composite picture would then be a corridor with

the outline of a person filled with stripes walking across it. Using these basic techniques, a series of complex visual effects are achieved." (Taken from *How We Did It* by Herb Gardener. Courtesy WCBS-TV Repertoire Workshop.)

8-32–34. Running Dancers: Busy World—People Running—Constant Motion—The Individual Trying to Keep Up With the World. (See diagrams Figs. 3, 4, 5.)

"Personal impressions of some of the dance sequences along with an explanation on how they were done is as follows: The inside of the dancers' bodies had a series of wavy stripes that moved from right to left to heighten the effect of motion. Two cameras and three videotape recorders were used. On Take 1 the camera framed the dancers at the top of the screen. The dancers were placed against a large blue canvas drop that curved down to the blue floor. This permitted even lighting so that a full figure could be matted. The background was a green slide that appeared wherever there was blue in the picture. The outlines of the dancers cut the "hole" in the background (green slide) and the "holes" were filled up by another camera shooting a revolving drum with stripes painted on it. This was recorded on VT-1 (Fig. 3). VT-1 then played it back to the studio where a wipe was used to combine the first level of dancers (tape) with the second level of dancers now being framed in the center by the camera (live). This composite was recorded on VT-2 (Fig. 4). VT-2 played this back to be combined with the third level of dancers using a wipe as before. The total effect was recorded on TV-3 (Fig. 5). During the first take, the music was fed back from the videotape in order to maintain accurate synchronization. The patterns inside the bodies were changed simply by switching a different video signal into the foreground. In each recording, backgrounds were matched so the wipe line did not show." (Taken from *How We Did It* by Herb Gardener. Courtesy WCBS-TV Repertoire Workshop.)

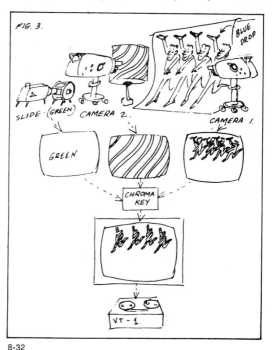

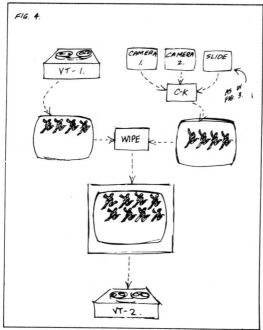

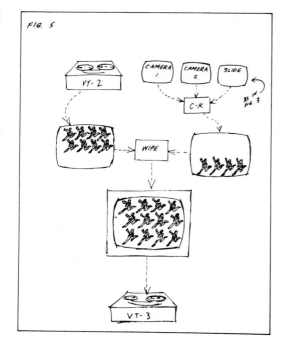

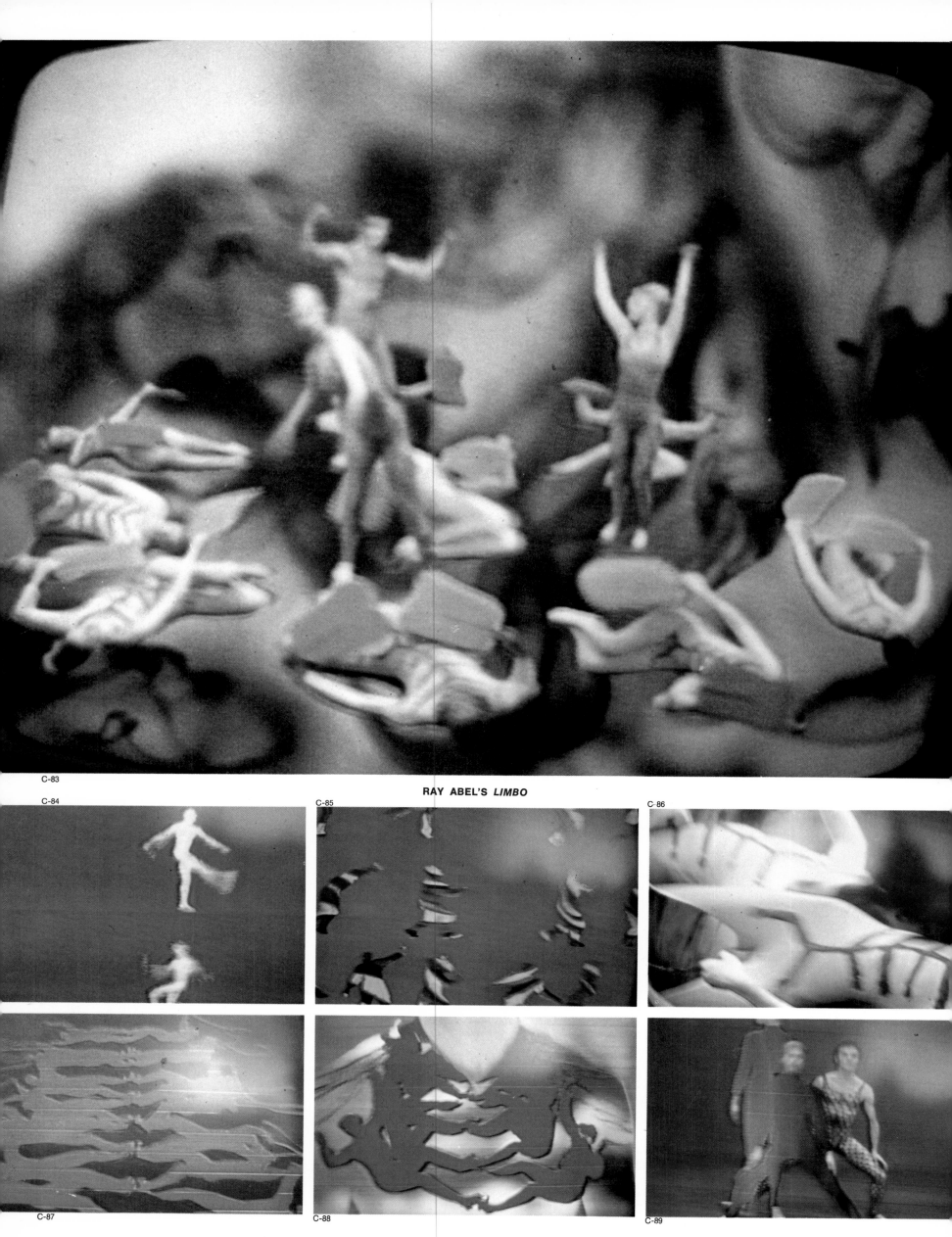

C-83

RAY ABEL'S *LIMBO*

C-84

C-85

C-86

C-87

C-88

C-89

8-35–38. Hole Four Quarters: People Caught in the Whirl of Everyday Life—The Man is Drawn Deeper and Deeper into the Hole. (See diagram Figs. 6, 7, 8, 9.)

"The effect split the screen into 4 quadrants and had the same dancers move from the 4 corners and disappear into the circle in the center. The camera was mounted on a crane to achieve a high, almost straight-down shot. A large plywood disc was placed on the blue floor. The dancers were in their normal costumes. Again, the Chroma Key was used. The background was a yellow slide and the inside of the bodies (foreground) was a revolving multi-colored spiral. These elements were reversed during the number. On the first take, the dancers moved from downstage camera right, and rolled over the center disc (Fig. 6). The videotape of this was played back to be combined with the same dancers now coming in toward the disc from downstage camera left. A vertical wipe was used to combine the two (Fig. 7). In order to give the illusion of the dancers coming in toward the center from upstage and still maintain their size and perspective relative to the dancers coming from downstage, a special device was installed in the color camera to invert the vertical scanning. When the first two sequences were staged again, the performers appeared to come in from the upstage right and left corner even though they actually moved from downstage (Fig. 8). Each sequence was taped and played back to be combined by using a wipe, until a total 4-quadrant picture was recorded (Fig. 9) (4th generation). At one point, the principal dancer appeared in his own costume simply by switching the camera shooting him into the 'hole.' " (Taken from *How We Did It* by Herb Gardener. Courtesy WCBS-TV Repertoire Workshop.)

opposite
C-83. Swiss Cheese sequence from the video ballet *Limbo*, produced by Ray Abel. Note the fan in dancer's hand (also see figure C-86). The fan is used for Chroma Key switching to literally cut holes in images placed in front of the dancers.

C-84-85. Running dancers sequence from *Limbo*.

C-86. Chroma Key switching from the fan held by the dancer to a smoke image on the second Chroma Key camera. From the *Limbo* Swiss Cheese sequence.

C-87. Nerves sequence from *Limbo*.

C-88. Scene from *Limbo*.

C-89. Sequence of Fire Girls from *Limbo*.

(Courtesy WCBS-TV Repertoire Workshop.)

8-35

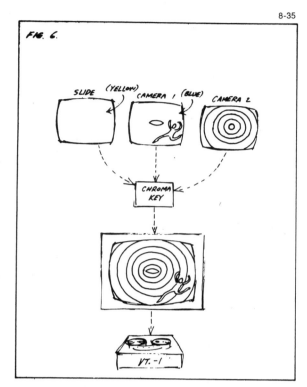

8-36

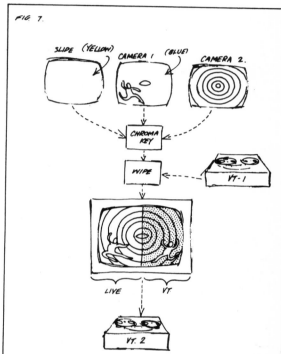

8-37

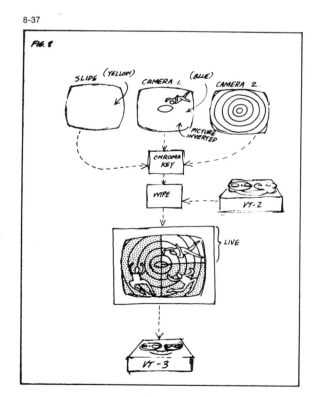

8-38

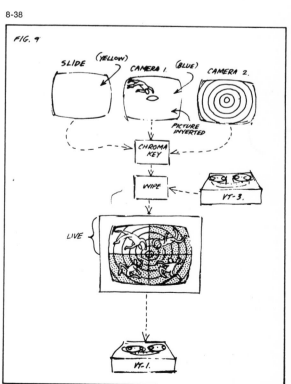

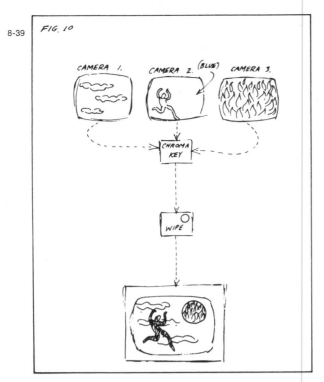

8-39. Sun: The Man is in Hell. He is Engulfed in Flames. He Attempts to Escape the Fire by Jumping Through a Circle of Flames Which Seems to be the Only Exit. (Diagram Fig. 10.)

"The dancer worked in front of the blue canvas drop. A cloud background was keyed in place of the blue and fire from another camera was inserted inside the dancer's body. A circle wipe was added in the upper right corner with fire inserted inside it. As the dancer jumped into the "sun" the circle wipe was expanded and repositioned to give the effect of swallowing the dancer (Fig. 10)." (Taken from How We Did It by Herb Gardener. Courtesy WCBS-TV Repertoire Workshop.)

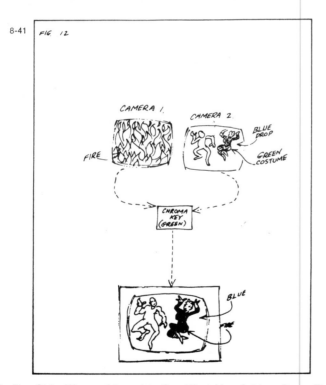

8-41. Fire Girls. We are Allowed to See What Man Seldom Does: The Inner Qualities of Women . . . Sometimes Glitter, Sometimes Fire. (Diagram Fig. 12.)

"This time, boys and girls were dancing together on the same camera. The boys were in natural costumes but the girls had 'glitter,' then 'fire' effects inserted where their costumes should be, giving them a transparent look. The simple answer to this one was to use blue costumes on the girls and place all the dancers against a background other than blue. However, in practice, it would have been very costly in time and materials to strike the blue backdrops blue. The girls' costumes then were dyed green so that the 'glitter' and 'fire' appeared everywhere there was green (Fig. 12). Incidentally, blue is normally used as the key because it is the most opposite color from skin tone. Any highly saturated color may be used except that the closer it is to skin tone, the harder it is to achieve a clean matte with people in the scene. Multiple recordings and a wipe were used to get two levels of dancers in the same pictures." (Taken from How We Did It by Herb Gardener. Courtesy WCBS-TV Repertoire Workshop.)

8-40. Hands: A Man is Threatened by Disembodied Hands and Arms. He is Tossed Aloft By Them and All of Life's Little Problems are Thrown at Him. (Diagram Fig. 11.)

"The principal dancer and the chorus were positioned in front of the blue drop, all on the same camera. The chorus members were dressed completely in blue except their hands and arms. This meant that wherever there was blue in the picture, the background camera shooting smoke would show through. The hands and the principal dancer's body then appeared as they were. At one point, the hands appeared to pull confetti and streamers out of nowhere and throw them in the air. The colored confetti was concealed with blue confetti covering the top of the pile. It was invisible until it was pulled out in the open (Fig. 11)." (Taken from How We Did It by Herb Gardener. Courtesy WCBS-TV Repertoire Workshop.)

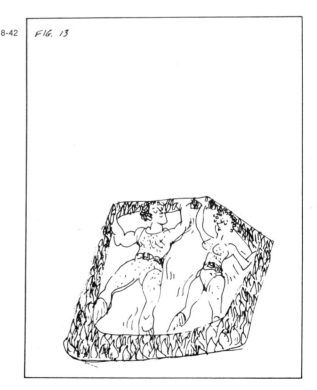

8-42. Doughnuts: Couples Surrounded by Rings of Fire. (Diagram Fig. 13.)

"Several couples were positioned lying on the floor. Each couple had a circular piece of stretch material that they could manipulate to surround themselves or take on various shapes. Fire was inserted in the shrouds giving the effect of a ring of fire around each couple. Here again, green was used as the keying color. The performers were seen in natural costumes while the shrouds having been dyed green could have another signal inserted within them (Fig. 13)." (Taken from How We Did It by Herb Gardener. Courtesy WCBS-TV Repertoire Workshop.)

DR. TOM DOUGLAS

jones

ARTIST, INVENTOR, EDUCATOR. COLORADO SPRINGS, COLORADO

My objective in the field of *STA* (Science + Technology + Art) has been to provide artists and students with means of observing and studying the mysteries of light and color and of applying the results to practical and aesthetic purposes. To that end I have designed and built a number of instruments for use in the classroom and studio.

One of these, the Colortron, is a small, easily portable cabinet containing controllable sources of colored light and a number of props and backgrounds. With these it is possible to demontrate such phenomena as additive color mixture, simultaneous contrast, afterimage, the effect of colored light on colored objects, complementary colored shadows, and other effects not readily perceived except in a controlled situation. All of this is important in merchandising, display, stage lighting, interior design, painting, photography, and other fields where color and light are vital factors. The Colortron is a tool for teaching and for experimentation.

Another device, the Chromaton, is a creative instrument for producing mobile or stabile abstract compositions in colored light. It was designed primarily for students of painting and design to make available to them, on a small scale, the resources for creativeness and expression that hitherto had been accessible only to a few inventors of "color organs" in their public demonstrations.

The Chromaton consists (a) of a portable cabinet about three feet wide with a translucent front upon which the effects produced within are projected, and (b) of a console by which these effects are controlled through a cable from a position in front of the cabinet. The cabinet contains numerous sources of colored light, which can be moved to any positions desired; slowly moving turntables carrying abstract shadow-casting forms; and several specialized projectors and miniature spotlights. The console contains many switches and voltage controls for the lights, turntables, motors, and projectors. All controls have calibrated dials so that any desired effect can be reproduced at any time.

While there are many incidental effects available at will, the basic compositions are produced by the abstract forms designed and constructed by the students or other experimenters. (Not all the experimenters are students: an engineer, a geologist, and a bank president, for example, have found relaxation and aesthetic pleasure in playing with the Chromaton; and artists, poets, and musicians have found inspiration.)

Speaking of musicians, students were asked to use music provided by a record player as a basis for their accompanying mobile compositions in colored light, seeking not a questionable and arbitrary correspondence between pitch and hue, but an intuitive translation in color, form, dynamics, and tempo of the *mood* of the music (Ravel, Debussy, Delius). The results were gratifying; and in my own experiments I found that music provided a needed framework on which to build the modulations and developments in color, form, and rhythm of the visual creation.

I also found that people who had no interest whatever in music or any other art were fascinated by this combination of sound and sight; and that people who scorned abstract painting were pleased with the Chromaton, with or without music. This was something strange and beautiful; but they didn't think of it as art. Therefore they could enjoy it. This example of the elemental appeal of lumia convinced me that it is here to stay and to grow in power and grandeur as science and technology bring new resources to the artist.

continued

8-43. Portrait of Dr. Tom Douglas Jones.

(All photographs herewith courtesy Dr. Jones.)

8-44. The COLORTRON is a portable cabinet containing colored light sources, various props and backgrounds and a remote control panel for the lights. It is used for studying and demonstrating the phenomena of colored light and their practical and aesthetic applications. Above, the cabinet open for a demonstration. Below, the cabinet closed for carrying or for storage.

8-45. The CHROMATON with its remote control console. The stark shadow on the screen can be turned into any number of compositions in an infinite number of color combinations by turning the knobs and switches on the console.

8-46. Some of the effects produced by the CELESTON. The actual effects are in luminous color, and the compositions are constantly, almost imperceptibly changing.

8-46

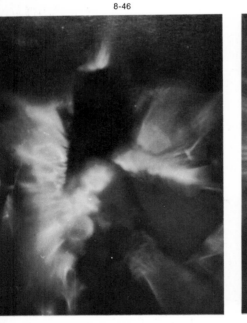
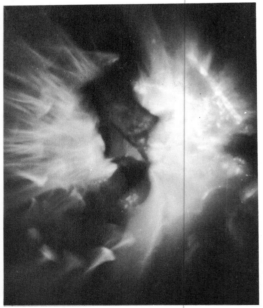

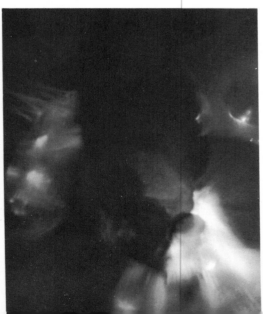

Another creative instrument is the Celeston, so-called because the effects it produces have so often been called celestial. It was at first one of the special projectors in the Chromaton, but it has emerged as a separate entity whose creations outshine those of the Chromaton itself. The creations are of a different kind, however, being more the result of accident (if there is such a thing) than of human calculation. Therefore the Celeston gives less opportunity to the student for original expression than does the Chromaton; but at the turn of a switch it does give instant inspiration, and this is a rare and essential commodity.

The Celeston is a small box about a foot wide containing two overlapping glass discs that slowly revolve; a projection bulb behind the discs, and a lens in front. The discs are studded with small prisms, beads, and bits of colored glass, which, as they slowly pass each other in front of the bulb, project, through the lens onto a viewing screen, a slowly changing image of truly celestial beauty. There is no control console, everything being preset; and the element of creativeness lies in the making of the discs and the adjustment of their relationship to each other.

The idea is not new nor original with me, but the Celeston adds certain modifications such as calibrated dials which make possible the repetition of any desired effect.

There are other instruments, all dealing with the use of colored light, and all, I hope, helping prepare the students of painting today for the world of lumia tomorrow.

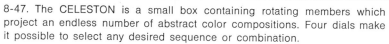

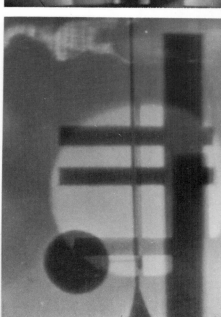

8-47. The CELESTON is a small box containing rotating members which project an endless number of abstract color compositions. Four dials make it possible to select any desired sequence or combination.

8-48. Compositions on the CHROMATON can be in color or black and white; static or slowly changing from one into the other. Three of the above compositions were produced by the abstract form on the left in figure 8-49; the fourth by the form on the right.

8-49. Three composite abstract forms designed and constructed by students for use in the CHROMATON. The center form appears on the screen in figure 8-45. The coordinated parts of these forms can be made to turn independently at the same or different rates, in the same or different directions, producing infinite combinations of colored light and shadows.

8-49

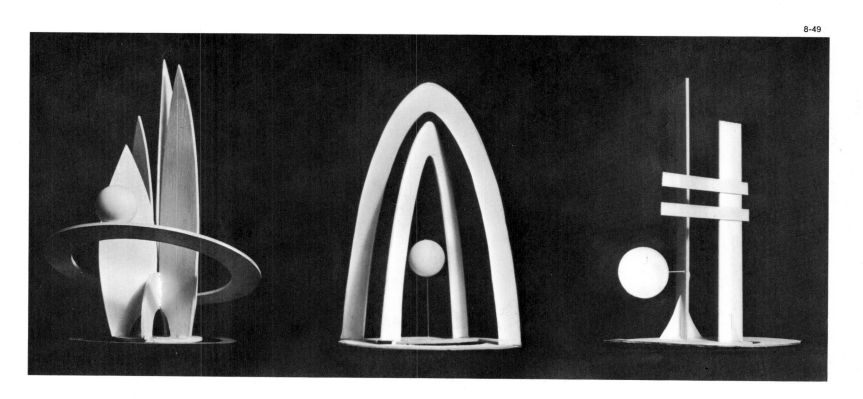

CHRISTIAN
sidenius

LUMIA ARTIST, SANDY HOOK, CONNECTICUT

8-50. Christian Sidenius seated behind his multiple Clavilux devices in his Theatre of Light in Sandy Hook, Connecticut.

In a Theatre of Light, we can use time more creatively than the motion-picture photographer can use it. When you are taking movies of people or things, you are chained to your photography by an element of time. If you disturb the time element, you disturb your audience. But when you deal with an abstract image, you may use the time element more flexibly. For example, here I can take a morphic shape and slowly change it to another kind of morphic shape, change its color, do this very, very slowly, picking up speed, faster, faster, faster, stop, and then very slowly transform back to the original image. Now if you were to do this with a human face, the audience would be quite disturbed because of the psychological fact of remembrance of what faces should be.

Lumia is a performing art. I've done some amateur theatrical work and it struck me that this was an exciting thing simply because we like human beings. We like to see what they are doing. The musician performing for you in the concert hall is more interesting than the record this same musician makes for you. This, again, is why a professor of physics lecturing is more interesting than a movie of a professor of physics giving his lecture. In one of our performances, we introduce a young woman. Her body interferes with the beam of light. It is an aberrant beam, not a pure, straight-line beam. This multifaceted beam destroys her image and transforms her body into something quite different. It abstracts the body, and then you see an abstracted body moving on the screen, which is very exciting.

You use many of the disciplines of the musician. You can orchestrate your image.

I am going on to new ideas and new directions. To me it is an open-ended art. There is no limit to what one can do. We can go on and on and on developing instruments. I've only begun to touch the possibilities.

(See color photographs of light environments by Christian Sidenius, Jackie Cassen, and Rudi Stern shown on page 199.) Stern and Cassen interviews appear in chapter 9.)

8-51. Sidenius sitting inside the Theatre of Light, built by himself and his wife.

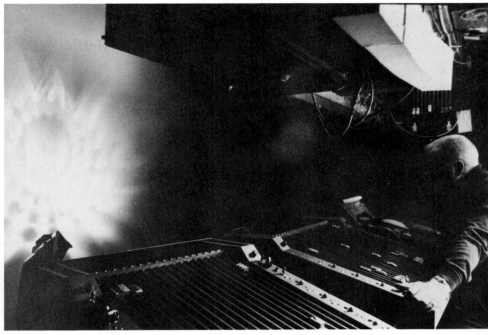

8-52. Sidenius at the Clavilux with a lumia projection on a transparent screen.

8-53. Sidenious with Clavilux and rotating table in his Theatre of Light.

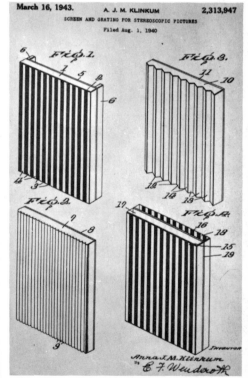

8-56. The lenticular screen developed by Mr. Keijzer for the stereoscopic viewing.

8-54. Sidenius' father-in-law, Albertus Keijzer, patented a method for forming stereoscopic pictures using the motion-picture camera, at left, the special projector, at right, and a lenticular screen in the background.

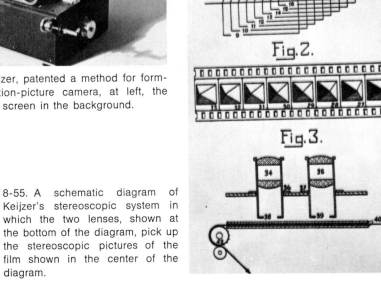

8-55. A schematic diagram of Keijzer's stereoscopic system in which the two lenses, shown at the bottom of the diagram, pick up the stereoscopic pictures of the film shown in the center of the diagram.

Jackie Cassen and Rudi Stern

8-57, 58. Sketches by Cassen and Stern for their light environment at the Architectural League exhibit, held December 14, 1967 to January 11, 1968. See facing page.

8-58

ENVIRONMENT V :
VIBRATIONS
JACKIE CASSEN · RUDI STERN
Architectural League of New York
41 East 65 th. st. N.Y.C.
Dec. 14, 1967···Jan.11, 1968

MIRRORED SURFACE
POOL & WATER SOURCE
FOUNTAINS
PLEXIGLASS BLOCKS
FIBER OPTICS CONSTRUCTION
SOURCE OF BLACK LIGHT
PATH OF LIGHT
PROJECTOR
SCULPTURE
GEODESIC SPHERE
REAR SCREEN
LIGHT ACTIVATED SOUND PATTERNS

8-57

opposite

C-90–C-97. Lumia sequences created for the author by Christian Sidenius in his Theatre of Light, Sandy Hook, Connecticut. (Courtesy Christian Sidenius.)

C-98, C-101–C-105. Photographs of the main room at the Architectural League exhibit, 1968, showing the effect of light projected on the wall. Environment by Jackie Cassen and Rudi Stern.

C-99, C-106, C-107. Use of ultraviolet light and strobe light. Water appeared to be arrested in midair as the strobe light hit the fountain. Cassen and Stern Water Room environment photographed at the Architectural League exhibit, 1968.

C-100, C-108. Kinetic balls (globes). Floors throughout were carpeted with foam-rubber mattresses so spectators could lie and meditate. Cassen and Stern Red Room environment at the Architectural League exhibit, 1968.

(Courtesy Jackie Cassen and Rudi Stern.)

C-90

C-91

C-92

C-93

C-94

C-95

C-96

C-97

C-98

C-99

C-100

C-101

C-102

C-103

C-104

C-105

C-106

C-107

C-108

CHRISTIAN SIDENIUS

JACKIE CASSEN AND RUDI STERN

ROBERT
fisher
LUMIA ARTIST, URBANA, ILLINOIS

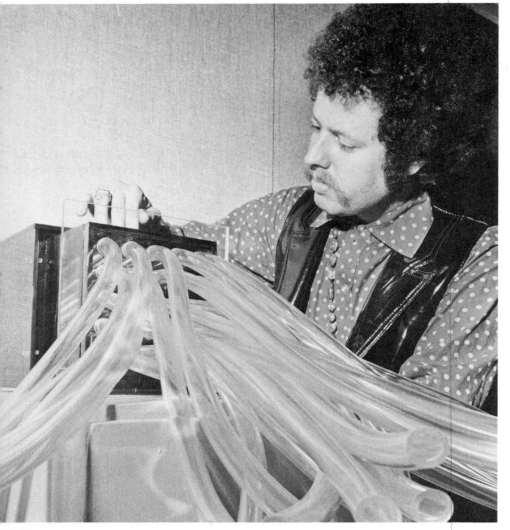

8-59. Portrait of Robert Fisher with one of his light sculptures. (All photographs courtesy Robert Fisher.)

"Those artists producing for the museums and collectors are holdovers from another age. They will pass, as the upper class diminishes or finally gets sated by this game. The mounted and stuffed art of the "big game" hunter finally bores him and his den becomes the repository of a past interest. The artists who pander to the needs of this class fill a void. But in the end, the void will engulf them and they themselves will be voided. Let us finish with the claim that these are the only artists and that their products are the only art. Deny this allegation these artists will, but their cliquishness, 'art schools,' 'art museums,' and social following, defeat any protestation. Time is not on their side, however.

"There is anarchy brewing, and it parallels in its intensity the desires of the Dadaists. 'The King is dead, long live the King' expresses the lingering malady of today. Tomorrow's credo is as far from this as one can get. It reads—'Art is dead; [. . .] art.' " (Taken from *The Artful Society* by Robert Fisher, 1969.)

Light sculptures

I find myself at odds with all that is going on. I am assuming the position of an absurdist. I do not reject meaning; I only find it ultimately meaningless. I enjoy form, but find the quest of perfection in form to be infinite to the degree of being pointless.

Technology is nothing more than a new medium, which is presently being "discovered" by the "artist." We are in a baroque or Victorian period when technical complexity in art is seen as an end in itself. We have ultimate do-nothing machines, which employ sophisticated means to achieve sophomoric ends.

The public is asked to contemplate the wonder and meaning of light sculpture, for example, in galleries a few blocks from Times Square. But how many stop to view the symphony of the Square's lights as the most natural expression of man using light as a medium? It possesses both form and function, is in a constant state of flux, and is magnificently environmental. With all its commercial connotation, it is much less pretentious than the light subjects that are being thrust upon us in the name of light sculpture.

This is an academic period in which formula painters, sculptors, happeners are saturating the environment with their empty visions. It's no longer possible to get excited about the abstract value of proportion, color, or forms in contemporary art.

Minimal forms, as big as they are, are boring. Op is boring. Pop is boring. Art is not only composed of trivia, but it, itself, is trivial. Without redeeming social value, it becomes the most obscene production of our time.

Why don't we kill it? A void will be created. A delicious, metaphysical void. Life purged of its excesses, art rid of its artiness. And to fill the void? We merely have to reverse the expression "when all things become art, art is dead." Art will find its way into the lives and activities of all people. The new museum will be the home, the street, the city, the highway landscape. The function of the older museums will be as repositories for an outdated form of expression called "art." A great epoch will have passed. An epoch that ended as they all have—in decadence, charlatanism, obsession, fad, excess. We are here in it, right now. Let's celebrate the Age of Art by rendering it obsolete.

8-60. A light sculpture designed by Fisher to commemorate the 10th Anniversary of the University of Illinois. This design was adopted by the university, and multiples of this light box were distributed to important alumni.

8-62. *Light Fountain—1967*. Height 6 feet, diameter 10 feet.

8-61. *Light motif—1966*. Height 18 inches, width 40 inches. The artist's first light sculpture.

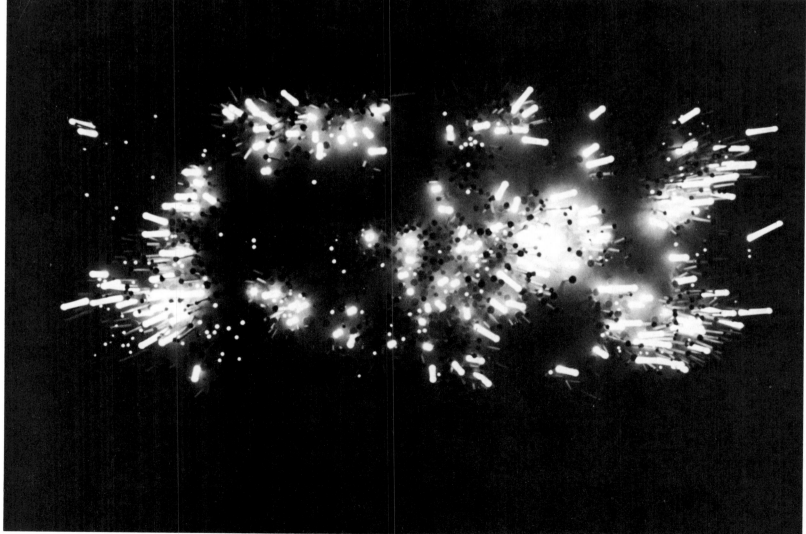

8-63. *Totem to an Electric Age*—1968. Height 18 inches.

8-64B. *The Light Bag* (portable carrying case)—1969.

8-65. Detail of *The Terrarium*—1973. Blown Plexiglas and laminated vinyl film in a plate glass enclosure. Height 15 feet, width 4 feet, depth 4 feet. (Commissioned by Bacon & Van Buskirk Glass Company, Champaign, Illinois.)

8-64A. *Architectural Model*—1969. Height 12 inches.

GERSHON
kingsley

ELECTRONIC COMPOSER, NEW YORK CITY

Gershon Kingsley, born in Germany, during World War II, went to Palestine, where he studied at the Jerusalem Conservatory. From there he went to New York and the Juilliard. He has studied at the Los Angeles Conservatory of Music and Columbia University. In 1966, he made an agreement, as a composer, to work with the Moog, "because of its new dimension of sound."

The musician and the Moog

Because of technology and research, there is an extension of all senses, as well as sound—a desire to go across previous limits in the senses. I am a composer. The logical development, instead of using natural methods to create sound, is using other forms—electronic devices—to create a combination of sounds. This, before, could not even be imagined by people. I think we are receptive to it today.

All sounds are now material for the composer and musician. You take any part of what you hear. Even the motor or the windshield wiper can be part of it.

This particular instrument was invented by R. A. Moog, an engineer. He specializes in designing and developing these instruments, in collaboration with musicians like myself. It can synthesize some things—a synthesis of the component of metrical sounds—but the other application of this particular instrument produces a whole range of frequencies. What we hear are frequencies that have no particular musical sound—like noise. It has no pitch—it's noise. We could get the frequencies, the richness of the

symphony orchestra. The only thing is that the sounds might not be those of a symphony orchestra.

But the instrument computer is meaningless until something is fed into it. You can affect the beginning of it— new music for the new instrument. People should realize that they cannot buck the new, cannot buck something that is very progressive.

To me, the greatest invention in modern times is the tape. You can cut it, splice it, change it around. The tape is actually the final medium that the sounds will have to go through. It can be played for performances, too. It's something new. It's alive to the public. When you go to a concert, you have a whole orchestra playing. Here you have a collage; it's a sound collage.

8-67. Kingsley at the Moog Synthesizer.

8-66. Gershon Kingsley in his studio.

8-68. Close-up of the Synthesizer.

8-70. Four different tracks are picked up on recorder's tape head in the studio.

8-69. The complete multimedia studio.

DR. JAN

larue

MUSICOLOGIST, COMPUTER-ANALYZED MUSICAL SCORES, NEW YORK UNIVERSITY, NEW YORK CITY

8-71. Portrait of Dr. Jan LaRue.

We haven't attempted to do very much with raw analysis, because we haven't established the criteria to feed into the computer to analyze raw material; what we have done is feed in a partially analyzed work, particularly a Haydn symphony of which we have made a formal analysis. We then feed in this formal analysis, controlled by the bar numbers. Bar one is *P,* a primary thematic function. Bar two is a continuation of that function. Maybe bars three and four are still continuations. Then, at bar five, a new idea—a new thematic function—comes in. And by feeding in a type of analysis that I call a timeline—which is nothing but a line on which all of these bars are marked—with the various phenomena of thematic function written above the line and harmonic functions below the line, a simply ordered graph of the piece can then be keypunched by almost a one-to-one code, nothing at all complicated. This gives you a base line on which to hang any other observation of the piece that you may want to make. For example, you can, at any point, feed into the computer a remark that a certain interesting harmony occurs at bar twenty-two, and then you could later ask the computer what thematic functions are associated with this type of

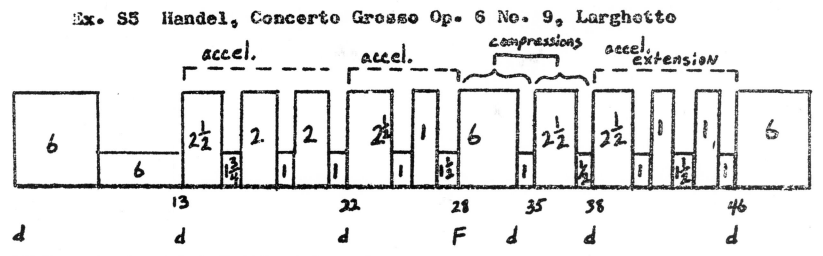

Ex. 85 Handel, Concerto Grosso Op. 6 No. 9, Larghetto

8-72. Diagram shows the analysis of a Handel Concerto Grosso, using a computer to determine the period of acceleration and compression in a short passage from the Handel work. (Courtesy Jan LaRue.)

interesting harmony. That's the useful point of this. This is a partially analyzed input and not a raw bit of data. A computer is not doing the analyzing; it is just doing the remembering and the correlating.

There is a kind of objective attitude toward the data that the computer furnishes that you might not achieve yourself. I'll illustrate this, with respect to the Haydn project, with something quite distinctive and interesting that the computer showed me, which had never previously occurred to me at all. Any Haydn symphony modulates; that is, it moves from one key to a new, contrast key. And our computer tabulation shows that in the second, the new key, there were in a group of thirty early symphonies more themes in the new key area than there were in the old key area. For some reason or other, I had never counted themes by key affiliation; it didn't seem important. But now, as a result of the computer analysis, I have an entirely new question to pose that I never thought of myself. I think every time you get a fresh approach, it stimulates you to new thoughts; really new ideas are going to come out of purely numerical manipulations of musical data.

DANIEL

DANCER, CHOREOGRAPHER, NEW YORK CITY

A dancer discusses the role of technology in his field— and finds it wanting.

The significant thing about my collaboration with Eric Salzman,* the electronic composer, is that neither one of us is a purist. We could go through an entire piece and not take advantage of modern technology, or we could, if necessary, make use of the most advanced technology. Or any combination. Neither one of us feels restricted in the sense that certain periods of art, or certain ways of expressing, are automatically ruled out because they are not "in," not fashionable, not this, or not that. Both of us feel that we are the children of a great library that goes as far back as one can reach, or up to laser beams. If you turned laser beams into music, and we needed it, and that was the only way to do it, we would do it. Neither one of us would feel any special joy or excitement in using something because it was new technology. As a consequence, we worked well together.

My premise in work is the people. The technology is really to be kept at a minimum. *The Peloponnesian War* turned out to be an extremely complex work. Orginally, it

*See Salzman interview in chapter 9.

was to have films and slides and whatnot. As I began to work, I realized that these things were not necessary, that the basic interaction was to an extremely complex sound situation, where a voice spoke the Peloponnesian War through the entire sequence. At intermittent times there were music, music collage, sounds, and then there were costume changes. Within the same short phase of movement, I would do utterly naturalistic movement and highly stylized movement. There were times where I was doing magic tricks, and times where I was doing a rather complex dance with a serial construction. The use of films and slides would have added another level of information, which was beyond the situation.

My excitement is people. The work I am doing now is focused on the space between people—what takes place between people. I do not put down the excitement of other artists with media. My sound equipment, when I travel, is as advanced a piece of technology as you can get. But if kazoos were right, I would use kazoos. To me, the greatest complexity, and the greatest fascination, is people.

So much for technology. *continued*

8-73. Daniel Nagrin opening the door to his studio on Bleecker Street, New York City.

8-74. Rehearsal hall where Nagrin teaches and practices the dance.

As a matter of fact, I'd like technology to work for us. I look forward to an inexpensive film technology so that we can become a literate art. I look forward to a creative approach to the videocassettes.

For a dancer in our culture, that's no way out. An actor can bum around for years, fight and struggle, and suddenly he's tops. A wild-haired guitarist can become a millionaire. I am not putting down talent. I am saying that technology works for them. We have no technology that is easy, cheap, and commercial. No record platter. No inexpensive film. Video is lousy. An awful picture. Very little choice of gradation. Small size, reducing the whole thing to insignificance and impotence, as far as movement goes. The only thing that works in television is the close-up. Or people talking or laughing or singing. Spectacle is meaningless in television. You can't have spectacle unless you have force, weight—you can't have force, weight, until you have size. What's a twenty-four-inch screen? Nothing.

Some serious people in the dance field have done poetic things with the use of juxtaposition of film and dance. The one thing that is really difficult is creating a dance film. The two mediums are competitive. Dance and sound work because you can't see sound and you can't hear movement. So they are like a man and a woman. Motion pictures are aptly named. The dancer is a mover; the camera is basically a mover. What the camera tends to do is paralyze the dancer. In order to have the figure contained in the camera, the dancer never moves. He's in the center of the frame. He's a little like some pathetic hunted man who's in a gunsight and is running, and the gunner keeps him frozen in the cross hairs. If you're too close to the figure, you don't sense the space that he's moving in. If you back up and get a sense of the space, you lose the weight-force of the dancer's body, because the dancer gets too small in the frame.

My feeling is that it is possible, but that one must look at it in terms of translation. If one tried to translate a Chinese poem into English, one would lose and gain. That's what has to take place, dance into film. There are two kinds of film. One is to record, and the other is to take dance work that already exists and translate it to the film medium. The most profound hassle is expense. Expense and the fact that the culture isn't that interested in dance. Therefore, who is going to put in the money? Dance as a film is a stalemate until something comes along that can reduce the costs of filmmaking.

8-75A—75H. Scenes from *The Peloponnesian War,* a dance recital by Daniel Nagrin, with music by Eric Salzman.

8-75E

8-75F

8-75G

8-75H

9 the forms of intermedia

The intermedia artist has at his command an extremely broad range of imaging systems and tools to create his art. Many of these forms are not new and have had a long and elegant history of their own; some, however, are of relatively recent origin: the holograph image, the laser, videotape, and electronic music. It is surprising, in reviewing the language of intermedia, to discover how recent many of these forms actually are. To a large degree, they flow from the explosion of knowledge after World War II.

We have also noted that the mixed-media artist has received direct support from members of the scientific community in using the more expensive pieces of hardware, especially the computer. Corporations have lent facilities to enable artists to extend their art in this direction.

A third development, which has real significance as we explore the realm of the media-based artist, is the involvement of the spectator as a participant in the creative experience in environmental art. There is a strong desire on the part of the intermedia artist to bridge the traditional gap between art with a capital *A* and the mass taste.

In this brief tour of the realm, we have also perceived that the development of enlarged-field painting contributed to the artist's interest in the relation of the scale of the painting to the spectator. As the size of the work increased, it became environmental. A painting twenty feet wide and forty feet high, exhibited with others of lesser proportions, by its very existence creates an environment.

I remember my feelings of being engulfed in Clyfford Still's works when I viewed them in the magnificent interior space provided for them at an exhibit mounted by the Albright-Knox Gallery in Buffalo, New York.

The interest in enlarged environments has been expressed by intermedia artists in great murals and collages, and in projected images, still and kinetic. Combined with these projections into the space enveloping the spectator have been multichanneled audio systems, which bring the nuances of electronic music and reconstituted narrative sounds into the same environment.

The artist does not intend to be alone in this somewhat frightening world. He is increasingly insistent on sharing his reactions with those around him. Art must move out of the gallery to areas where the masses can understand and enjoy it.

An artist wants to give pleasure. His work is like the fun houses in the amusement park, which are true childhood intermedia environments. The kinetics, the surprises, the distorted images in mirrors are familiar, yet different, as they express the contemporary artist's powerful urge for relevancy.

Environmental Art: Expo '67 as a Total Environment
The National Film Board of Canada Pavilion: *Labyrinthe*

The Canadian government planned and presented to the public a total environment in the remarkable World's Fair, Expo '67. The exhibition's location, on a series of connected islands in the Saint Lawrence River near the center of Montreal, set the keynote. It was in itself a special environment. Each pavilion was a carefully planned environment, so that the shrill commercial pitch that mars most large exhibitions was not present. Expo '67 had a theme that held firm throughout its time.

Labyrinthe

Intermedia techniques were widely used for entertainment and education at Expo '67. Multiprojection projects were common denominators in exhibits from any far-flung and diverse cultures. Entire pavilions dealt with the pantheon of media, offering environmental experiences in varying degrees.

The total environment came closest to full realization in Canada's *Labyrinthe* pavilion. Few visitors will forget the psychological impact of what they might have fancied would be a purely entertaining show. As they moved through halls and rooms that trancended physical realities, they became, whether they wished it or not, participants in an emotional labyrinth.

The total concept and technological details, which created the unforgettable atmosphere of *Labyrinthe,* were partly the work of Thomas C. Daly, Ian MacNeill, and J. Creighton Douglas of the National Film Board of Canada. Coupled with photographs taken at the time, their words recreate a little of the magic that was *Labyrinthe.*

Thomas C. Daly

Tom Daly is a film editor to the bottom of his soul. He can, and does, do many other things for the film board, but his work with the five-screen presentation in the third and final room of *Labyrinthe* was his most important commitment at that time. He described the editing problems of five visual and audio tracks where the shifts from screen to screen required a special sense of editing continuity. On the other hand, the editing "problems" were just the challenge that Daly desired. He told me of the mock-up they made of the five screens in an old airplane hanger so they could test the concept in practice long before the pavilion building was constructed.

Daly is a warm and open man, a consumate film editor, and someone who has solved that most difficult of all adult riddles: how to get paid for things you love to do.

Ian MacNeill

Ian MacNeill was a producer for the *Labyrinthe* exhibition. He worked with the many talented producers who put together this most sophisticated of all environmental exhibitions. He recalled with great pleasure the meticulous planning that went into the three main rooms for the pavilion. One sensed the pleasure he had experienced in being involved in such a well-conceived project. Each of the three rooms exploited a different visual concept: the floor-wall interactive image; the infinity star room, which suggested an endless space; and the five-screen multiple display of the last major room.

J. Creighton Douglas

The first time I tried to interview Creighton Douglas, I doubt he would have seen the Queen of England, let alone the Prime Minister of Canada. I visited *Labyrinthe* when the exhibition was in full swing and Mr. Douglas was in charge of the administrative show. The entire pavilion represented the best thinking of the National Film Board of Canada, and Douglas had been in on the planning from the very outset.

Later on, I returned to Montreal and the bustle of the final exhibit had long since subsided. Douglas is a careful, precise man, who impresses one as being deeply concerned with communications as an art form.

The Czechoslovak Pavilion: Expo '67

For imaginative applications of multimedia techniques, the Czechoslovak Pavilion was notable. Fresh and vivid impressions were made on visitors to Emil Radok's *Diapolyekran*, Josef Svoboda's *Polyvision,* and Dr. Raduz Cincera's *Kino-Automat* theatre. In varying degrees, people became involved—in the Kino-Automat's film *One Man and His World* to the extent that they determined, by voting, the course of the story.

Emil Radok

Emil Radok is an important Czechoslovak artist who has collaborated with Josef Svoboda at many important international expositions. Radok is a master photographer, animator, and creator of what surely ranks as the most ambitious still slide-projection system ever developed by man. It would be almost impossible for the layman to grasp the complexity of Radok's projection technique. When the audience at Expo '67 saw his masterpiece, entitled the *Creation of the World,* they were witnessing the most remarkable still, slide program ever shown.

In an interview with the author, Radok described the complex Diapolyekran as an attempt to combine the aesthetics of Cubism and naturalistic painting for a new kind of imagery. The mural was composed of a screen twenty feet high and thirty-two feet wide, made up of 112 cubes, each two feet square and mounted so that they could move backward and forward in space to a depth of three feet.

Two slide projectors were mounted on a rack behind each cube. Since each projector held eighty slides, 160 images could be projected on each cube during the presentation of *Creation of the World*. In fourteen minutes, 15,000 images appeared on the screen. Rakok explained that six pieces of information had to be fed to each module every fifth of a second during the fourteen-minute show.

Although the concept of modular mosaics is a simple one—an old one to us, as old as Ravenna, or as recent as the card formations of students at halftime on the tube—Radok's *Diapolyekran* was designed in such a manner that it combined the power of the cubist still image with powerful kinetic sequences. The system was designed so that at one moment only one cube of the 112 in the system was illuminated. Then, suddenly, the entire field of remaining cubes could be illuminated in dazzling sequences until an entirely new form of audio-visual presentation emerged. Because the artist could control every cube independently, he was able to intermix and juxtapose partial visual elements in a totally original manner.

An additional aspect of the presentation was the fact that each cube was mounted on a "sled," which could move toward or away from the audience as the computer program dictated. Here again, we tend to concentrate on technical effects, while the real issue is that an artist of Radok's stature could take such a complex system and create a stunning work of visual art.

Josef Svoboda

Josef Svoboda is rapidly gaining in international reputation as one of the most important artists working with environmental art and new kinetic light forms. He has enjoyed a distinguished career in Europe as one of the leading experimental artists where he successfully combined motion pictures, live actors, dancers, kinetic light effects, and multiple audio effects. His mastery, however, does not come from his use of multiple media effects with live action, it comes from an inherent good taste which utilizes a medium only when it will achieve an artistic result.

Although the author has not been able to interview Mr. Svoboda personally, he has carried on a correspondence with the artist, which resulted in the rich photographic record of his career presented later in this chapter.

Recently his reputation was enhanced in the United States with the production of the late Göran Gentele's version of the opera *Carmen* at the Metropolitan Opera House, New York City. Svoboda designed the lighting for this remarkable production.

At Expo '67, Svoboda's *Polyvision* proved to be one of the most important environmental displays ever created by an artist. The room for the display was fifty-five feet long and over twenty feet high. The stage was more than twenty feet deep. The presentation required multiprojectors in which over 8,000 slides were used, as well as eight 35 mm looped film projectors located above the display. Each film was over 300 feet long and ran during the entire projection of the slides. There was also multichanneled musical accompaniment.

Kinetic effects were coupled with visual projections—rotating globes and drums, and cubes that moved in space, toward and away from the spectator and left to right. Computers with programmed tapes controlled the spectacle—a pale, inadequate word to describe this offspring of art and technology.

Kino-Automat

The Kino-Automat's film *One Man and His World* was a kind of cinema by jury. From time to time the action considerably came to a stop, so that the members of the audience could vote on the direction of the story line by pushing one of two buttons on the seat armrests. Should the husband give shelter to a lovely blonde clad only in a bath towel, with his wife due back any moment? Or should he close the door on her? Voting results were flashed on two panels at the side of the screen. Social psychologists, taking solemn note of the proceedings, observed that the audiences tended to vote on the side of a fling for the husband.

Young Intermedia Artists

Les Levine uses disposable components for the creation of an art experience. Stan VanDerBeek worked with scientists of Bell Laboratories on computer-generated graphic problems. Robert Whitman uses lasers to solve an aesthetic problem.

They and others take from the technological tool box the things that appear good and right to them for the shaping of their visions: motion pictures, lumia, laser, virtual images, holograms, multichannel sounds, television with stereo-audio and visual channels, computer generated films.

Les Levine

One of the most original intermedia artists working today is Les Levine. Having received his training as an industrial engineer, he has made use of this orientation during his concern with intermedia and environmental art. An interesting example of this influence could be seen in his environmental exhibition, entitled *Star Garden* at the Museum of Modern Art, New York City, late in the sixties. For the exhibit, Levine had large, plastic domelike shapes constructed to focus the attention of the spectator-par-

ticipant. Another example is his work with what he called "disposable art." These were plastic modules vacuum-formed over a mold and sold for a very small sum. The purchaser was invited to use them as long as they proved interesting, and then to discard them.

Stan VanDerBeek

Stan VanDerBeek's home, multimedia studio, and editing facilities are located in a beautiful wooded plot about forty miles north of New York City. John Cage and other avant-garde artists live on the cooperatively-owned land. VanDerBeek has explored the full range of multimedia iconography, from multiple still projection to stereo-video programs for public television in the Boston area.

In his studio VanDerBeek has constructed a hemispherical dome. Here he can control motion-picture projectors mounted on remote control turntables, slide projectors, and related hardware, to create startling multi-impression showings. In a separate editing building, he has animation facilities, which can be used to generate his films.

He has also spent a good deal of his recent effort on computer-generated films. Recently, he joined Gyorgy Kepes at Massachusetts Institute of Technology as an artist-in-residence. Currently he holds a similar post at Syracuse University, Buffalo, New York.

Robert Whitman

Robert Whitman has worked as intermedia environmental artist for many years. He has shown a strong interest in the use of reflective surfaces as part of environmental shows. This interest was shown at his Finch College Museum of Art exhibit, again at the *Pond* exhibit held at the Jewish Museum in New York City, and most recently in his work at Expo '70, and at MOMA in 1973.

The *Pond* exhibit exploited the virtual image technique familiar to NASA simulation scientists. Simply stated, a real image is a mirrored reflection. With a flat mirror, the point of focus is on the surface of the mirror. On the other hand, if the artist or scientist employs a concave mirror, an unusual phenomenon occurs: instead of reflecting an image on the concave face of the mirrored surface, the reflection focuses out in space—in thin air. The point of focus or the distance from the mirror's surface depends on the diameter of the concave mirror. The larger the mirror, the farther away it focuses. Whitman exploited this principle brilliantly at his *Pond* exhibit. He had eight-foot-diameter concave mirrors formed out of plastic: when the spectator stood in front of the mirror, his inverted reflection simply stood out in thin air. Combined with the concave mirrors at this exhibit, Whitman employed Mylar reflective surfaces, which were activated by audio vibrations. Much of his work has been collaborative with scientists. In this context, it is interesting to speculate on how much the artist owes to the scientist. During this writer's tour of the realm, he never found an artist who did not give full credit to the importance of the scientist's contribution.

The New York University Group

Under Boyd Compton's leadership, the Intermedia Program of the New School of the Arts had a brief existence at New York University. Compton brought Len Lye (featured in chapter 2), Anthony Martin, Morton Subotnick, and other important artists to the school to teach and work with the students in one of the first formalized intermedia programs in the country. The emphasis was on the concepts of mixed-media environmental spectator-activated art.

Anthony Martin

Anthony Martin has developed some of the most original spectator-activated environments in the country. His "Interaction Room," originally shown at The Howard Wise Gallery, has subsequently been displayed at other art centers around the country, including the Museum of Contemporary Art in Chicago.

I first met Anthony Martin when I photographed him at his "Interaction Room," then being displayed at The Howard Wise Gallery. Martin is a dynamic young artist who has thought out the problems of spectator involvement very carefully, so that the spectator activity results in a genuine involvement. His method for the Interaction Room was to create four projection systems that sent multiple images to its four walls. Located in the center of the room was a pedestal with four spectator switches. Participants pushed one of the switches to activate a particular projection system. Four colors designated the different projection zones, and each one related to the particular philosophy of the visuals in that zone. Martin had prepared all of the stunning visual material.

At a later date, I caught up with the artist again, at the NYU Intermedia School. Here he showed me more of his work, and we taped the interview contained in this chapter. I was particularly intrigued with a drawing of a virtual image multimedia device Martin had on the wall. This was planned to use the same visual simulation techniques developed by Joseph LaRussa for the Apollo simulators; it seemed most interesting to me that this young artist was employing essentially the same conception for aesthetic rather than training purposes. It also implied that artists and engineers, although working in different areas, are seeking similar visual solutions.

Martin and Morton Subotnick, a composer of electronic music, have also developed environmental shows for Fillmore West and the Electric Circus.

Morton Subotnick

Composer Subotnick and artist Martin worked independently on their own collaborations before joining the New York University staff. While Subotnick was teaching music composition and analysis at Mills College in Oakland, California, he became interested in inventing a modular system for electronic music. With the help of Boyd Compton, he obtained a Rockefeller Foundation grant and worked with engineer Don Buchla to produce the system now known by Buchla's name.

Multimedia Opera

Dr. John V. Gilbert

The concept of a multimedia or intermedia opera, as noted by Dr. Gilbert, the composer-director of such an opera, has a long and respectable tradition. To a large degree, Gilbert sees it as having grown out of the great intermedia operas of Richard Wagner, in which Wagner wrote the scenario, researched the history of German folk music, expanded the concept of the opera, revised its discipline, restructured the relationship between the voices and the instruments, and in general created in his *Ring* cycle, through his setting and staging, one of the most remarkable intermedia performances yet conceived.

Wagner called his "intermedia" operas *Gesamtkunstwerks*. The term means "an all together work"; it helps define the word "intermedia." Intermedia means an integration of stage effects with other art forms.

Gilbert's multimedia opera *Rotation* deals with the conflicts between youth and age, illusion and reality, and the quest for absolute meaning to life, with the several philosophical positions on the relevance of absolutes.

In the multimedia opera, because of the nature of the performing art, there is a return to the audience as spectators. The audience remains seated and observes the activity of an extended stage through multimedia projection, but it does not become an active participant in the sense that the audience participates in a pure intermedia environment.

Opera Today

Patricia Collins/Herbert Kaplan/Al Berr

A remarkable group of young artists has gathered around Patricia Collins, the artistic director of the "Opera Today" group. Together with Herbert Kaplan, music director, and Al Berr, the managing director, Miss Collins has developed a strong new direction for opera in America. In a sense, the group has integrated live voice, dance, and ballet with film, still-photograph projection, and recorded voice and music. This is no small order of achievement. The aesthetic results are perhaps the most professional integration of visual and aural media with live performance this writer has seen.

Opera Today has received widespread notice for its first major effort *Spatial Variations on a Theme by Benjamin Britten.* The film sequences for the performance were created by Elaine Summers; the music (Britten's song cycle, based on Rimbaud's love poems) was directed by Herbert Kaplan; Norman Walker choreographed the production, which was admirably danced by Tony Catanzaro, Mario Delamo, Pamela Ladimer, and Alice Gill; and the beautiful libretto was sung by Michael Best. This group created a masterful moment for the new opera conception. Some of the photographs in the section on Elaine Summers show her filming Pamela Ladimer, the dancer, for portions of the "Spatial Variations" performance.

Opera Today is currently preparing a major new work on the Gulliver story. It will integrate an even more ambitious mélange of media and live performance.

Cinema Dance

Elaine Summers

The cinema dance carries the audience farther along the path of participation toward the ultimate encounter in the exchange of blows and caresses in the Living Theatre.

Elaine Summers combines her first love, the dance and choreography, with her second, motion pictures, in theatre-dance performances that bring the audience into participation. She creates and makes her own films, choreographs the dances, plans the settings, directs the performances, and dances in them. In the congenial quarters of the Judson Memorial Church in Greenwich Village, New York City, the dance-theater presentations sometimes become tribal happenings, with members of the audience flashing lights at random from individual hand-held mirrors onto stage and performers.

Intermedia Systems, Inc.—Extension to the Real World

Dr. George H. Litwin

Inevitably, the concept of intermedia as a way to create environments would be applied to the world of business and education.

Intermedia Systems, Inc., was set up to program environmental simulations for educational, business, and research purposes. Multimedia technology is the tool for creating environments that have particular kinds of psychological effects. Intermedia is building the hardware needed for programming the software. The programming and delivery systems are conceived in totality, to be made available to the client as a whole.

One of their basic functions is to produce intermedia materials for use in schools, with a view to providing our culture's media-oriented youth with a greater sense of relevancy in their studies.

Dr. Litwin, president of Intermedia Systems, Inc., is a psychologist who teaches at Harvard University. Creative director Gerd Stern is a pioneer in the field of intermedia. He is also a founding member of the mixed-media group USCO, now disbanded, which created kinetic sculptures and media environments shown at many museums and galleries. Litwin and Stern were on the teaching staff of the Harvard Graduate School of Business when they began their collaboration. They are joined in the project by two young specialists, Michael Callahan, technical director, and Donald Pasquella, visual program manager.

Gerd Stern

Gerd Stern is one of the most influential intermedia artists working at the present time. He has been able to translate the implications of McLuhan into a powerful aesthetic statement. He has had an extremely varied career for such a young man. In the late sixties, when the psychedelic and the mystic were influencing so many artists, Stern created, at his "church" in Garnerville, New York, an equalitarian community for a whole generation of emerging talents. His fellow artists created a cooperative approach to creating kinetic light environments, audio extravaganzas and a whole series of interesting multisensory works. Stern told me rather ruefully, after the USCO group had scattered in diverse ways, that their own success had defeated the concept of a cooperative artists' community. In its original conception, any artist who wished to live at the church and work on projects was welcome. This persisted for some time until the site began to be noticed in the popular press. Suddenly the teen-age population of Garnerville, which had hardly been motivated previously towards culture, descended on the church with a vengeance. Sheer numbers did the whole thing in.

One of Stern's most interesting projects before he went to the Harvard Business School to teach multimedia, and later form Intermedia Systems with Litwin, was to develop a total sensory bombardment for a group of doctors who had been studying effects of sensory deprivation at the Johns Hopkins Medical School. It occurred to them that they might do well to study the antithesis of sensory isolation, and they came to Stern to help them prepare the experiment.

Michael Callahan

Michael Callahan is a young electronics expert with commanding skills. He specializes in developing the "hardware" that makes multimedia systems work. In the beginning, artists hooked up three or four Kodak Carrousel projectors to a simple switching unit. The limitations of this technology, however, very quickly became apparent to artists who wanted to literally "bombard" the eye with hundreds of images simultaneously. Callahan started out with Stern at the Garnerville church, then went to Boston when Intermedia Systems got going. He has since advanced to the point where he is one of the most knowledgeable young men in the country in the use of audio and visual multi-channel equipment.

Donald Pasquella

When I met him, Don was taking many of the still photographs used by Intermedia Systems. Later, Pasquella went on his own to become a teacher of intermedia technique as well as perfecting his own concept of the medium.

A Definition of Intermedia

In essence, all of the intermedia experiences strive for a greater sense of spectator participation. Eventually they wish to eliminate the word "spectator" from the vocabulary of the arts. The spectator is replaced by the colleague-participant in the tribal community of intermedia experience.

The Videocassette and the Underground

It has become apparent in the early years of the seventies, that many artists who were originally attracted to film have turned their attention to the immediacy of expression they can experience with the videotape medium. With film, the artist constructs an elaborate shooting sequence and finally, on an appointed day, begins to shoot film. The medium has one inherent drawback for the creative artist: the footage exposed in the camera cannot be viewed until it has been developed by a film-processing laboratory. There is no greater trauma for the filmmaker than waiting for the "rushes" of his previous day's shooting. All sorts of gremlins intrude—from missed shots on location to chicanery and incompetence at the processing labs.

With videotape, no such technical barriers exist. It is possible for the videotape artist to immediately "play back" the sequence just taped. If it is satisfactory, the artist knows immediately. If, for some reason, he wishes a change in the scene, he merely redubs over the dis-

carded scene. As we have already noted with the work of Ray Abel and Herb Gardener, the videotape medium offers remarkable visual freedom for the creative director and for the engineer working closely with artists and musicians.

In its early years videotape did suffer from the scandalous lack of compatibility between various manufacturers' recording devices. Furthermore, the videotape recorders were prohibitively expensive and available primarily to the broadcasting networks. In time, less expensive machines were developed and the Japanese finally decreed the E.I.J.A. standards for half-inch reel-to-reel videotape recorders. With this half-inch compatibility, many young artists turned to the medium with a vengeance. The cost of good recording equipment came into the range reserved for high-fidelity audio components. The medium, however, still had a major drawback for the artist. The general public shied away from reel-to-reel players because they found them difficult to load and use.

In the late sixties Peter Goldmark developed the first cartridge-loaded videocassette player, the CBS/Motorola EVR player. The system caught the attention of artists who longed for quick and easy distribution of their video message. The EVR system did not live up to its promise; it was followed, however, by Sony, which did. Soon Panasonic, RCA, Cortrivision, and many other competing systems will enter the race. In essence, a new standardization battle will be mounted, in which the genius of the free-enterprise system will be sorely tested. After many hundreds of millions of dollars loss to the protagonists, one or two systems will emerge to capture the public interest in home videoplayers. The artists interviewed for this section see this potential. They envision a new form of underground communication in which their special vision and insight will reach an ever-widening audience.

Rudi Stern and John Reilly at Global Village, Eric Salzman and Jackie Cassen at Channel 13, and independent artists such as Eric Siegal, Woody Vasulka, and Arthur Ginsberg typify extremely talented artists who are exploiting this new medium.

Rudi Stern and John Reilly, Global Village

Rudi Stern and John Reilly come from very different backgrounds. Stern established a reputation for himself as a lumia artist over a period of years. Recently, however, he turned his attention to videotape as a medium. He joined forces with a highly talented filmmaker, John Reilly. Reilly was well established as a university film instructor but felt that his medium of expression was limited in the academic milieu. Together, Stern and Reilly forged a new voice in video by seeking topics of profound anti-establishment insight. They viewed videotape as an egalatarian medium and they hoped that the videocassette would enable them to establish an alternate form of television journalism in which they would speak directly to their "disenfranchised" generation with relevant videocassette journalism. They called their loft *Global Village* and opened it to creative artists of great talent. One program, entitled *Richard II,* starred Rip Torn in one of the most scathing political satires this observer has ever seen. It juxtaposed a "Shakesperean" Richard being prepared for a television appearance with scenes dubbed from network appearances of Richard Nixon commenting on the American involvement in the Vietnam war. The production used multiple monitors with three-channel switching to intermix the program material. Currently, Reilly and Stern are serving as consultants to community groups who wish to create videotape programming to achieve new social goals.

Eric Salzman

Author, critic, composer, and videotape producer, Eric Salzman is a man of many talents. He is widely known for his work with WBAI, a listener-supported radio station in New York City. His trenchant criticism of contemporary music is reflected in several books and articles.

The author first encountered his talent when he attended Daniel Nagrin's performance of *The Peloponnesian War.* Salzman created the audio score for the three-hour performance—a brilliantly-created intertwining collage of sound, using an electronic score intermixed with a classic recitation of the Thucydidies epic. He recently joined forces with Jackie Cassen at Channel 13 to create a remarkable color videotape entitled *Ecolog.* The force of the medium of videotape is explored in depth: multiple images, superimpositions, colorized black-and-white images, live broadcasts, and burlesque juxtapositions of broadcast commercials with studio effects create a devastating tableaux.

Jackie Cassen

Videotape producer-director and lumia artist, Jackie Cassen in undoubtedly one of the most talented young artists working in the videotape medium. She has created a remarkable series of works as creative director for experimental programming at Channel 13. Her work with Eric Salzman was alluded to above. Her recent *Life of Charlotte Moorman* is a touching classic on the psychological origins of an artistic personality. The videotape is filled with hauting juxtapositions of Miss Moorman's childhood, her parents, her crowning as a beauty queen, and with her current success as the concert cellist who scandalized the musical world by appearing bare-breasted on the stage while studiously playing classical cello pieces.

Ms. Cassen has also distinguished herself with the development of highly abstract images using a colorizer (an electronic device that assigns arbitrary color values to black-and-white videotape images) and a Putney synthesizer.

Woody Vasulka

Videotape artist. There are thousands of young artists around the world who have discovered the videotape recorder. They have become enchanted with its instant recording and playback capabilities. The fact that they can edit it freely with another recorder and a few simple switching devices has opened a new world of effects for them. Everyone now is a Cecil B. DeMille. With the advent of light battery-operated videotape recorders equipped with sound capability, Stan Brakhage's concept of the autonomous, walking producer-director-artist-reporter has become a commonplace reality. Unfortunately, the increased volume of videotape productions has not resulted in quantum jumps in video aesthetic development.

Woody Vasulka is an exception. He has evaluated the medium as just that—a medium for expression. He has not tried to force its potential for effects' sake; on the contrary, he works like a stranger on a newly-discovered planet, carefully exploring the stones and artifacts close to his landing zone. He confesses a kind of awe at the magnitude of videotape when combined with color synthesizers, electronic-effects devices, such as the Putney, the Buchla, and the Moog. The visual effects that can be achieved are infinite.

Vasulka is content to work with the abstract image, refine it, and then project it through multiple monitors. When economics permit, his dream is to control a hemispherical space with thousands of monitors, which will be programmed to create a continuous flow of images.

Arthur Ginsberg, Video Free America

Arthur Ginsberg is a remarkable young videotape artist. He has gathered around him a very powerful group of young artists dedicated to creating an alternate form of television journalism. They began their operations in the San Francisco area a few years back. One of their early productions was entitled *The International Frisbee Contest.* The group, using several cameras, recorded a tongue-in-cheek contest staged in Berkley to find the world's most proficient Frisbee athelete. The entire contest was a put-on to the tragicomedy emphasis placed on sports events by the broadcast media. Ginsberg and his group videotaped interviews with the contestants asking "straight" questions on technique, the glory of breaking the "five-hundred foot barrier," and sundry other delights. The net impression of the show was a wonderful parody on the American passion for sport as an expression of patriotism, manliness, respect for mother, and apple pie, all combined as a lay rosary, week after week on the tube.

Interviews

Interviews with the personalities discussed in this chapter follow. Photographs illustrate the subject matter of the interviews and the theme of the chapter.

THOMAS C.
daly

FILM PRODUCER, NATIONAL FILM BOARD OF CANADA, MONTREAL, QUEBEC, SUPERVISING EDITOR, *LABYRINTHE*, EXPO '67

There are moments in your life when you actually understand something—moments when all kinds of previously disconnected things get connected in your mind. You suddenly see the relationships, and it opens you up to the wonderful sense of the interrelationship of everything in the universe. You have experienced this moment of connecting them for yourself.

It was moments like that that we were trying to achieve in the audience in Theatre One, in *Labyrinthe*. Moments where there would be an experience of relating things without thinking too much about it, just feeling and understanding things. The story of *Labyrinthe* is, if you like, the unfolding of the psychological stages of growth in a person as distinct from the physical ages and stages.

Labyrinthe's first room represents the universal starting point where each individual seeks to achieve everything by his own importance—the person against other people. It is a very narrow view of life. Even the screen formats are narrow. It is hard to take in the two screens at once; you find that you have to look at one or the other. It represents that part of life where you feel that you can go to the ends of the earth, when everything is going for you with physical strength and energy. Nothing is going to stop you. But by the end of this picture you discover that there are other forces besides yourself that somehow get in your way. Things kind of grind to a halt. You really don't know where to go, but if you stay like this, you aren't going to be happy. You are not going to find the meaning in life.

Now the fact that, in this "First Theatre," you actually have to get up, make a move, and go in search of something else is symbolic of one's psychological development.

The next step is that you must physically leave this theatre, and go to "Theatre Two."

Theatre Two didn't really work. It was intended to be the moment when you go apart. You realize that somehow you have come to nothing; something else must be found; you feel very, very much alone. It is almost like this in the desert or the wilderness, and then comes the discovery that you are in a labyrinth and you do not know the way out. What went wrong with that theatre, in a sense, is that you should be there alone. But it is the one theatre where everybody meets everybody else, where there is glass on all sides reflecting and multiplying the audiences' sounds and images. The actual concentrated presence of all those people creates a kind of interplay

9-1. Thomas C. Daly, Film Producer, National Film Board of Canada, Supervising Film Editor for *Labyrinthe, Expo '67.* (All illustrations courtesy National Film Board of Canada.)

with everybody. One doesn't feel alone. One feels quite the opposite.

We found that the programming of Theatre Two on the sound track was too serious. Everybody wanted to laugh when they were in this atmosphere, you see, and they couldn't. During the first two weeks of Expo, we reprogrammed it, to make it into a pleasurable kind of entertainment, where people would feel that, yes, there is something else.

At the end of Theatre Two, there is this problem: You can't go back, you don't want to go back, but you don't know where to go. Nevertheless, you have had a taste of something. You see the possibility of a new world, and "Theatre Three" has to do with "the search." And this search comes on in the five-screen theatre. The essence is that you can sit in quiet, and the theatre is so designed that you are remote from other people. There are only a few near you on your own level, with four rows of seats at the most. There are three levels, with two rows on the top. two on the bottom, and four in the middle. . . .

You now have a new perspective, with a multiplicity of impressions and some choice as to where you want to put more attention. It is a matter, so to speak, of doling out the proper proportion to everything that you must feel simultaneously.

continued

In terms of myth, *Labyrinthe* deals with innocent childhood, confident youth, then disillusioned youth. Then come the wandering in the wilderness, the search, and the coming to grips with the "monster," which turns out to be an aspect of one's self. You expect it to be outside. Then the destruction, or the controlling of the monster. St.-George-and-the-Dragon is one of the images for this from way back. Every man has these elements—the St. George element and the Dragon element.

Perhaps the most valuable thing one could do at a world's fair is to work with the universal element in all individuals.

IAN

macneill

PROGRAM PRODUCER, NATIONAL FILM BOARD OF CANADA

9-2. Ian MacNeill, Programme Producer.

We want to go on and explore things that we started in *Labyrinthe* and continued for the World's Fair in Osaka. We don't want to do this just for fairs; we want to find other audiences. Traveling shows. Environmental shows carried to places where people already are. Places that they pass every day, for instance. Perhaps we could have something like this in subway stations. Perhaps on that long corridor in the airport, along the moving sidewalk. Maybe there is something to do on those walls. These are some of the things we want to look into.

The point about programming is that, if you have good filmmakers and they represent a cross section of Canadian viewpoints—tastes and attitudes and experiences—and the right proportion of immigrants among them, over the years their interests will effectively produce films that make up a good program. All you have to do is encourage good people in their good ideas, and you are going to end up with an exciting and well-balanced film program that is, in the best sense of the term, "in the public interest."

J. CREIGHTON

douglas

CHIEF OF PRODUCTION SERVICES, NATIONAL FILM BOARD OF CANADA

If you go back through *Labyrinthe's* design, you'll find that there is nothing really new in it. It's a new combination of things, but I can't think of a single thing that hasn't been done somewhere else, some other time, by somebody else. But we did succeed in bringing these all together and marrying them and making them work.

In spite of the unbelievably long waits—our record queue was seven hours—it held the audiences' attention very well. There were many reasons why this was so. Some people saw it as an integrated, overall, artistic creation. Other people were interested simply because of the variety of pictures. It had something for everybody, all ages and tastes. A rather useful factor was that it didn't depend on language at all. We had tours of visiting Russians, who understood no English, and they thought it was great. The commentary was the last thing that was added. Long scripts were written and there were lots of arguments about how much we had to have. Eventually it worked down to very little, and in fact there was a group of us who claimed that what was there was not necessary. The pictures spoke for themselves.

9-3. J. Creighton Douglas, Chief, Production Services, National Film Board of Canada, in his office *(at desk)* with Pierre Handfield, Technical Supervisor for the Canadian Expo '67 pavilion. (seated, left).

9-4. Long lines waited to enter the *Labyrinthe* pavilion. The record queue was seven hours. During Expo '67 *Labyrinthe* ran 5,545 shows (one every twenty-three minutes, for thirty shows per day) and the total audience was 1,324,560 persons.

9-5. Along the way, the walls with reliefs depicting ancient labyrinths of Egypt and Chartres prepare viewers for the psychological labyrinth they are soon to enter.

9-6. Another kind of experience—the austere corridor leading to the exhibit.

9-7. The wall/floor projection for Chamber 1, *Labyrinthe*.

9-9. Audience between viewings at *Labyrinthe*.

9-8. Photograph showing the galleries available for the audience in the wall/floor projection in Chamber 1, *Labyrinthe*.

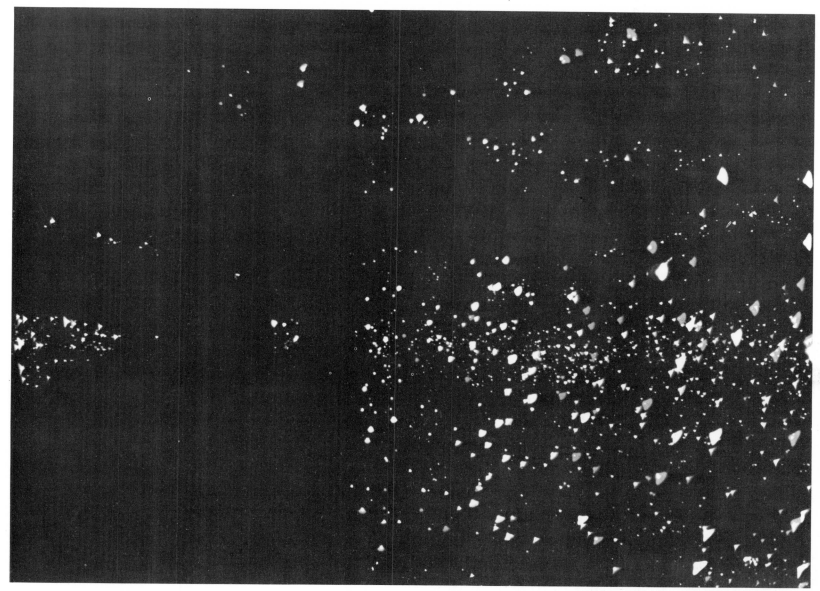

9-10. The Star Chamber, *Labyrinthe*.

9-11. Five-screen projection room showing console in foreground, screens at upper left.

9-12A. Close-ups and long shots of a crowd appear simultaneously.

9-12B. Five segments of the same view are shown on the five screens.

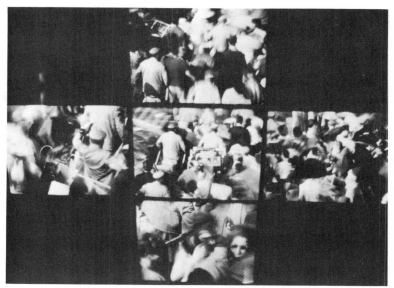

9-12A   9-12B

EMIL
radok

CREATOR OF THE DIAPOLYEKRAN, CZECHOSLOVAK PAVILION, EXPO '67, MONTREAL

9-13. Emil Radok planning his virtuoso light and music display "Creation of the World," a multimedia projection called *Diapolyekran* to be shown at Expo '67. (All illustrations courtesy Emil Radok; photographer, Zdenek Stuchlik.)

The Czechoslovak Pavilion: Expo '67

Although Diapolyekran, otherwise called "mosaic projection," lies explicitly within the visual domain, the initial phase of the work did indeed entail a literary idea. Nevertheless, it is a special discipline of the visual arts, enabling the creator to tell a story through the use of individual, ever-changing pictures, and even allowing him to elicit dramatic emotions. Let us but recall certain medieval paintings that possessed similar qualities.

In selecting a theme suitable for mosaic projection, I tried to recall simultaneously both literary and pictorial images, which would then interact. Despite its essentially narrative nature, mosaic projection requires that everything be expressed by shape and color devices. As the theme must be very simple, the literary side is restricted to the expression of the basic idea. For Diapolyekran I worked with the theme of the creation of the world, the external motif being the constant development of Nature. The inner motif, however, consisted of an abundant transformation of shapes, colors, and structures. Every program for the Diapolyekran has to have literary and pictorial poles, both of which create a unity.

It remains to be determined how to express a particular theme on the given projection system.

The simplest action can be captured only in certain of its phases. A picture that represents one phase changes either suddenly or gradually into another, successive phase of the action. If the change occurs suddenly, we may work with contrast, which brings about a dramatic effect. In the latter case the concrete picture changes first into a total abstraction, and then back into a completely identifiable picture. This method allows the achievement of unusual aesthetic reactions, which resemble somewhat those achieved by kinetic art. On the Diapolyekran, however, these have a unique, inimitable character.

This form of expression is made possible by the use of minute elements of photographically captured reality, in which the shapes, colors, and spaces are no longer able to speak for themselves but instead have a greater ability to relate to one another and create concentrated, new, and more important realities.

I have been working in this area of artistic expression for several years; at the Brussels World Exhibition in 1958 I exhibited the first Polyekran on eight screens. I believe that in mosaic projection I have so far advanced the farthest.

As you know, the picture in this case consists of 112 fields, which create the mosaic proper. Every field is equipped with two slide projectors, which permit either a change in the whole picture, or in any of the fields independently of the others. The time of any of the changes can be accurately programmed. This yields the particularly important required rhythm. Individual illuminated fields may create in the darkened space either different geometrical figures or participate in the creation of a complete integral picture consisting of 112 fields.

This enables us to achieve a pictorial "stream," with a high metamorphic capacity, whose expressive ability is further enhanced by the fact that each of the fields can be mechanically adjusted into three positions, thus changing the flat surface into a pictorial relief. Every pictorial symbol also has its special significance. Diapolyekran creates a synthesis of harmonies of shape, color, and architecture, all of which are eminently capable of being combined with music.

The creative process itself consists, therefore, of the transformation of the action phase or structure into the mentioned spatio-temporal pictorial stream. *continued, 227*

9-14. A view of the audience and the screen at *Diapolyekran*, "Creation of the World," during a showing at Expo '67.

The environmental Diapolyekran *at the Czechoslovak Pavilion, Expo '67: The screen, composed of 112 blocks, each two feet square, is twenty feet high and thirty-two feet wide. The program used up to 15,000 slides, which were projected in a period of fourteen minutes, telling the story of human skill in transforming raw materials into finished products for man's comfort —"The Creation of the World."*

overleaf

9-15. Scenes from *Diapolyekran* display at Expo '67 demonstrate the use of selective illumination to create a visual pattern.

Each of the 2' x 2' cubes, equipped with two slide projectors, moves backward and forward by electronic command, flipping slides at the rate of one every fifth of a second. Control of this highly complicated light and music display required 240 miles of circuitry, using both optical and electronic devices. The program was created and photographed at the Skoda Works, Pilsen, Czechoslovakia. Selected segments from the program, starting in the upper left-hand corner, extend to the bottom of the first column, return to the top of the second column, proceed to the bottom, and continue in that order.

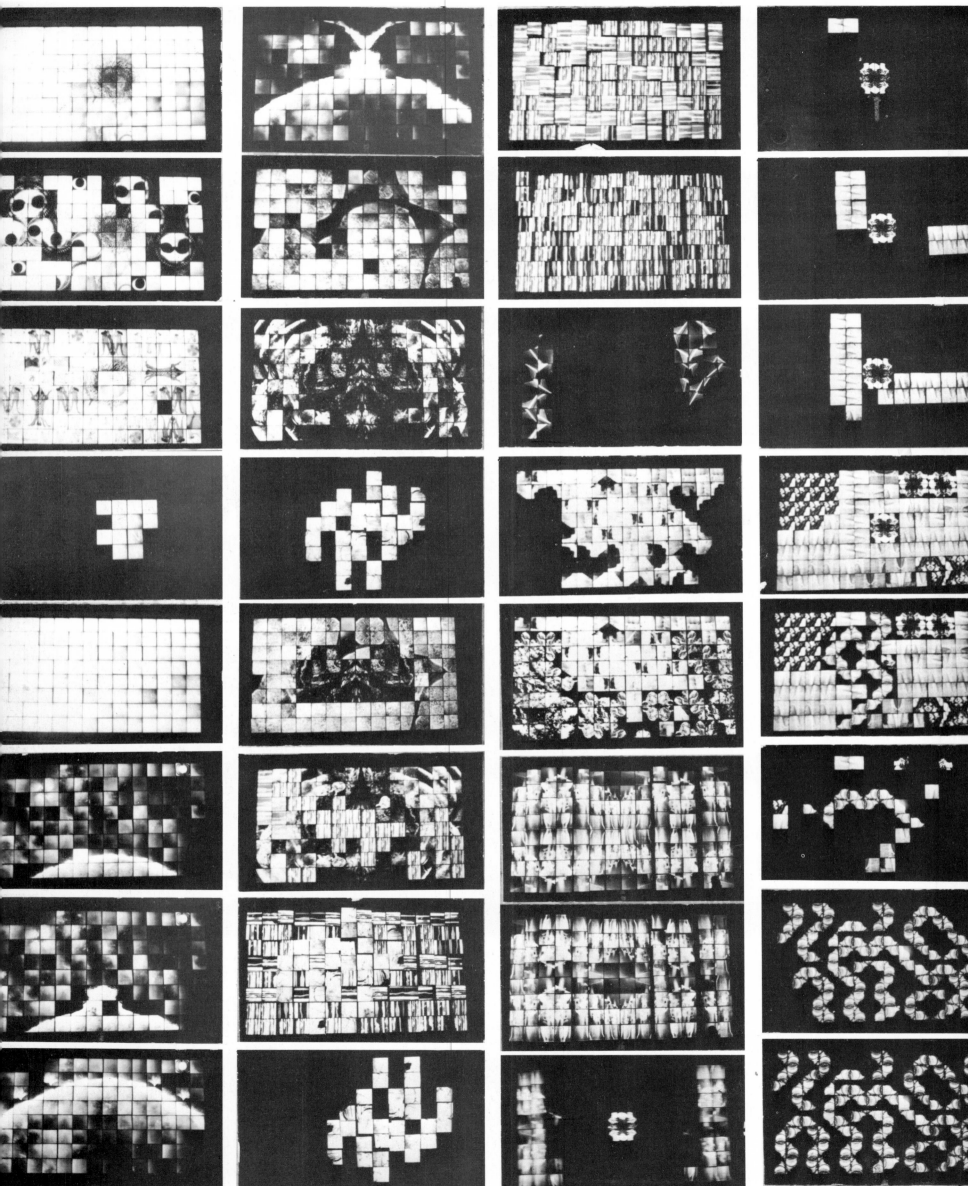

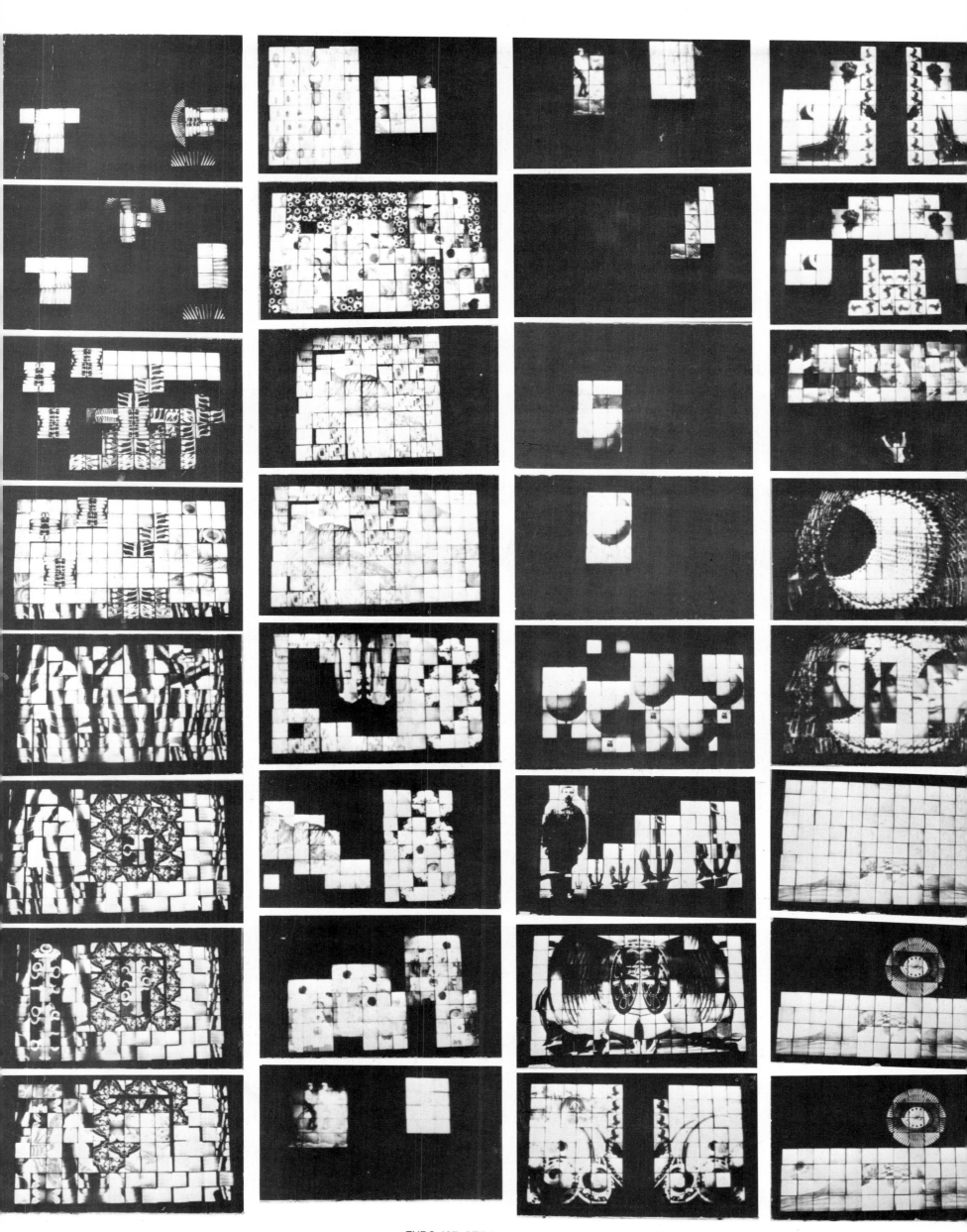

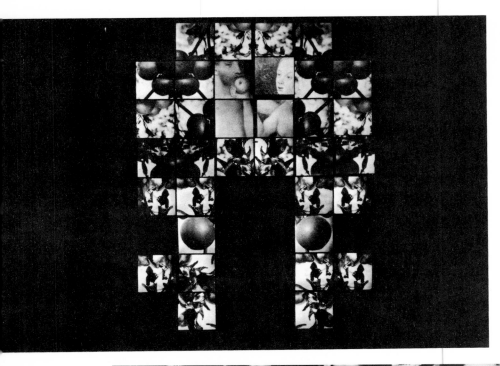

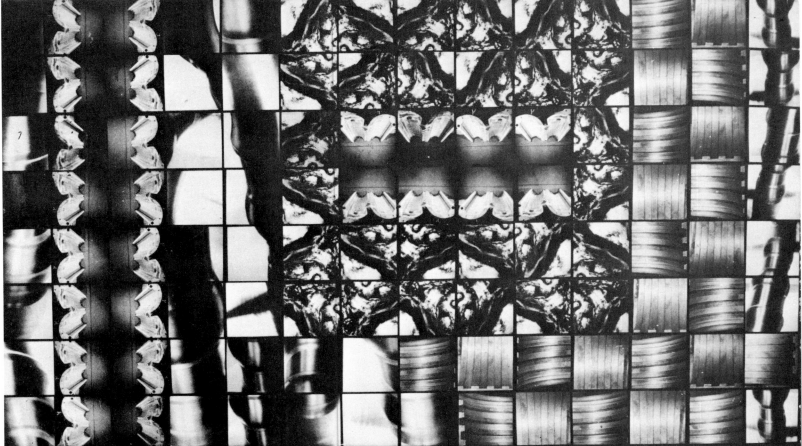

9-16A. Sequence from *Diapolyekran*. This sequence is interesting when compared with the companion photographs, figures 9-16B and 9-16C. Notice how radically the visual field can be altered with this technique, using 112 independent modules, each capable of projecting a different slide.

9-16B. Sequence from "The Creation of the World" *(Diapolyekran)*. Here every module is illuminated with a slide. The dramatic shifts from a fully articulated field to selective patterning in figures 9-16A and 9-16C is quite remarkable.

9-16C. Startling juxtapostions of figure-ground relationships can be seen in this photograph. Objects can appear as separated from their field or surroundings, or as integrated into the surrounding as the designer desires.

9-17A, B. Control console for manual override of the *Diapolyekran.*

9-18. Backstage at the Czechoslovak Pavilion.

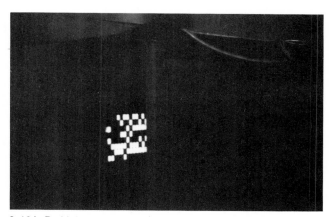

9-19A, B. Light-sensing devices used to program the six functions of each *Diapolyekran* projector.

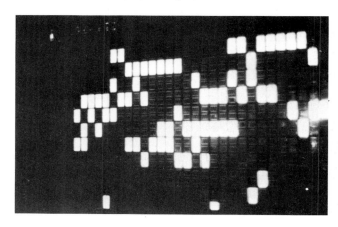

Unfortunately, the process of realization in this system is not simple. An uninitiated viewer is probably unable to fathom the complexities related to the creation of a program. It begins with individual ideas of a purely artistic nature, then moves into the sphere of mathematics, and ends in a vast and very specific technology, which requires the discovery of completely new organizational and technical methods.

To illustrate some of the most important facts, I will quote a few numbers: the program that ran for fourteen-and-a half minutes consisted of 13,000 pictures. To that end, a large number of photographs had to be made, from which were selected 200,000 cutouts. These represented the selection material, which was used to assemble the mosaic pictures.

The program was first made on a small model. Every part of the mosaic included in the model had to be registered and coded. It was necessary to mark its position on the plane and in space as well as on the time axis.

Since the picture could change every fifth of a second, it was also necessary to identify every one of these time phases. Each of the 112 fields was registered in three codes, which meant identifying 1,461,000 pieces of information. For the automatic reproduction of this record during the showing of the program, the technicians had to work with much larger amounts of information, which reached tens of millions. Naturally they used a computer.

The work on the program took one year and employed a whole staff of artistic, technical, and other personnel. The work was very intensive; during the final three months it was necessary to work fifteen to eighteen hours a day in order to complete the program on time.

I regret very much that in view of the above facts I will probably not be able to work on this or any other comparable system that can be realized only at large exhibitions of an important nature. Nevertheless, I do believe that contemporary society—which is currently at the stage of highly civil, intimate, and individualistic art—will move toward the renaissance of monumental art forms, since science and industry have been operating in those proportions for a long time. Diapolyekran, or the mosaic projection, is, in my opinion, an art form that reacts to that reality.

Note. On the following six pages, instead of a formal interview with **Josef Svoboda,** we present a photographic record of outstanding Svoboda achievements.

JOSEF
svoboda
INTEGRATED MEDIA ARTIST, CZECHOSLOVAKIA

9-20. Portrait of Josef Svoboda. Svoboda is one of the leading European artists working with integrated media. His work has influenced an entire generation of European and American artists. (All illustrations courtesy Josef Svoboda.)

9-21. Scene from *Laterna Magika I*. Svoboda pioneered the full integration of the live performer, film, lumia, and other visual effects. Notice that the performer appears live and in film simultaneously.

9-23. Svoboda pioneered the projection of images on three-dimensional sculptured forms. This is a model the artist created for his production *Die Soldaten*.

9-24. Sketch of photographic material for *Die Soldaten*. A powerful visual analogy is created between Goya's *The Disasters of War* and scenes from the Nazi invasion of Eastern Europe.

9-25A. Three-dimensional model of Svoboda's remarkable *Polyvision* environment at Expo '67. Most of the cubes, cylinders, and cones were mechanically activated so that images projected on their surfaces have a remarkable kinetic quality.

9-25B. Compare this photograph from the actual *Polyvision* environment with the model for the set, shown above. Notice how the final ''performance'' is articulated on the three-dimensional surfaces.

9-26

9-26–29. Scenes from the *Polyvision* environmental exhibit.

This ten-minute exhibition supported by specially composed background music creates the impression of a projection in space, since it is aided by ingeniously placed semi-transparent mirrors and moving objects that produce subtly ambiguous illusions. The globe on the left rotates in a counterclockwise motion. Above it is a slotted barrel-like image, which rotates horizontally in a plane and alternately picks up images and rejects them. At the right of the globe is a concave vertical element that looks something like a ship's capstan. This also rotated. When images were projected on it, the slats alternately picked up and rejected an aspect of the image. We can see the reflection of the globe on transparent mirrors directly below. In turn, all of these images are interrupted by the three-dimensional cubes, which move in space, backward and forward, vertically and horizontally. The conglomerate effect is one of fantastically brilliant environmental illusion.

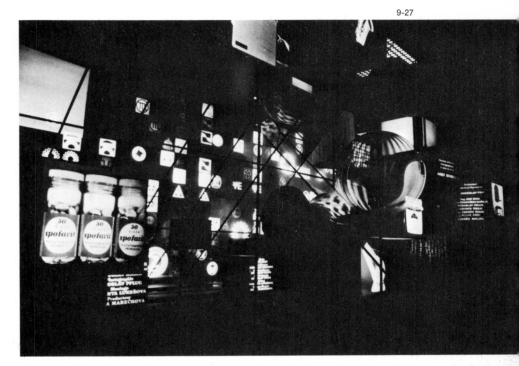

9-27

9-28

9-29

9-30

9-32

9-30–34. Projection equipment used for the *Polyvision* display.

Polyvision *told the story of Czechoslovakia's highly diversified industry and occupied a corner fifty-five feet long and twenty feet high in the Czechoslovak Pavilion. On a twenty-foot-deep stage, some 8,000 color slides, with eight films of 300 yards each, were projected on thirty-six stationary and moving cubes and rotating objects. The performance ran for ten minutes and was supported by background music specially composed to create the impression of a projection in space.*

9-31

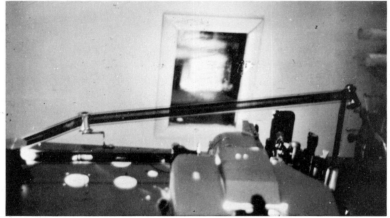

9-33

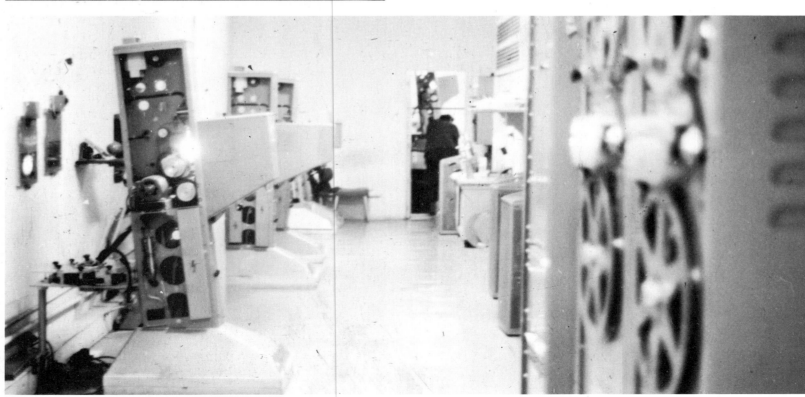

9-34

9-35A. Scene from *Die Reise* (The Journey) designed by Svoboda. This work of Lars Johan Werle was performed at the Hamburg State Opera in 1969. Each cube in this environment served as a projection surface.

9-35B. Projection on multiple cubes from *Die Reise*. Svoboda has emerged as a preeminent protagonist of the integrated stage image.

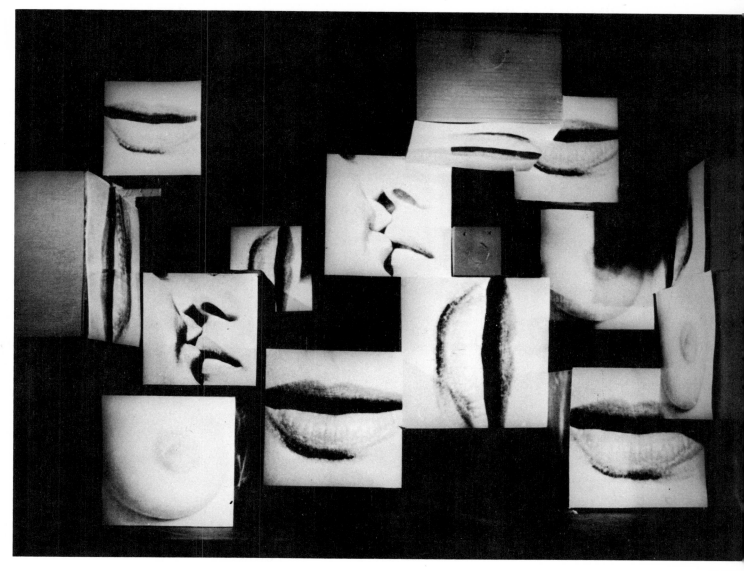

The Kino-Automat Theatre at the Czechoslovak Pavilion, Expo '67

9-36. This 127-foot movie theatre was programmed six times a day. It offered a 45-minute film with active audience participation. The movie story runs its innocent course for a while, then stops. The actors invite the public to make changes as they see fit. For instance, should the hero kiss the blonde or pursue the brunette? By pushing the button on the seat, the audience was permitted to vote, and the result was electronically computed. The tally was projected on two scoreboards flanking the screen. This do-it-yourself theatre, where every visitor became an inventor, was the first of its kind in the world. The inventor was Dr. Raduz Cincera.

LES
levine
INTERMEDIA ARTIST, NEW YORK CITY

Les Levine, an iconoclast in a day when "anything visual that you put in front of a person has already been accepted," was born in Dublin, Ireland, in 1935, and went to the Central School of Arts and Crafts in London, England. He had three years of industrial design there, went to within one month of graduating, and dropped out. He has been in the United States since early 1964. His work-in-progress design for manufacturers in Canada and the United States influenced his current work with vacuum-formed shapes produced from his ideas—but without his supervision—in packaging factories.

To me, art and fine art are two different things. Art can be an antique object; it can be a beautifully made plate, a tapestry, a well-designed building. But fine art cannot be used for societal function. It cannot have any societal utility. Fine art's primary function is only related to the idea of art.

Art is a broad term that can be related to anything. You can say that architecture is an art; clothing, if it is well made by a great designer, is an art. You can say furniture is art. Within art's broad definition, you can say anything is art. But when you come to fine art, you have no subfunction. Its only function is to be viewed as an aesthetic experience.

I think that any sound that a musical instrument makes is music. I think that anything made from art products is art. Oil paint in the tube is an art component, and no matter what you do with it, what is finished is going to be art. Now whether it is going to be good art or bad art is questionable. But it is going to be art of some level, in the same way that anything that comes out of a piano is going to be music. It is nothing else, it has to be music. It's a musical note of some sort. It's a component of music.

With the disposable objects, I was making components for the creation of an art experience. I did not consider the panels of polyexpandable styrene works of art in themselves. I considered them components for an art activity, in the same way as the tube of oil paint is a component for an art activity.

First of all, there was a choice from over 150 kinds of disposable components, and selection relates to the whole Abstract Expressionist movement, where the whole painting is made up by accidents in selection. So the audience, by the idea of choice, became a part of creating the art. If you chose more than one disposable, you became involved not only in choice but also in composition. How were you going to put those together? Why did you choose these two? You chose those two because you knew that, put together, they came out in an arrangement that aesthetically was pleasing to you. Therefore you were put in a creative frame of mind by these things. You were, in fact, in the same position as the painter deciding if he would put, let's say, a man into his landscape or not. And as it went on and you chose more and more (Philip Johnson took a whole wall of disposables, for example), then you were involved in a very complicated decision.

There is no mold involved. It is merely done by vacuum-forming over a shape or an object. I have it done in factories. Any sign manufacturer does it. Any packaging manufacturer could do it. I did not supervise. I wanted to remove myself as completely as possible. At the time, I had a lot of people around my studio and I asked them to make choices about things like that.

In the first group, I wanted to choose only things that related to historical art ideas. So I used bottles, which related to still-life—bowls of fruit—various things that we all know have been painted ten million times. Just by taking the bottle and placing it on the vacuum-forming machine, in two seconds you had the drawing of the thing, the relief shape of it.

Practically every industry in the United States has a service organization. I usually start off by going to the engineers' association, or the plastics society, or whatever. That was in the beginning. My work has taken a turn. A lot of people in industry, and in science, know about it now. Surprisingly, a lot of people have come

9-37. Les Levine standing inside of one of the plastic modules used in his *Star Garden* exhibit at the Museum of Modern Art, New York City.

9-38. Scale model of modules used by Les Levine for his *Star Garden* exhibit.

9-39. Levine's studio. Two television cameras, a TV screen, and a portable videotape console are prominent features.

9-40. Levine working on a layout for an environmental exhibit at the Architectural League. A member of the League's board, he helps to judge shows there.

forward and offered their services for various projects.

Environments must be by nature passive. There is no possibility for aggressiveness in environments. There is no possibility for different levels of attention. Everything has to be on the same level of attention—everything. The closest example of what environmental art is all about is the street. You walk through the street and everything is happening on all different levels, and that is an environment. Now as soon as you start looking at a billboard, you are out of the environment.

I've used the word *place,* rather than environment, for my works. I think the real concern in environmental art is to change the iconic image from the contemplative to the overall experience.

STAN
van der beek

MULTIMEDIA ARTIST, STONY POINT, NEW YORK

Stan VanDerBeek had what he calls a "pretty uninteresting child-hood. . . . Very straight parents. . . . Middle class environ-ment. . . . The whole scene." His schooling was at a science high school, where he took all the art he could get, the National Academy of Design, Black Mountain College, and Cooper Union, where he was fascinated by architecture. Out of this he feels came his focus on environments. . . . All these studies and in-fluences led to the theatre, and then to films, particularly ani-mation.

I was interested in theatre, as such, but my experiences with actors were always rather difficult. You have an idea of a play and you try to get them to bend to your ideal. In effect, they are only instruments for you, and their own egos just burst through; that either destroys the scene I have in mind or in various ways it just is impossible to lead them to it—unless you are a master psychologist— to get them up to that "edge" I have in mind. I never found the combination that would make it work. I got discouraged quite easily and then I started the film, which was a private form I could truly control, and—in this case particularly—animation, where I was absolutely every-thing. I was entirely dependent on my vision, on my hand, on my technique. I could do it my own way, at my own time. And for relatively little money I could produce the illusions that could go way beyond the stage—the literal stage, with the problem of the four walls, the visual boundaries, the surfaces of the stage, always inhibiting you, literally, because theatres are small; or whatever the staging problems were. Also, I like the ideas of infinity, space, and instant change, which movies have. What I'm summarizing is that I had an interest in architecture, which was environmental. I had an interest in technology, which was in a sense social and manipulative techniques. I had both those things. And I was interested in personal private expression, in which I was trained: how to use my hands and how to write poetry—to fantasize—was something I had slowly developed. Black Mountain in a sense per-fected that for me. I mean the importance of my self as a spokesman for myself. I went through a public school system in New York City that said I was literally to be blotted out in the mass, and I fought my way through to some self-observations. Then I went through a series of agonizing training periods, which now I see clearly as background that prepared me for a kind of integration of art and technology.

9-41. Stan VanDerBeek standing in front of his specially constructed pro-jection room near his home outside New York City.

(At the time of the interview, VanDerBeek was working on com-puter graphics, in collaboration with Ken Knowlton and Max Mathews, at Bell Laboratories.)

I'm in the middle of about six or seven computer proj-ects at the moment (i.e., I have produced twelve com-puter-animated films). They're all studies in graphic format. I'm calling the whole series *Poem Fields*. They use words in poems I've written translated into graphics, moving graphics. Just to explore graphology, these shapes mov-ing and shifting around the patterns that they make. I'll be integrating them with live images at some point. Literal images, also computer-generated images, but I haven't got to that state yet. The system is quite subtle. I have a lot of control over it, and I'm only just learning. I did a lot of work in the area of calligraphy, brush and pen-and-ink drawings. I wrote poetry in the fifties. I combined it into kind-of-unrealistic books. Enormous books. Two-foot-by-three-foot-pages. Like the Chinese did. I was always in-trigued with that idea of a "picture" language. So this is a fortunate experiment—a continuation of my interest in these areas.

9-42. A montage of interiors of the artist's home in an artists' cooperative near New York City.

This tremendous interest in communication, in multimedia, seems unique in our Western culture. We're still on the outer edges of it. Expo '67 was a major public demonstration of it, where over 70,000,000 people experienced multimedia.* Curiously enough, in terms of history, multimedia ideas were presented way back at the Paris Exposition of 1908, or thereabouts, where a simultaneous 360-degree screen projection system was already developed.

There was a big gap during which multimedia fell into a hole; the "talking" motion picture dominated our media logic. Now, suddenly, it's come back again. Now that it's here, where will it go? Clearly it is going into education. You can make a clear prediction that it is going to become a very integrated part of the education "culture." We are evolving a nonverbal visual symbol structure. This is a basic tenet. I've been working on this thing for twelve years now. It just needs to be developed. The tools are here—TV, Super-8, Instamatic cameras, holog-

*Interestingly enough, the total population of Canada is only 20 million!

raphy. They need to be orchestrated. Now we have to find the talent that can handle this orchestration.

We're getting transmission now to 400 million people at the same time from a satellite thirty-nine miles up. They give us a little stage show or a boxing match. What's next? Here's somebody cracking cosmic jokes. That's show biz. In the best sense, it's show biz.

It is imperative that we quickly find some way for the level of world understanding to rise to a new human scale. This scale is the world. The risks are the life or death of this world. Man is running the machines of his own invention, while the machine that is man runs the risk of running wild.

Technological research, development, and involvement have almost completely outdistanced our emotional and socio-"logical" comprehension. It is imperative that every member of the world community join the twentieth century as quickly as possible. Technical power and cultural "overreach" are placing the fulcrum of man's intelligence so far outside himself, so quickly, that he cannot judge the results of his acts before he commits them. The process of life as an experiment on earth has never been made clearer. Man does not have time to talk to himself, man does not have means to talk to other men, the world hangs by a thread of verbs and nouns. It is imperative that the world's artists invent a nonverbal international language.

In this context, I propose the following: that immediate research begin on the possibility of a picture-language based on motion pictures; that we combine audio-visual devices into an educational tool—an experience machine

9-43

9-43, 44. Scenes inside the hemispherical dome used by VanDerBeek to create prototypes for his multimedia exhibits.

9-44

9-45A-H. Sequential series from VanDerBeek's *Movie Mural*.

9-45A

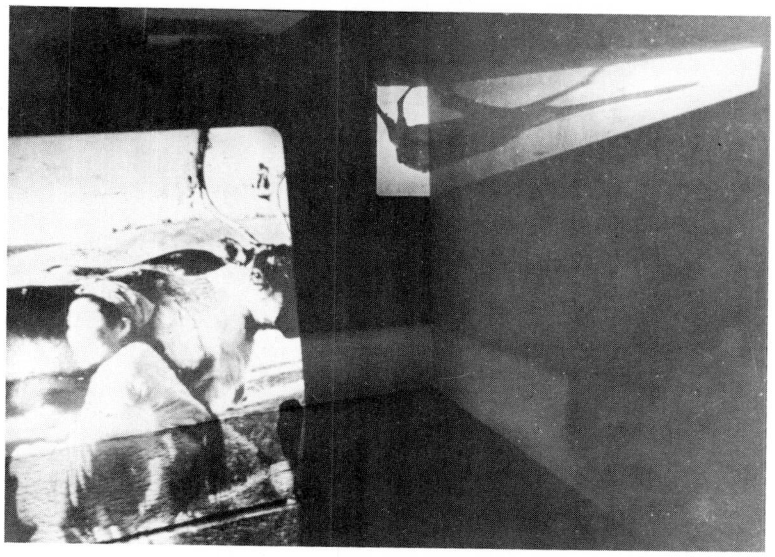

9-45E

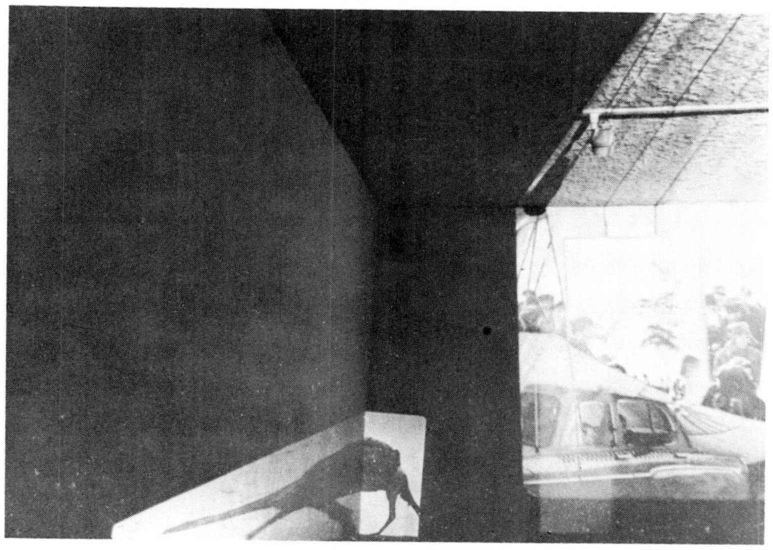

9-45B

9-45F

9-45C

9-45G

9-45D

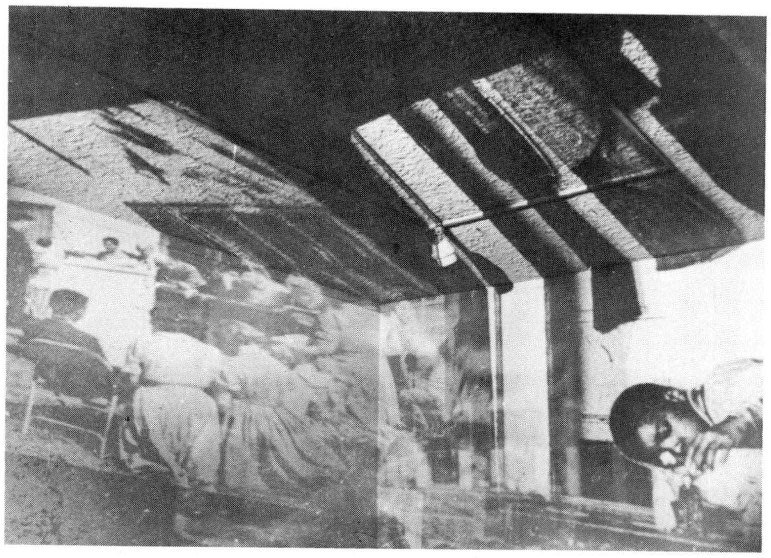

9-45H

9-46. Device developed by VanDerBeek, called *Primitive Projection Wheel*. The observer can spin this bicycle wheel and, as he stands at face height to the slits, he will see a primitive motion picture on the inside of the wheel.

or "culture-intercom"; that prototype theatres, called "Movie-Dromes," be developed immediately, incorporating the use of such projection hardware. I shall call these prototype presentations "Movie-Murals," "*Ethos*-Cinema," "Newsreel of Dreams," "Feedback," "Image Libraries."

The audience takes what it can or wants from the presentation and makes its own conclusions. Each member of the audience will build his own references and realizations from the image flow.

The purpose and effect of such image flow and image density (also to be called "visual velocity") is both to deal with logical understanding and to penetrate to unconscious levels; to reach for the emotional denominator of all men, the nonverbal basis of human life, thought, and understanding; and to inspire all men to goodwill and "inter- and intro-realization."

If an individual is exposed to an overwhelming information experience, it might be possible to reorder the structure of motion pictures as we know them. Cinema would become a "performing" art and image library. Such centers would have artists in residence who will orchestrate the image material at their disposal, integrating it with live actors and performers, leading to a totally new international art-cinema form. In probing for the "emotional denominator," it would be possible by the visual power of such a presentation to reach any age or culture group, regardless of background. There are an estimated 700 million people in the world who are unlettered; we have no time to lose or miscalculate.

9-47A–M. Scenes from a computer-generated film created by Stan VanDerBeek and Ken Knowlton at Bell Laobratories. This film was exhibited at Expo '67. (Courtesy Bell Laboratories, Murray Hill, New Jersey.)

9-47A

9-47B

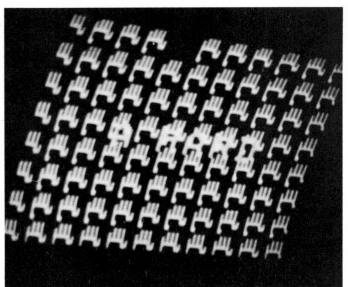

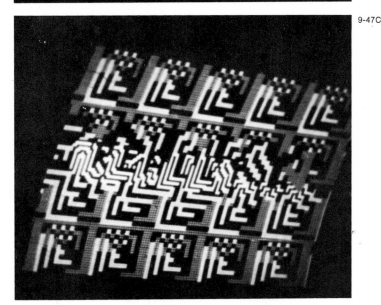

9-47C

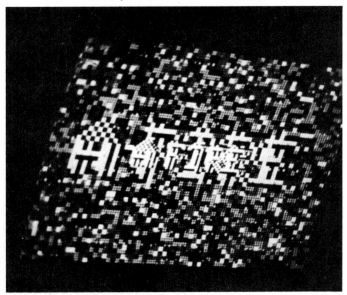

9-47D

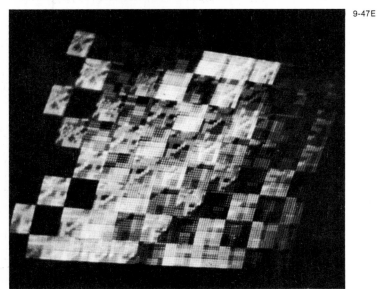

9-47E

9-47F

9-47J

9-47G

9-47K

9-47H

9-47L

9-47 I

9-47M

9-48. *Found Forms,* VanDerBeek's multiprojection film performance at an Intermedia Festival in Tokyo, 1969.

9-49. A telephone mural transmitted from the Center for Advanced Visual Studies, MIT, to the Walker Art Center, Minneapolis, over a two-week period, by way of a Telecopier and telephone. The mural, entitled *Panels for the Walls of the World, Phase I,* was created by VanDerBeek in April 1970.

9-50. Stan VanDerBeek in front of his telephone mural at MIT, Cambridge, Massachusetts, 1970.

ROBERT
whitman

INTERMEDIA ARTIST, NEW YORK CITY

The skeptical approach of artist to scientist and the indifference of scientist to artist marked Robert Whitman's first meeting with his collaborator, Eric Rawson.

WHITMAN. I met Eric about a year and a half ago. It was through E.A.T. I wanted him to advise me, to be a consultant. At the first meeting, he had no time. He said, "Look, I can talk to you now, and give you an hour some time, and two or three phone calls, but I don't have any more time than that."

Since then I think that Eric and I have been on the phone practically every day. He comes in at the drop of a hat, and we're very good friends. He worked with me on my laser exhibit.

9-51. Portrait of Robert Whitman seated at a mirrored table.

9-52. The artist in his loft studio.

KRANZ. *You didn't know anything about lasers when you started?*

WHITMAN. I knew a little bit about it. I was interested in it but only as a freak of nature. . . .

KRANZ. *What did the laser offer you?*

WHITMAN. It didn't offer me anything. That's what I was trying to say. It was just a freak of nature. I made a problem that, as it turned out, could be solved by using the laser.

KRANZ. *What was the problem?*

WHITMAN. Well, to draw a red line around the room, and then to have it erase itself. And it turned out that the laser was the best way to do it.

The artist has to move into the technical world. It's a way to get things done efficiently. If the artist is going to

get involved in any kind of a project, he has to deal with technology. It's the easiest way to do things. You can't program a whole thing of activities if you don't know anything about it.

People feel threatened by technology—they say it's making a mechanical world, a dehumanized world. But it is only a *tool* just like any other one—but easy. Maybe people will criticize somebody for making it easy, but I am not going to do more work than I have to. I am not going to stand around the Jewish Museum and pull switches for a couple of months. It is silly—because it is not important. That is not what the piece is about. If there is a threat to what people think of as "art," then what they think of as art isn't worth it. The work should be exposed to all the dangers it can have.

9-53–54. Views of the Whitman loft, New York City.

9-54

9-55. Mirrored table and environment at the Finch College Museum of Art exhibit entitled *Projected Art*.

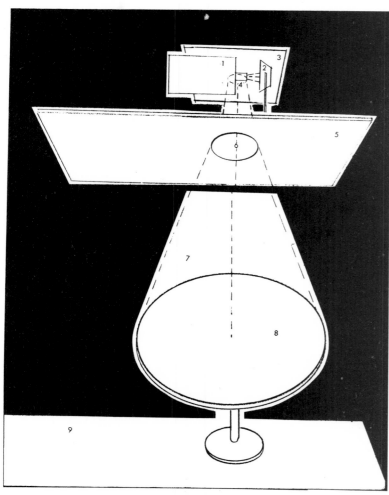

9-56. A demonstration of the way Whitman created his *Dining Room Table* exhibit at the Finch College Museum of Art.

Number 1 is the motion-picture camera; number 2 is a mirror to diffuse the image; number 3 is the ceiling; number 4 is a second mirror, which deflects the projected image downward to the surface of the table (number 8); number 5 is the ceiling of the gallery; number 6 is a hole cut in the gallery to allow the projection to reach the table; number 9 is the floor of the gallery.

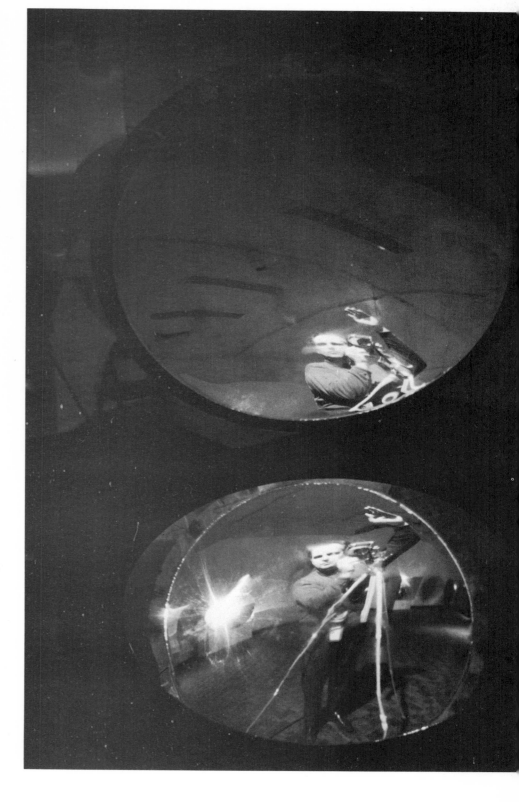

9-57. View of the author photographing two concave mirrors in Robert Whitman's *Pond* exhibit at the Jewish Museum, New York City. This exhibit was held from October 18, 1968, to January 5, 1969. Whitman's interest in mirrors is shown in this view: the two concave mirrors create a virtual image, one in which the spectator appears to be standing in space.

9-58–60. Scenes from Robert Whitman's *Pond* exhibit at the Jewish Museum, New York City.
(All photographs reproduced courtesy Robert Whitman.)

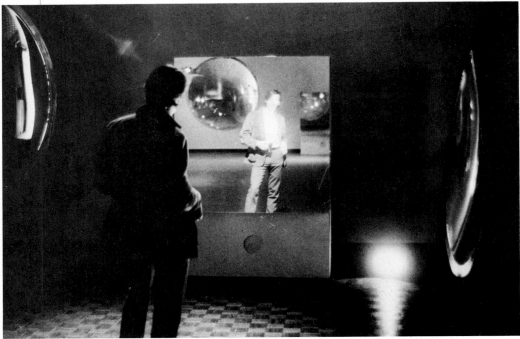

ANTHONY
martin
PAINTER, INTERMEDIA ARTIST, LIGHT COMPOSER, NEW YORK CITY

I am interested in the dynamics of light and how they can be compiled to make a meaningful work for performance or as a sculpture—combines of focal plane imagery, light in space, video, laser, optical arrangements. There are new disciplines required in order to achieve the simplicity that can communicate fundamental things and be a rich experience, to be aware of many possibilities and yet reveal them in an uncomplicated way. Combining energy forms in art is infant; there are unique things about a young medium.

Interaction Room is a situation of human beings and certain images and certain themes. It is a combination of the way they move with the images that are being projected and the sounds that are being created. It has its own quality. The piece is evolving. It is changeable. At the installation I had some prearranged switching. I've done away with them because they made people feel the events were being programmed. The way it is now, viewer-particpants have nearly complete control, if they want it. This area of work has evolved to making more specific process-oriented sculpture. In another work, *Well,* viewers observe downward a changing relationship of waveforms, images in space, and other reflected light as they move small elements and their hands. I want to see a society in miniature create itself in the space at a given time. A miniature society of people acting together, looking at each other, looking at the images, feeling the colors and the sounds that are activated by them, and then interacting with each other by making choices about what they want to have happen, a receptive format.

Is the experience new? The use of materials is new; the choice of materials is new; the form is new. The difference between a painting and a light composition can be seen as a difference in materials and format. I continue to paint. The use of technology doesn't create a completely new aesthetic. As a matter of fact, it regenerates some of the very oldest tribal aesthetics. It's a new art form. My performance composition *Tensions and Light Time Drift* employs dynamics of moving spectral light and a sound-producing light pendulum applying a system of common values in energy exchange. The content is a mode of tensions, question, release, an enterable experience, as are older art forms.

9-61. Anthony Martin, painter and environmental artist, stands under the yellow light in his spectators activated *Interaction Room.* He is looking at a wall portraying creatures that existed before man.

Physiologically, light is directly connected to a person's motor activity. What is its nature beyond that? Painting and sculpture have unleashed vision. Applying light as a natural resource, freed by electricity, enables a new palette. Perhaps as a free tool, it can help turn a light on in a human being dying from his own ill-conceived products. A natural far-reaching communication is at hand.

(See color photographs of Martin's work shown on page 249.)

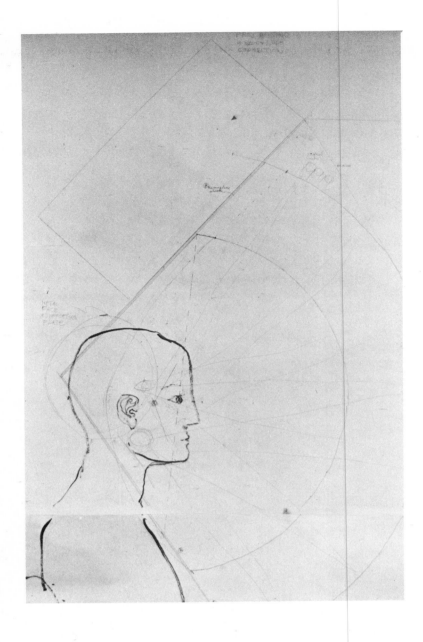

9-62. Diagram of virtual-image technique used by Martin, probably for the first time in an art exhibit. This enables the spectator, who places his head in a box, to see a three-dimensional motion-picture image in space. The technique is the one used by scientists in simulations.

9-63. The *Interaction Room* was exhibited at The Howard Wise Gallery. Shown in the photograph is the overhead projection device. Martin created and coordinated the transparencies used for projection in the room.

opposite

C-109. Portrait of Anthony Martin.

C-110. Martin under yellow light, with pre-historic figures in the background.

C-111. Close-up of the artist, showing projection apparatus above him.

C-112. Martin looking at an image projected on the wall.

C-113. Martin's *Interaction Room* at The Howard Wise Gallery. Later, the room was shown at the *Options* exhibit in Chicago.

C-114. Artist Martin created all the transparencies used in the show and coordinated them for their greatest impact.

C-115. The projection apparatus.

C-116. Martin standing in front of a projected image.

(Courtesy Anthony Martin.)

C-109

C-110

C-111

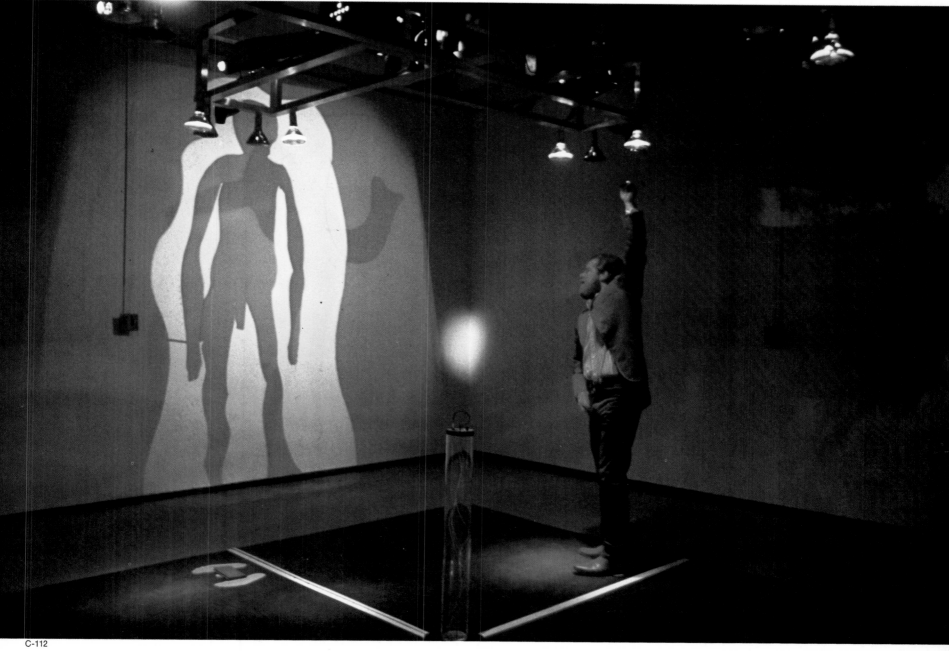

C-112

C-113

C-114

C-115

C-116

ANTHONY MARTIN

MORTON
subotnick
ELECTRONIC COMPOSER, CALIFORNIA INSTITUTE OF ARTS

9-64. Morton Subotnick, electronic composer, with the Buchla.

While in California, Subotnick co-founded the Mills College Performing Group and the San Francisco Tape Music Center. At the same time, he held posts as Assistant Professor of Music at Mills College and Musical Director of Ann Halprin's Dancers' Workshop Company. He was Musical Director of the Repertory Theatre at Lincoln Center during its first season, and, from the fall of 1966 until the spring of 1969, Subotnick was involved with the Intermedia Program at the School of Arts at New York University. He was Visiting Professor in Composition at the University of Maryland for the academic year 1968-1969. He was also Director of Electronic Music at the Electric Circus in New York City.

When the electronic composer finishes the composition, it exists in its total form, already performed. It is as if the composer were there himself, performing the piece over and over from that moment.

With the Buchla you can produce anything you can produce with the Moog. It is the compositional approach that is different. The Moog system is more like an instrument. You actually play it. It is a performance instrument with a normal keyboard and normal action. You can't approach a Buchla as a traditional instrument in any shape or fashion. The keyboard is different from what we customarily call a keyboard. You approach a Buchla almost like an analogue computer in which you actually program materials.

Let's get this straight. Electronic music isn't anything. There isn't any such thing as electronic music. There are composers who are working with electronic means. Most of them are not interested in recreating traditional sounds. Usually they attempt to develop new sounds or to add new qualities to old sounds—to extend the language. There is a group that believes that the electronic function is not to perform, but to realize a musical idea. In other words, it is conceivable that you might have a very complicated musical idea—or produce one on paper—that nobody can play, because of technical problems and human limitations. Things have been produced for the xylophone in which there are eight different dynamic ranges from loud to soft, going at a fantastic rate, and each note at a different dynamic. No xylophone player can actually do that, but if one could, it would be a stupendous sound. This, then, could be the role of computerized music. In this case, you would want to reproduce the instrument for which you had originally conceived the composition. This isn't to say that you wouldn't eventually create new instruments, but you are not, in this case, dealing with the module because you want a new sound. It's because you want a more perfect rendition of what you have written.

It is usually assumed that because a machine is involved in a production, it is mechanical. But it is only mechanical as you program it. From a composer's standpoint, the expressive qualities of a performance can be calculated so that you know that this note is just a little longer than that note, and starts like this and ends like that. You have the machine producing, as I have with the Buchla, a musical performance that is not just a mechanical performance.

We use the word "mechanical" to mean rigid and inflexible. Machine-produced music is inflexible in that it is not going to change, but that does not mean that it is unmusical or not expressive. The composer actually performs it by providing the proper information to the machine (to produce it as if it were an orchestra). It is as if you could give the conductor every single detail to do in the whole orchestra. My view of it is that electronic music has a very special personal quality, in that the composer goes through all the processes from beginning to end. He conceives it. He creates it in terms of his musical ideas. And he performs it. He keeps creating and he keeps performing, because then when he finishes the composition it exists in its total form, already performed. He hands

9-65. Subotnick seated before the Buchla.

Subotnick is the first composer in history to be commissioned to write an electronic composition for the record medium. This work, Silver Apples of the Moon, *was adapted subsequently for ballet use by the Netherlands Ballet Company, the Ballet Rambert of London, and the Glen Tetley Dance Company.*

it to somebody, and it is as if the composer were there himself performing the piece over and over again from that minute.

When a painter finishes a painting, it always remains the same. It never changes, and we accept this as a personal gift from the painter. We look at it, and know that it will never change, and isn't it wonderful? I can't understand why people deny this to the composer. They allowed it to the painter because they had no other choice. The composer needed someone to perform the music— an imperfect human being. Performed live, it was always a different performance. There was no way of recording that original performance. But now the composer has a choice.

9-66. Another view of the Buchla and the composer.

Since July 1969, Subotnick has held the position of Associate Dean of the School of Music and Director of Electronic Music at the California Institute of the Arts.

SCENES FROM MULTIMEDIA OPERA BY DR. JOHN V. GILBERT
A SCENE FROM OPERA TODAY PRODUCTION

DR. JOHN V.
gilbert

MULTIMEDIA OPERA COMPOSER, NEW YORK UNIVERSITY

Wagner thought of himself as a musician, but he also saw his role as that of philosopher and writer. He had a number of ideas that he wanted to bring to culmination, and he felt from observation that the arts must inevitably merge. Such a viewpoint encourages the artist not to limit himself, but to say, "I can do all of this." He would begin to search for a form that incorporated all these ideas into one form. This is what Wagner called his *Gesamtkünstwerk,* an all together art work.

The fact that he chose remote legends as subjects was in keeping with the whole century and an awakening interest in looking into the past in a systematic way—the foundations of modern musicology and research. Wagner utilized historical research, delving into legends and myths for his subject matter. He wanted to find the roots and heritage of his own culture and enshrine it.

Here was a German, with an already highly developed

opposite
C-117. Dr. John V. Gilbert at the Putney Synthesizer.

C-118. Scene from Dr. Gilbert's one-act multimedia opera *Rotation.* Dancers Jill Kalotay and Sherry Popkin, like a pantomime Greek chorus, "comment" on the action.

C-119. Group of principals in *Rotation.*

C-120. Set for *Rotation,* showing projections on the sides of set.

C-121. One of the principals in *Rotation.*

C-122. Scene from *Rotation.* "The Critic" to the audience:

> "Don't be fooled by them.
> I'm sure you can see
> That I
> Am the only competent eye . . ."

C-123. *Rotation* set seen from the balcony.

C-124. A scene from Opera Today's production *Variations on a Theme by Benjamin Britten.* Total environment surrounds the singer, dancers, and audience. Projected films and slides are coordinated with the performance. (Courtesy Opera Today, Inc.)

(Courtesy Dr. John V. Gilbert.)

German tradition. Here was a composer with an ability to deal with words, to conceive his libretto, to oversee the entire production, to produce an art work different from earlier operas. He was deeply steeped in the symphonic tradition of the dramatic "working out" of musical ideas. It was a logical step for a composer with such a background to develop the *leitmotif* (in which a musical idea represents a character or theme) to a greater extent than it had been used before. In other words, his music represented characters and ideas the audience was to follow aurally as well as visually. Such music attempted to be philosophical, to say something in ways that other arts could not.

Wagner transformed musical ideas to correspond with the action of the drama. For example, each time the idea of death might appear the audience would hear a theme representing death. Later on, the action of the drama might suggest joy in the meeting of lovers, but underscoring this action in the orchestra, the death theme portends that the lovers are doomed. Wagner synthesized an abstract musical figure with a specific action and theme. Wagner's *Gesamtkünstwerk* was difficult to achieve in such a collaborative venture as an opera. Since he appears to have been a musical entrepreneur, if he were alive today he might have been a film producer and director, conceiving the entire finished work, including the musical score and the editing!

I think Wagner was trying to achieve what the film did achieve—a real union, a kind of "all-together art work" where the music, the visual impact, and the verbal or literary aspects are brought together in one work.

(All illustrations for this interview appear in color on the facing page.)

PATRICIA HERBERT AL
collins kaplan berr

OPERA TODAY, INC., NEW YORK CITY

9-67A

9-67C

9-67A, B, C. Portraits of Patricia Collins, Artistic Director, Herbert Kaplan, Music Director, and Al Berr, Managing Director, Opera Today, Inc.

9-67B

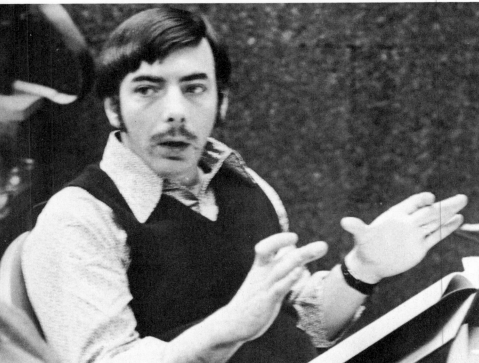

A talk with artistic director Patricia Collins, music director Herbert Kaplan, and managing director Al Berr on the successful integration of various media and many artistic disciplines into an aesthetically-controlled operatic performance.

KRANZ. *What is the purpose of Opera Today?*

COLLINS. To revitalize lyric theater by finding new forms, and by lyric theater I mean any form of theater that uses music as a means to develop and extend a dramatic situation. Our choice of music lies somewhere between the pop medium and full scale "grand" opera. We are very interested in doing opera—expanding it in directions that traditional groups will not undertake.

KRANZ. *Does that mean that Opera Today does only new works?*

KAPLAN. Absolutely. Or at this point we certainly think so, because that is what's needed. But beyond that, what we want is not just an investigation of a musical form. Certainly as important, perhaps at this point more important, we want to define new directions for the physical forms through the use of contemporary technologies. As a matter of fact we have coined a phrase for what we're up to. We call it "techno-lyric theater."

KRANZ. *How did all this come about?*

COLLINS. Well, at a certain point in my career and also in Herb Kaplan's, we found ourselves working for a small opera company in upstate New York. There we each fell in love with the flexibility, the richness, the "multi-media" possibilities inherent in opera.

KRANZ. *In other words, the size of the event?*

COLLINS. Right. The scale one is capable of portraying in opera—the multi-leveled quality, with the music saying one thing, the words another, the scenery saying another, and all adding up to a portrait of a single moment considerably more complicated than straight musical theater. We often, in those days, discussed our desire for our own form of theater.

KAPLAN. I think we all became bored with the way opera was being treated in this country, which was really just renewing old productions. Whether they were "new" or not, they were, in concept, old productions.

COLLINS. But I certainly sensed that the world didn't need another small opera company. Later, in order to get some managerial experience, I joined the City Center Joffrey Ballet as production supervisor. While I was there we did a production called *Astarte,* which was the first large scale mixed-media piece for theater! I . . .

KRANZ. *That turned you on?*

COLLINS. It did, and I decided we could pursue a whole form of lyric theater in the direction of multimedia. Herbert, who was by then with the American National Opera Company, became our music director and Al Berr, from being general manager with the Joffrey Ballet, became our managing director. That's how Opera Today started.

KRANZ. *I can imagine your concentration on multimedia getting in the way of the singers' egos. How do singers react to all this technology in and around and on top of them?*

COLLINS. Well, if they are really good performers they use it as an extention of themselves—which is exactly what the media should be. It should be an electronic means of extending their personalities, extending the

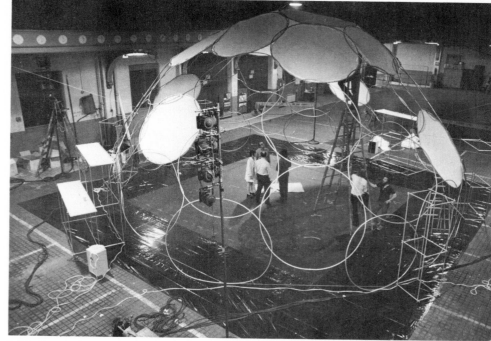

9-68. Opera Today environmental dome under construction.

characters they are portraying. The performers we have worked with so far have found it enormously exciting—something to play off, in decor, texture, color, sound—a continual subtext they can do something with.

KRANZ. *So it all comes back to the individual talent again?*

BERR. Of course, always. The bigger the challenge, the harder one has to work, and so the more exciting the work can be.

KRANZ. *Your first production in this form was given last year, wasn't it?*

9-69. Control center outside the dome, including computer, quadrasonic tape deck, and lighting controls.

9-70A. Completed dome without projection.

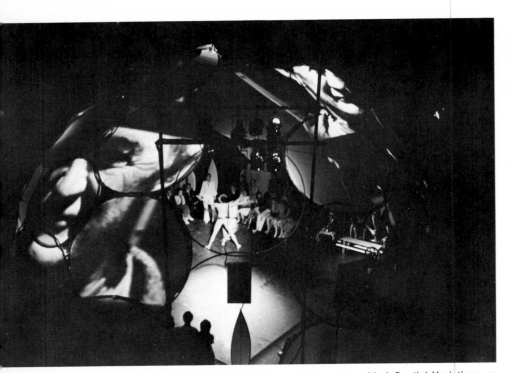

9-70B. Scene from Opera Today performance entitled *Spatial Variations on a Theme by Benjamin Britten.* A dome of interlaced aluminum hoops encloses dancers, singers, and the audience in a total visual and aural environment. This film, developed especially for this performance by Elaine Summers, was projected on the hoops from four banks of projectors. (See color page 252 figure C-124.)

9-71. Spectator-level view of a scene from *Spatial Variations.* Live voice was intermingled with recorded voice, while live dancers were juxtaposed with filmed and projected images, which evoked the mood of the music. In some instances, filmed portions of the live actors appeared simultaneously with the live action.

BERR. Yes, in June 1970 at the Medical Armory here in New York City. It was titled *Spatial Variations on a Theme by Benjamin Britten,* and it was staged for tenor and four dancers.

KRANZ. *As I remember, it involved a special environment—something like six film projectors, eight slide projectors, a computer, and quadrasonics. Wasn't all this technology hard to tame?*

COLLINS. It's not a matter of taming it, it's a matter of understanding that mixed-media and the technology it uses is an animal all its own; it is headstrong and it is

going to go in certain directions. But if you believe in the ability of technology to extend perception, then you begin to listen to what media wants to say. You dare to let it go rather than resist it. You find that it teaches you how to say the things you want to say in a manner never dreamed of.

KRANZ. *How did you develop the interplay between the live voice and the recorded voice in Spatial Variations. . . ?*

KAPLAN. There were practical reasons for this. One of the cliches of traditional opera is that of a soprano standing in the middle of the stage singing the aria. We did not want to sacrifice the vocal art every time the singer became physically involved in the production. When our director wanted the singer to be particularly involved in the action, we put those moments on tape. Once we started we went further because of the incredible effect we got. We found we could fool the ear, play the live singer against himself or against just the echo of his voice and so on. Of course an enormous amount of care was taken with the recording. It was done in sixteen tracks dubbed down to four. We had, and will always have, very creative sound engineers. That's one of the wonderful things about the mixed-media form. It requires the closest collaboration in all areas. No one person can have expertise in all the technologies.

KRANZ. *Can you elaborate?*

BERR. Well, for example, in putting people together for our work, we soon discovered that we could not use talents unless they were capable of a close collaboration, of taking criticism, changing direction, responding to the ideas of others. This interplay is pivotal to the creation of a mixed-media work. In most productions media is applied as an afterthought in a sort of booster or supportive relation to the production. That is why it so often fails. The media must be conceived along with everything else —hence the importance of the word *collaboration*.

KRANZ. *But surely collaboration has always been of prime importance in theater?*

COLLINS. Theater has always given lip service to the idea of collaboration and then gone on to develop its work on the dictates of a single talent, and still function superbly— as for example the 1950s' work of Elia Kazan—a kind of "auteur" theory of theater. But we have found that once you become involved with technology, really closely involved with technology, the producer works at his creative peak. He permits the people most familiar with the technology to function as artists on an unprecedented collaborative level. It is no longer a matter of an author handing you a script and your effecting it; the authors did indeed hand us a script for our current production *Gulliver,* but since then we, the director, the composers, the designer, the filmmaker, and the sound people have been kneading it, helping to form what the audience will finally see.

KAPLAN. In a collaborative project of this scope, even

9-72. Scale model of *Gulliver* environment for the planned Opera Today production. (Scale ¼″) (Courtesy Opera Today, Inc.)

This photograph shows proposed renovation plans for an existing movie house to make it into a multimedia production environment. The Opera Today group plans to construct a new floor that will cover the former orchestra section of the theatre. The curved tiers at left represent the present theatre's first and second balconies. The block-like sections at left and right foreground, combined with a third section behind the metal projection towers, will be reserved for audience seating. The shiny black surface in the center is reserved for the performance area.
Movable projection screens (about twenty feet high) can be seen in the performance area. A large projection surface will be provided by the existing proscenium, seen in the left foreground. Additional projection areas may be added to the balcony and theatre walls.

the director has found it hard to make a move without considering every implication. For example, the environment that he, we, and the designer developed affected the flow of the action, which affected the placement of twenty-five or thirty speakers, which affected the work of the composers, who needed to know, *before writing,* the direction from which certain effects would emanate.

COLLINS. Meanwhile, the filmmaker wanted to do certain things with imagery that affected the action, which affected the direction of sound, and so on. With this medium, no one can make a move without affecting somebody else. Nobody grabs the ball and runs down the field with it.

BERR. *Gulliver* has been an exciting education in the disciplines of mixed-media. We hope when it is done it will be a synthesis of all the things we have talked of today.
(A scene from Opera Today is shown in color on page 252.)

ELAINE
summers
INTERMEDIA DANCER AND CHOREOGRAPHER, NEW YORK CITY

My real excitement is light and kinetic visual forms—the interaction in space of projected images and kinetic forms. For that reason I use film, and use it with live bodies, creating an environment in which there is an interchange and exchange between the component parts

—audience, film, and performers. There is a magic happening that is difficult to explain verbally and can only be experienced in space. Therefore, it cannot exist on a TV screen or in a single or multiscreen projection.

Intermedia is the interaction of the performing arts—

9-73. A portrait of Elaine Summers in her studio.
(All photographs reproduced courtesy Elaine Summers.)

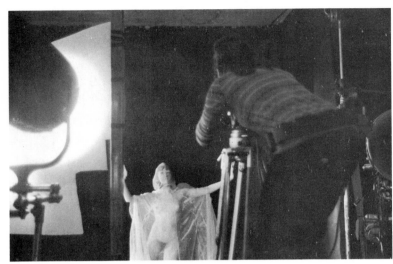

9-74. Elaine Summers photographing the dancer Pamela Ladimer for a film.

9-75. Elaine Summers rehearsing the dancer Pamela Ladimer.

film, dance, theater, music, and light—in space, as differentiated from expanded cinema or multiprojection, which is multiplicity and simultaneiety of projected images upon a surface. In both forms there is the collage of image upon image, which has tremendous impact. We are able to see and absorb much more than we realize—seeing, feeling, sensing in many ways at once. Intermedia offers the possibility of suggesting the complex of our experiences, echoing our fantastic ability to respond with multiple feelings to a single experience and to collage them in our mind verbally and visually. Simultaneous presentation of multiple forms gives a new dimension to our understanding and perception visually and spatially.

For a particular intermedia work, I very carefully work out the kind, size, and number of screens, i.e., translucent, opaque, split, vertical, partial, horizontal, or floor-to-wall screens. These screens may be constructed of inexpensive materials, like stretch jerseys and plastic yard material in white. The space and performers, in relation to the images, give infinite possibilities of exaggeration of action and space, distortion of performers' sizes and actions, and strange juxtapositions. If the performer is behind the screen, he may appear as a shadow and thus be integrated into the filmed image. If he moves between the projected image and the wall, his body will become a screen that makes visible the unseen image existing in the air. These elements combine to destroy realities and to create spatial and kinetic illusions.

In disciplining myself to stay in my own studio and to work, I began to develop along a completely strange (to the usual concepts of dance training) way, which was internal, meditative, and quiet—developing action kinetically and organically rather than decoratively and competitively. I was thinking a great deal about film—that it was a media that could transcend, through illusion, the reality of gravity and space. I think we all desire to be free of the limitations we experience as bodies in this world.

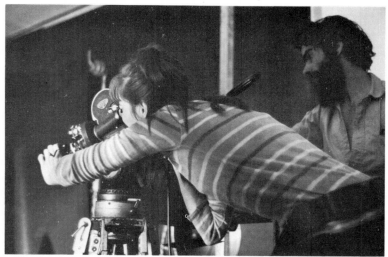

9-76. Elaine Summers and her assistant cameraman and editor, Dave Gearey.

9-77. Intermedia lighting expert Jay Jerome Washington in Elaine Summers' studio.

9-78. Costume designer Judith Haugan painting the costume of dancer Pamela Ladimer.

9-79. Finishing touches on painted costume in preparation for film at Elaine Summers' Intermedia Institute.

9-80. Elaine Summers in her studio kitchen with Dave Gearey.

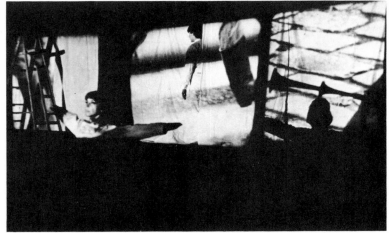

9-81. Dancer Pamela Ladimer rehearsing at Elaine Summers' studio.

9-82. Scene from *Fantastic Gardens,* an evening of dance presented by the Judson Dance Theatre, February 17, 18, and 19, 1964, at the Judson Memorial Church in New York City. Dancers, from left to right, are: Sally Gross, John Worden, Carla Blanc, Tony Holder, Ruth Emerson, Sandra Neels. (Photograph by Al Giese.)

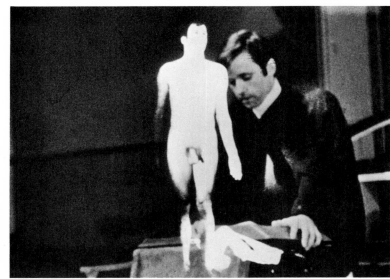

9-83. Final scene from *Another Pilgrim*. Script and music by Rev. Al Carmine. Camera work and editing by Elaine Summers. The minister was played by John Hendricks. (Photograph by The Ken Thompson Group, Inc.)

DR. GEORGE H.
litwin

CHAIRMAN OF THE BOARD, INTERMEDIA SYSTEMS CORPORATION, CAMBRIDGE, MASSACHUSETTS,
AND PRESIDENT OF HUMANA, AN INTERMEDIA COMPANY CONCERNED WITH EXPERIMENTAL LEARNING

A motivation man meets a media man.

My own special field is motivation—human motivation. In the last five years or so, I've been doing research at the Harvard Business School*, in which I've been trying to get a handle on motivation from the point of view of managers, teachers, parents—people who have responsibility for motivating others. After a lot of study, I emerged with the notion of what we have come to call climate, or organizational climate, as a critical factor in understanding motivation. By climate, we mean the nature of the environment as perceived and experienced by the person who lives there. Not as it might actually look, not as it might be described by someone else, but as the person feels and experiences it. Motivation is, in fact, heavily determined by the psychological environment or climate.

There came a point when I realized that what I was doing had a frustration built into it, because, though I could analyze climates and understand their impact, I couldn't do anything about it. . . . And it was just at this time that I met Gerd Stern. In talking about what we were doing, we discovered that we were working on different sides of the same problem: I was studying the psychological effects of environment, he was creating environments that had distinct psychological effects.

We have done several things together. We set up a project at the Harvard Business School to work on problems of understanding psychological climate, using media as a tool for stimulating business climates, looking at their effects, and understanding better how they operate. We set up a similar project in the Harvard School of Education, pushing a little further into the use of this kind of environmental simulation as a way of sensitizing teachers to the climates they create. The third thing we did was to teach a joint seminar, which was offered at the Harvard Business School, the School of Education, the Divinity School, the Design School, and at MIT. It created a tremendous amount of interest.

We formed a company, Intermedia Systems, to begin to do some things we thought needed doing, such as building hardware to control this kind of environmental system and learning to program media environments to create particular psychological effects. We got a staff, people with real skill and background in photography, sound, and programming, who could create these concepts.

*Technically, the Harvard Graduate School of Business Administration, commonly called the Harvard Business School.

9-84. Dr. George H. Litwin, formerly president and genius of Intermedia Systems Corporation, is now Assistant Professor of Organizational Behavior at Harvard University Graduate School of Business Education.

Intermedia Systems Corporation—a group of young artists trying to use multimedia technology to create environments that have particular kinds of psychological effects, with educational applications a priority.

We are trying to use mixed media—multimedia technology—to create environments that have particular kinds of psychological effects. The educational applications are really manifold, for organizations, for management education, for adult learning, and for improved curriculum approaches in our colleges and high schools. We are talking about man's environment. It's been here all along. It's been influencing us all along. What we are saying is: we can begin to have some control over the environmental influences on our behavior, attitudes, and motivation. We don't have to live with whatever happens to have been created. We can program environmental influence, using media technology, and this opens up major new possibilities for learning, and for the improvement of living and working environments.

In some cases, we actually try to simulate, realistically, environments in industries, schools, ghettos, and so on, for the purpose of learning about them. We are doing something beyond that, however; we are programming certain kinds of idealized environments—which may or may not exist anywhere, but which would have a particular quality—to learn about how they work, to help teachers and managers understand new possibilities, and to demonstrate the vast potential of programmed media environments.

GERD
stern

PRESIDENT AND CREATIVE DIRECTOR, INTERMEDIA SYSTEMS CORPORATION, CAMBRIDGE, MASSACHUSETTS

9-85

9-85. Gerd Stern, Creative Director, Intermedia Systems Corporation.

A conversation with Gerd Stern in his home and studio workshop in an old church, the former USCO *Shrine,* Garnerville, New York.

STERN. Is painting as a medium dead? Is the horse dead? It is pretty lively, biologically speaking. The horse isn't dead, but the function of the horse is changed. The function of the book and the function of the painting have changed radically. Mainly, the book doesn't have to do a lot of things it didn't do very well, because we now have movies and television. It would be nice if we could get the painting back to its original role of celebrating a kind of an instant of revelation. Right now, painting is simply a frame and a signature. You go to a museum and you see this kind of chicken-head-bobbing, where people are looking for the label. They don't really *see* the painting.

There's not a painter in the world who paints his painting to hang in among other paintings and be looked at for a split second like a comic strip. But that's how painting is used today. I don't think that's a very good role for it. It was different entirely when you had a painting in a cathedral as an object for someone to sit in front of and pray and meditate.

Well, that's a painting and you use it to fill some function, but this business that the museums and galleries have foisted on us, or the collectors, where the walls are plastered with pictures—you know what the pictures are in a collector's house? They're money! They might just as well be money upon the wall.

KRANZ. *Are the environmental aspects of multimedia presentations conceived primarily to fill the full range of peripheral vision, or do they have other, more significant aspects?*

STERN. I think the best way to deal with it is as a surround. It doesn't merely fill the peripheral vision; it fills the whole field. At its best, it simulates an environment, and it allows you what McLuhan calls "antienvironment." Antienvironments give you perspective on environments.

When you're dealing with environmental parameters, you have to be prepared to create and to simulate all kinds of environments. The principal show that we've done—at the Riverside Museum—was basically a meditative and contemplative environment. All our earlier performances in auditoriums were overload environments. The Jewish Museum thing gets overloady because the Lower East Side is an overload situation. It was strange. Those old people would come in and one old woman said to me: "Why is it so noisy?" I turned around: "Isn't it noisy down on the Lower East Side?" She said: "But this is a museum."

I could have played the Lower East Side with sounds of birds and rushing water. That would have been something else. It wouldn't have been a simulation of the Lower East Side, now or then. It's one of the best things we've ever done. We went out and recorded people from an old people's home. They had come over fifty years ago. And we got records from those days, and we mixed it with material from now. It really worked. That's the simplest, most vital thing that you can do with audiovisual techniques. You contrast one thing with another. The seashore with the urban environment. The simulation is not intended just to replace the natural environment.

There are many motivations; the purely artistic motivation of creating an experience; the motivation of depicting an organizational climate in order to examine the productivity of the climate. We perform many experiments. We don't entirely know the reason why we are doing them. We have the technology at hand, and when technology

9-86. View of Gerd Stern's church-shrine-home at Garnerville, New York.

comes to hand there are certain natural things you do with it, and there are certain inspired comprehensions that lead you on. The natural sequence is slow. The inspired jump is a gift, even if you only make it once in a while.

continued on page 268

9-87A

9-87A, B. Two views of the entrance to the Stern residence.

9-87B

9-88. The artist's child.

9-89. A tree grows in a home.

9-90. The artist examines an early intermedia control box.

9-91. Light box made by the USCO group.

9-92. USCO kinetic sculpture.

9-93. Multimedia report made by
Stern to General Electric. *opposite*

9-94. Gerd Stern and intermedia artifacts.

9-95. Light symbolizes the USCO philosophy.

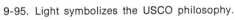

9-96. Gerd Stern's workshop, complete with the thousands of electronic
elements that invariably clutter the intermedia artist's life.

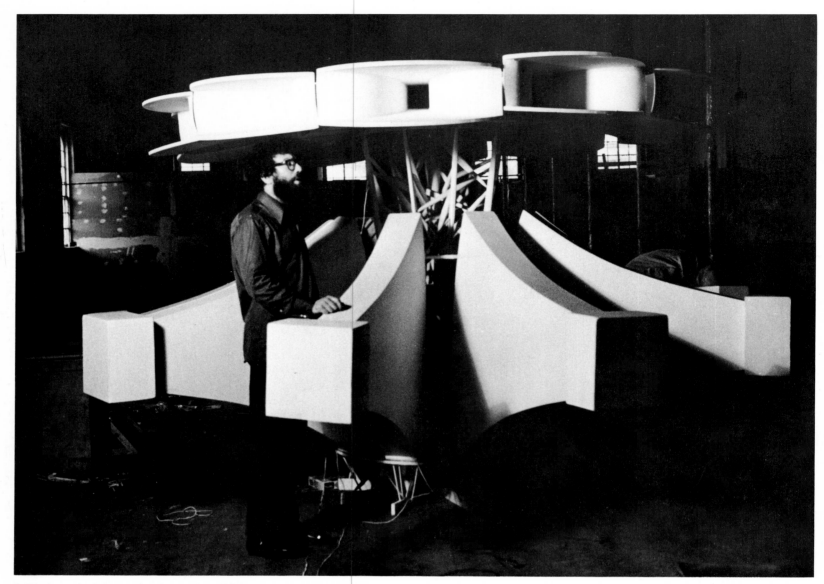

9-97. Acoustical form, developed by USCO, exhibited at The Brooklyn Museum.

Speaking of his work with Michael Callahan, technical director of Intermedia Systems, Inc., Gerd Stern threw a light on the mysterious process of interaction between artist and technologist.

Mike and I have been working together for six years, going on seven, and actually anything we've done in the technical world, Michael has created. It's an interesting ambivalent phenomenon. You make a demand for some effect—I do—and Michael creates the circuitry and hardware that does it. In turn, that leads on to a demand for another effect, because you see now what you can do with it. Then the visual, or let's say the slide, isn't quite up to it, so then you create new software, and then you think of what the next step would be if you could only do this or that—and you've got something else going. And after five or six years, you've got a Frankenstein. You've got that pile of surplus equipment that you see lying all around here in this workshop.

opposite

C-125. Canvas cupola of *Shrine,* an environment by Gerd Stern and the USCO group.

C-126. Meditation light in the shrine. Detail.

C-127. Central sculpture is the focal point of the meditation shrine.

C-128. Shrine wall.

C-129. Figures of a man and a Hindu deity were superimposed.

C-130. Entrance to the shrine.

C-131. A corner of the shrine.

C-132. Optical effects create illusion for meditation.

(Courtesy USCO.)

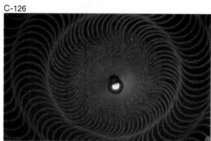
C-126

C-128

**GERD STERN
AND THE USCO GROUP'S**
SHRINE

C-129

C-125

C-127

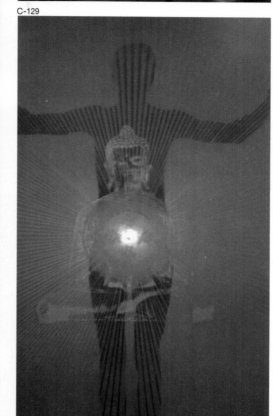

C-130

C-131

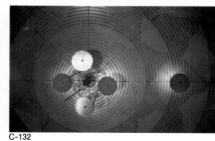
C-132

MICHAEL
callahan

TECHNICAL DIRECTOR, INTERMEDIA SYSTEMS CORPORATION, CAMBRIDGE, MASSACHUSETTS

9-98. Michael Callahan, Technical Director, Intermedia Systems Corporation.

KRANZ. *What is the potential of the new, relatively inexpensive computer for the field of intermedia?*

CALLAHAN. Having the computer will give us a lot more potential for action. . . . Actually it will simplify the hardware, having a small general-purpose computer where programming is in software rather than in hardware. We'll have more versatility. We'll be able to control more functions on projectors. A big thing would be in the programming area. Although making up a program with the tape is possible, it takes a lot of thought and a lot of work to get the tape punched. Punching it is not the hardest part of it. It's creating the program, keeping track of all those projectors, knowing what projector is doing what. If, indeed, a lot of these things could be delegated to the computer, it would be a big step in getting sophisticated media shows out to the real world.

KRANZ. *Do you think that you're really involved in the Kitty Hawk stage of intermedia, in terms of what it can become?*

CALLAHAN. I think so. I think the field is going to continue to grow and pretty soon some of the very large companies will jump into the hardware, which will be interesting. Right now we don't have an awful lot of competition, which is one thing. Competition does, you know, put hair on your chest. Stimulates growth.

KRANZ. *In terms of some of the shows that you're putting together now, I gather that your interest is moving toward the educational ground.*

CALLAHAN. I don't want to start criticizing the American educational system too hard, but I think a lot can be done in the whole educational industry, not just in the public schools. I think it's a little grim now, and somewhat lugubrious.

KRANZ. *Do you think that it's possible that creative artists, filmmakers and intermedia men would be able to bring a freshness to the pedagogic process?*

CALLAHAN. There's no question in my mind that new techniques, not only media techniques, are in order; that there are people around who could do them. Right now, we're still pretty much dependent upon commercially available slide film projectors. We're beginning to build up the talent required to design the projection equipment. I think as the techniques evolve, we'll get . . . well, the equipment is going to become smaller, lighter, cheaper, easier to use.

DONALD
pasquella

INTERMEDIA ARTIST AND TEACHER

After consuming a fairly large dosage of words from a wide range of artists, educators, businessmen, politicians, radicals, experts, and critics, I get the feeling that there are a lot of carpetbaggers running around loose—along with a sprinkling of frauds, charlatans, and fools, all of whom love to blah-blah-blah about their latest thing, spinning fantastic word-webs glistening with store-bought phrases. Why do they do it? Why do artists get caught up in this? I mean, they come on very strong about their things, guiding us poor mortals through the hidden mysteries of their work. Then you see their stuff and it's junk, really insipid and unimaginative, poorly done, and you wonder what these guys are up to.

When I look at their things, I start believing that people have missed the point about pollution—that the worst crime is not the pollution of the air, earth, and water. The worst crime is the pollution of the individual creative spirit. We are constantly bombarded with a veritable multimedia cacophony of ugliness, brutality, dishonesty, and trivia. We celebrate and honor the semblance of things rather than the thing itself, no matter whether it is quality, creativity, honesty, vitality, security, education, love or food. All of this is damaging us as human beings. You know, artists are both the offended and the offenders.

I believe that an artist has a moral obligation to do the absolute best he possibly can all the time and constantly learn from everything, constantly work to become better. His work should strive to be integrating—a real partnership between hand, head, heart, and soul—and integrating also in terms of the artist sharing something of himself with an audience. The artist must learn to become an alchemist transmuting grossness into fineness, ugliness into beauty, turning lead into gold. I mean, really changing for the better not only himself but also, through himself, his environment and the people as a whole.

(See color photographs of USCO production *Shrine* shown on page 269.)

9-99. Donald Pasquella, formerly Visual Program Manager for Intermedia Systems Corporation, is currently associated with a well known university.

C-133

C-134

C-135

C-136

C-137

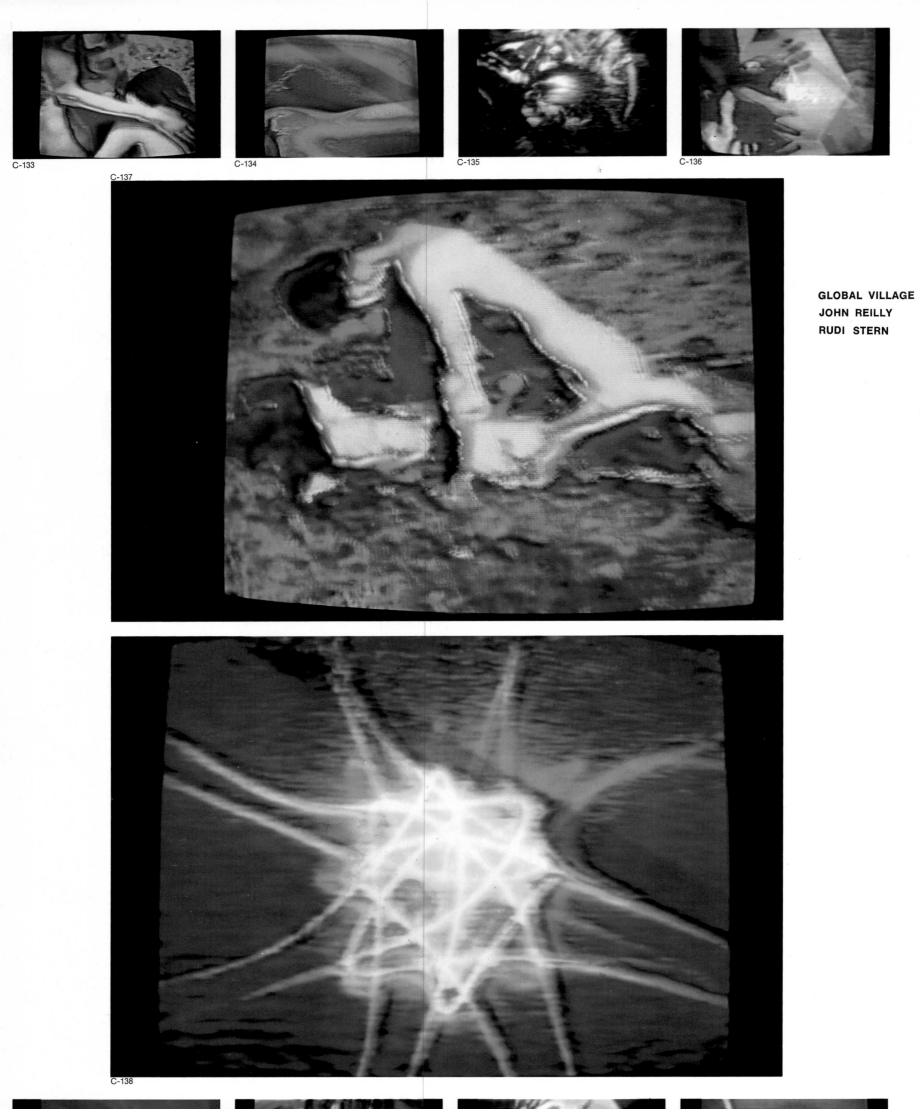

GLOBAL VILLAGE
JOHN REILLY
RUDI STERN

C-138

C-139

C-140

C-141

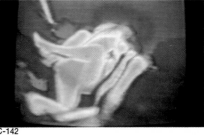

C-142

RUDI JOHN
stern reilly

INTERMEDIA ARTISTS, GLOBAL VILLAGE

STERN. Our collaboration began when we opened Global Village, in October 1969, as a new kind of theatre experience that would involve a video multichannel environment—a room in which people could interact. Part of that interaction would then be fed back through the environment as part of the information.

Why the name "Global Village"? It had a good sound for what we were planning to do, because it involved simultaneous action on many fronts; it involved exchange; it involved the concept that each point of receiving information would also eventually be a place of generating information.

Using multivideo channels was for me an extension of what I had been into. It meant going beyond the aesthetic, more sensual, experience of light projectors, to offer a kind of information that seemed more relevant, more in keeping with the time we are living in. It is a different time from 1965-66, when I was working with more meditative and contemplative environments in which one could focus in on oneself. Multivideo channels reflects a time in which important information has to be shared, and shared on many different levels.

opposite

C-133. Synthesized color from the Global Village video composition *John and Samantha.*

C-134. Synthesized color from the Global Village video composition *Bodies.*

C-135–136. Kinetic compositions, Global Village.

C-137. Synthesized color from *John and Samantha.*

C-138. Laser composition, Global Village.

C-139. Video composition using ARP Synthesizer, Global Village.

C-140. From a video environment at Global Village.

C-141. Kinetic composition, Global Village.

C-142. Bodies in motion, Global Village.

(Courtesy John Reilly and Rudi Stern, Global Village.)

REILLY. I had the realization that here was an extension of studio video, that I need not be locked into a studio—which is the fault of broadcast companies—you are quite literally locked into a studio—but could extend that into the street, into homes, into offices, actually anywhere. You are battery-operated and self-contained. With that extension, plus the fact that film required a continuity of thought over a period of time—these two factors coming together opened up a new artistic outlet for me. It was as if a storyteller suddenly had a radio invented, and he was invited to do a talk show in any way he pleased. This technological step gave me the freedom to express some of the ideas I'd had.

I recall one incident that gives an example of my realization of how multichannel might work. It was 1964 and I was doing what amounted to a memorial TV special on the Kennedy assassination. I went out on the street and shot material with people. I had a second source of information in the form of some footage from Kennedy's life. A third channel was two black men sitting in the studio talking about what they thought of the Kennedy administration—how it related to blacks. I produced and directed this show in a traditional television studio. I was assembling all this information into one channel, which was being broadcast, but on the three monitors there were actually three channels of information. I certainly had not envisioned Global Village, but I knew at that point that what I was seeing in the control room was a far richer experience than what was being broadcast.

STERN. We are involved in several new areas. We have the Global Village Resource Center, which is funded by the New York State Council on the Arts. This enables us to work with many different kinds of groups. They range from Krishna Consciousness to Daytop Village, which is a drug rehabilitation group. We are able to give these groups a voice, a way of expressing themselves via video that they haven't had before. These tapes are for internal use, for training or teaching purposes, or for presentation material that they can send out to other groups around the country.

Another area is our involvement with the New School in setting up a Center for Experimental Video. We have just received a seed grant from the Rockefeller Foundation to develop a series of courses and workshops that will enable us to experiment with this. *continued*

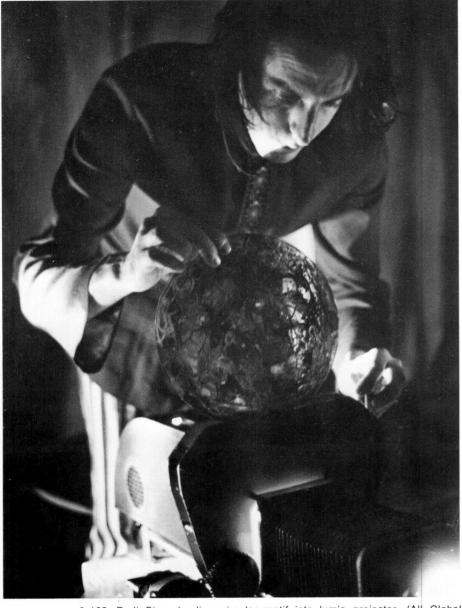

9-100. Rudi Stern loading circular motif into lumia projector. (All Global Village illustrations courtesy Rudi Stern and John Reilly.)

video you tend not to do it. You tend to involve other people, in crews, in editing. You work as a collective, in effect.

In our collaboration in Global Village, the fact that we have shared equipment and shared time enables us to complement each other in terms of the pressure involved in maintaining an operation like this. We can give each other freedom once in a while to go out and do a project, while the other person looks after the structure.

STERN. The day the astronauts were walking on the moon and the headlines were filled with it seemed the right moment to ask people of very modest means how they felt about the expenditure of these sums of money and how that very dramatic national gesture related to their lives. We did the interviewing on Essex Street on the Lower East Side. The responses were interesting as a kind of counterpoint to what was happening on the broadcast channels.

We can give a voice to groups with divergent opinions, a group like STAR—Street Transvestite Action Revolutionaries—who welcomed videotape as a needed voice. A couple of them have been in here and have seen the mix in our program. The whole experience of taping very

9-101. John Reilly at the Global Village workshop, New York City. (Photograph by C. Kosof.)

REILLY. When Rip Torn developed the show in which he played Richard III as Richard Nixon, my contribution was specifically in the area of video. Rip developed the whole aspect of the takeoff on Richard III. There are incredible parallels all the way through it. What I added to it was three channels of information. Richard III was being played against the grid of information, including actual broadcasts of Richard Nixon, some of the Kennedy assassination footage, and related scenes of the play. We worked out a way of integrating both the video grid and the ongoing stage part in front of the grid. We developed it over a three-day period and finally taped it. It's really a collaborative thing.

We are at a point now where an artist alone painting in a loft is becoming an anachronism. Anyone working with technology must be involved in studios, in equipment. There are crews involved, a rapport with cameramen and technicians that didn't exist a few years ago. The filmmaker-artist can literally go out alone, but with much involves showing people the equipment. It's not a complete cycle unless the people get a chance to look behind the camera, to shoot some material themselves, and to see the final edited result. Without that, it's still the same old conventional movie man who arrives, sucks up the images, and disappears.

REILLY. There's an analogy here with Ralph Nader's realizing that law school graduates were going and working for the large law firms, which in turn were working for General Motors, and nobody was working for the interests of the poor guy who drove the car. Video is an alternative means of communicating with people. It's a means that I think will expand into community cable systems, and to cassettes, into many areas. We've had examples of it with the underground press. We've had it happening most strongly in New York with listener-spon-

sored radio. But we had no examples in this country of its happening with video until the emergence, now, of people working primarily with half-inch tape, beginning to show tapes in colleges, communities, beginning the very first steps of community cable systems. It's a horizontal means of distributing information, as against the vertical stacking of a TV network.

STERN. What interests me most now, which never interested me as much before, is people. Most of the things I'm doing involve looking at people and having people look at each other, as opposed to kinetic or aesthetically oriented compositions, which for me at the moment have pretty much lost significance or relevance.
(See Global Village color photographs shown on page 272.)

9-102. Detail from *Innertube,* a videotape by John Reilly and Rudi Stern. (Photograph by Jay Good.)

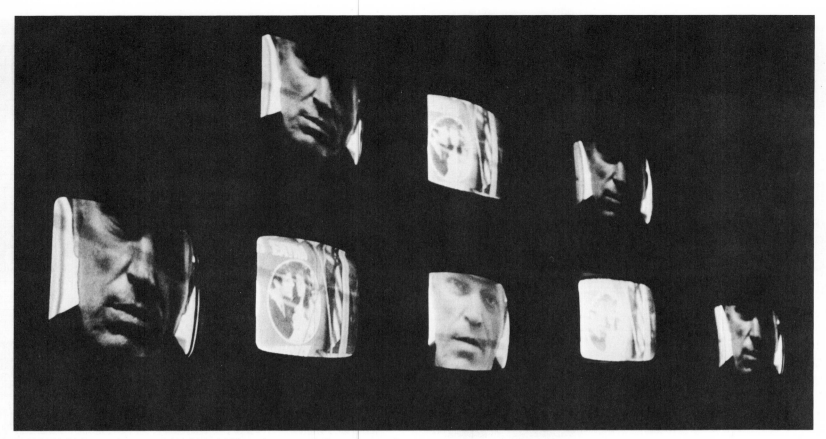

9-103. Multiple monitors used by Global Village for presentations. Some of the monitors are equipped for a colorized signal, which converts the black-and-white image into vivid and startling colors. (Photograph by Seiji Kakizaki.)

9-104. Spectators at a Global Village showing in the downtown loft section of New York City. (Photograph by C. Kosof.)

ERIC
salzman

COMPOSER, MULTIMEDIA & MUSIC THEATRE, BROOKLYN, NEW YORK

The crucial problem of contemporary life is the impact of technology—the relationship of the individual to mass technocratic society. Virtually all contemporary artistic expression responds to this central problem in one way or another. Technology oppresses me, therefore I use it; I fight back with the very thing that is being used to oppress me. Either technology controls us or we control it.

These questions are not just abstractions. Technology dominates our lives even where we least expect it. Music today is thoroughly dominated by recording technology. Some incredibly high percentage—perhaps 90 per cent—of our musical experiences today pass through loudspeakers. The sound of pop music is the sound of canned music. New concert halls are built to sound like stereo sets. Young performers try desperately to sound like their own recordings. Music is studied through records; printed music and music publications are no longer the main channels through which musical knowledge passes. Sound can be synthesized without the aid of any actual performers. Recording compaines select the music directors of our great orchestras. The only music publications for the general public are record magazines. Any sound that exists can be raw material for listening experience. The entire musical heritage of mankind as it exists is, in potential and increasingly in actuality, available; the esoteric experiences of yesterday are pop commonplaces of today. Music pursues us from elevator to airplane to shopping center, with an incredible information overload. For better or for worse, music and its relationship to our lives has changed drastically in little more than a decade or two.

Consciously or not, every musical artist is influenced by these realities, and the experience of the last few years suggests that there are two principal ways that composers have dealt with this situation: escapism or confrontation. There are several kinds of escapisms. One is that so-called conservatism, which attempts to continue with one or more of the older traditions of music. Another kind of escapism is that very current retreat from the buzzing, blooming confusion into a perfect, created, interior world. This often takes the form of abstraction, which is sometimes called minimalism: the gesture, the single experience occupying the entire universe. A closely related form is often called concept art: an idea in the singular carried out to its furthest logical extension or conclusion. Minimal and conceptual art are, in fact, a return to or an

9-105. Portrait of Eric Salzman, composer of electronic music for *The Peloponnesian War* (Nagrin), *Ecolog* (Cassen), and many more intermedia works.

extension of the notion of style in romantic and modern art. The view is from the hermit's cell: sackcloth and ashes. One rejects the universe, the functioning interaction of ecological units, in favor of the single, isolated, extended, ego-powered idea or event stripped—as an "experiment" or a self-indulgent denial—of its connections with other ideas or events.

Obviously, by "confrontation" I mean exactly the opposite: maximal instead of minimal, ecological instead of conceptual, humane instead of abstract, outgoing, rich, and engagé instead of inward, stripped, and self-indulgent. Such an art would be the true reaction to the romanticism and egotism of nineteenth- and twentieth-century art. It would be participatory, multilevel, multimedia, collaborative, and expressive of the human and social situation that gave it birth. This is the real meaning of the multimedia and music theatre forms now being born.

Any sound, any musical experience, is possible, available material. Traditions are nothing more than certain

Charlotte Moorman

C-143

C-144

C-145

C-146

C-147

C-148

C-149

C-150

C-151

C-152

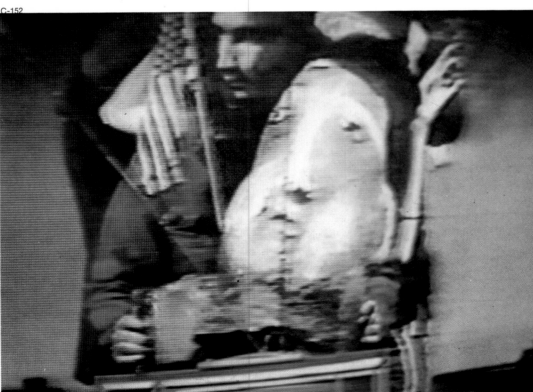

JACKIE CASSEN
ERIC SALZMAN
ERIC SIEGEL

C-153

C-154

C-155

C-156

C-157

C-158

specific kinds of experience commonly shared by larger or smaller groups of people. Any artistic statement is possible. You can do anything, and, surprisingly, that takes us back to an old insight: it isn't what you do, but what you do with it that counts.

The burden of romantic art and its stepchild, modern art, is imposing, egocentric, authoritarian, and non-humane. Some contemporary artists, with or without technology, would keep this view of art alive, with the result that many young people reject art altogether. But, contrary to the common opinion, a deeper understanding of contemporary life, including technology and media communications, can lead to a richer, more complex, more humane art. It will be an art not of fashion or of mode, but of concern, of involvement. It will involve interaction and feedback with its audience. It will speak to people and

their concerns and it will seek to reintegrate the art, so long divorced from reality, back into the fabric of our lives. Art and the artist will no longer be something apart; the new art will grow out of and express the conditions that gave it birth, and in that conjunction technology will assume exactly the significance it assumes in our everyday lives. Technology is not an end in itself, but it has already shown an incredible capacity for changing our heads, the nature of our lives, our experience, and even our society. It is also technology that offers us some of the best possibilities for an understanding of the nature of these changes, and this must be the principal role of the new artist and the new forms—media, multimedia, environmental art, participatory art, theater, music theater, whatever—that are being and must contiuue to be created.

(See also "Daniel Nagrin" in chapter 8.)

JACKIE

cassen

TELEVISION AND VIDEOTAPE ARTIST, NEW YORK CITY

I was using the art of light to create an atmosphere, or environment, of contemplation. Now I am using television —the most sophisticated possible medium—to do the same thing. Thomas Wilfred once said, "The Bach of the art of light is yet to be." He was hopeful in terms of the advancing sophistication of technology. I think that if he were alive today, he would see, in this technology, the evolution of a Bach coming about.

With the advance in technology, we have an increased responsibility, working through the medium of broadcast, to change our consciousness. We are at the beginnings of the realization of Teilhard de Chardin's ideas of the

growth of world consciousness. His basic philosophy was that the planet Earth, and all organic life, is a living entity in itself, as a whole. The new degree of evolution that has to come about involves the scheme of consciousness over the planet. Every individual cell mind, every spark of divinity (which is what we are) constitutes a world mind. What Chardin calls the Nuosphere. The advancement of the planet to a higher degree of consciousness is what is happening with us now.

One of the things we are trying to say in our use of television is: look here, these are some of the bad things

opposite
C-143. Title frame from the Jackie Cassen videotape program on the life of Charlotte Moorman, avant-garde cellist.

C-144. Charlotte Moorman during the shooting of the Jackie Cassen videotape of her life. Inserts on her bodice were achieved with Chroma Key switching to another camera.

C-145. Video superimposition of mother and grandmother on a portrait of Charlotte Moorman. Juxtaposition of psychic background with real-life response is implied.

C-146. Psychological portrait of Charlotte Moorman. Her portrait as an adult performer has been superimposed over a childhood portrait.

C-147. Abstract design created by Cassen by using a colorizer played through a Putney Synthesizer. Images on the screen can be modified ad infinitum.

C-148. Variation on a theme, by Cassen. Color video image was created abstractly with electronic image. Often the intensity and brightness of the colors are greater than those created through color videotape cameras.

C-149. Abstract image created by Jackie Cassen with color synthesizer.

C-150. Color videotape image created by Eric Siegel on a synthesizer developed by Siegel with the help of Howard Wise. The device enables the artist to modulate color, scale, and image definition at will during the actual performance. (Courtesy The Howard Wise Gallery. See also "Howard Wise" in chapter 2.)

C-151. Color videotape image created by Eric Siegel. He attracted attention of influential leaders in the art and technology movement, through important works such as War Trip, Einstein, Symphony of the Planets, and other videotape programs. (Courtesy The Howard Wise Gallery.)

C-152. Scene from finale of the Eric Salzman and Jackie Cassen videotape program Ecolog. A pâpier-maché sculpture of Lieutenant William Calley, seated above a television set, is wheeled into the visual field.

C-153. Opening scene from Ecolog, depicting horrors of the concentration camp and man's inhumanity to man.

C-154. Portrait of a live actor in Ecolog.

C-155. Black-and-white videotape image translated into color values with a colorizer, by Cassen. This device converts the varying values of a black-and-white videotape into vivid nonrepresentational colors.

C-156. Abstract image of Richard Nixon created through distorted uses of media sequence. From Ecolog. This scene was intermixed with scenes of sales of drug and soap products, as well as a sequence with a "hard-sell" religious presentation.

C-157. Sequence from Ecolog that parodies sale of drugs as being similar to political and religious presentations.

C-158. Religious "message" superimposed over television commercial promoting "Gary Cooper Week." From Ecolog.
(Cassen works shown courtesy Jackie Cassen.)

9-106. Portrait of Jackie Cassen in front of a light sculpture.

the medium has been used for. These are some of the indignities that have been put upon you by broadcast television. It's like a tank that has run you over. You've related to it only in a passive way. You've been overwhelmed by it. It's time that we fight back, that each person accept responsibility for this tremendous means of communication, this tremendous means of raising the level of thinking.

This is particularly true for the artist. What we are hoping to do—Eric Salzman and the group—is to advance the consciousness of the planet through broadcast by doing a real work of art. In the collaboration, the group's background is music. They were working with sound and action and movement. They wanted to get some light and some media into it. Over the course of months, we've developed some of the techniques used in *Ecolog*.

We came up with a theme of society in the context of television: a man is relating every night to television and so is his neighbor; how does that affect their relationship to each other?

I spent the next six weeks glued to the television every night. I taped everything I could off the air—the great mythological things that are happening to us. It's all mythology right there on television.

You can see how contemporary media is being used. We're choosing victims. We are making our arena, our sacrificial victims, our Roman trip happens right here in our living room. We choose a guy like Lieutenant Calley —we make him through the media—we need a victim, somebody to blame for our own guilt. So we take this guy and mock him up and then chop him down. Then we expiate our own guilt through Lieutenant Calley, right at home, right through the television set. This is another theme we're trying to get at in *Ecolog*. Here's this violence in the street. We're looking at it every night.

Compared to other media, tape has tremendous immediacy. You can put it into the hands of a child, and he can see what he's done and go on to do something better. A community group can learn to use the media almost immediately. Because of the simplicity and the immediacy, you can see what you've done, learn right away from your mistakes—and get a clear tape for a second time around.

I've been designing and building projectors; I've been building light sculptures. Each one is a thing unto itself. The first time I got inside a control room, that was it. Goodby everything. This is where I belong. Every artist belongs in television. That's where he can have the most impact. The gallery is over. The cassette and broadcast is "where it's at." Both industries have a responsibility to the artist, and to society through the artist. The artist has a responsibility to get himself in there and to get his work into the media.

(See *Charlotte Moorman* and *Ecolog,* color page 278.)

WOODY
vasulka
ELECTRONIC ARTIST, NEW YORK CITY

KRANZ. *How did you happen to get into the electronic world with your art form? Were you trained as a scientist or an artist?*

VASULKA. I was a movie-maker in Czechoslovakia—the Film School of Prague. Before that I was a writer. In film, the picture was too strong for me. I couldn't put any illusion into it. I was following straight documentary realism in a sociological sense—films on alcoholism, on the draft problem. I went to Iceland and did some typical geographical impressions, very straight documentary in the Flaherty tradition.

Then I got involved in multiscreen through a friend. Soon I was working with three screens, five screens, a very little single screen. Once, when we were faced with putting together about sixty viewing modules for an exhibit, I suggested television, because I thought that was a natural multiscreen. Actually, it was. We put together a system that was fifty-six modules, and six channels of different program distribution. Because the signal is flexible, it could be distributed, it could be multiplied, it could be activated into other media. Sounds could be translated into images. The flexibility is totally overwhelming.

In my experiments with film—as in 360-degree space recording—I never really built a projector, because that's when I realized that a motion-picture projector was nineteenth-century machinery. All those wheels and turns. The signal itself suddenly gave the freedom of space, in the sense that you could distribute or duplicate an image immediately. Our only limit, actually, is amplification. If you have more monitors, then you've got kinetics. You've got a moving image, from one to the other, so you get that enlarged space. The kinetic portion of the image is more important than the image itself. Then I finally got free, because I didn't have to follow any realistic concept. I got interesting effects. The whole gate to it was the signal.

KRANZ. *Do you, as an artist, feel that you are giving up a part of yourself by working so closely with these advanced electronical systems?*

VASULKA. First of all, I would say it's so vast, the electronic medium—not only television but the whole spectrum—that at first it just gets you. You don't know what to do with it. Then you select a fragment, and you go through that little section. Of course, behind that first wall

9-107. The author with Woody Vasulka at the Avant Garde Festival, Lexington Avenue Armory, New York City, November 1971. (Photograph by George Beker.)

there is another wall. You can go through in many ways. The thing to do is to allocate your piece of electronic reality, and work in that little piece—to limit yourself, and just work with one of them.

KRANZ. *So your answer is that instead of being a restricting thing, it is almost a limitless world for exploration?*

VASULKA. It is totally inexpressible how much you are offered by the media. It is so vast that everything written from the nineteenth-century on can never match it. You will find more stereotypes in literature—you can never match these stereotypes in electronics; it's incredible. It's as if all the history of man would suddenly stop, and start again with a universe that has never been explored. That kind of electronic universe is such a challenging thing— it would be loads of fun to try to do some documentaries.

9-108. Woody Vasulka videotape exhibit at the Avant Garde Festival, 1971. Multiple monitors were arranged in a circle. As spectators stood in the center of the circle, images passed from one monitor to the next to create an interesting visual environment. (Photograph by George Beker.)

9-109. General view of the Avant Garde Festival. Thousands of young spectators sampled the electronic wares. (Photograph by George Beker.)

ARTHUR
ginsberg

VIDEO FREE AMERICA, SAN FRANCISCO

The video screen of today is like the hearth of yesterday,
a source of personal and group enlightenment, very much
like the fire, only instead of giving out pure light,
it is giving out information.

There was a time when man's need for information was heat and light. He rose and slept and worked by amounts of light. His major need was to get the light and the heat so that he could work. We do that now pretty much by information. Consequently, what we've got in the video screen is the hearth of the future, and it can make good fires or bad fires. We can program intelligently and make it a source of enlightenment, or we can create information pollution.

Our thrust at Video Free America is to change television, to have it there to give information, feedback on what's happening, information for pleasure—not a huge political tool, but a source of personal and group enlightenment, a contact from group to group and place to place, very much like the hearth fire, only instead of giving out pure light, it is giving out information. That information can be anything from music to personal letters, to current events, to process tapes tracing human energies. There is a lot of beauty in process—it could be cooking, it could be anything. Process tapes tell a lot about ourselves—how we, as organisms, exist. When we shoot a process, we follow arms, we follow hands, we follow the motion of the energy. It's there, and looping. It's like a piece of music— you can go away and you can come back. It's there for your appreciation. We can make this thing give sense to our existence.

But that is a far cry from the present underground stance. Someone has said that, in the fifties, everyone in underground video would have been social workers, and in the sixties, they would have been in the Peace Corps. Do-gooding, save the world, join up with something, but don't break my camera!

That political trip is not really where it's at. Creating an information hearth, preventing information pollution, putting visual thoughts into the environment—that, to me, is where it can be.

So we are for changing television by creating a new kind of television and new forms for it. We are not talking about newspapers, or writing, or lecturing. We are talking about making as many kinds of tapes as possible, about mixes, about being able to just pour it back. That's where the group comes in. We work independently, and we work together. We all do something for the group; one

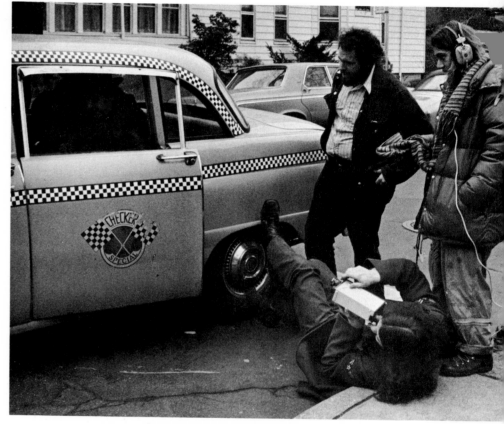

9-110. Arthur Ginsberg (striped shirt) on location for Video Free America, with crew Skip Sweeney (with camera) and sound man Schulman (with microphone). (Photograph by Alan B. Tepper.) (All illustrations courtesy Video Free America.)

does most of the administrative work, another most of the production technical work, another the fund raising. We are not tied together by anything but a need for each other. That is the structure, the key to any momentum or whatever success we are having.

There is a standard world-wide media structure, it's a ripoff. It leaves the subject of an interview bewildered by an irrelevant, or even alienating process. Most interviews are not in depth. The interviewers ask preplanned questions. They don't look you in the eye because they are thinking ahead to the next question. What they are interested in is the product of the words—am I getting what I am after? They ask. You answer. They take away the information and edit it. You never see what has been edited. Someone sees and hears you on television. The most important things were not said. *continued*

9-111. Scene from Video Free America production *The Continuing Story of Carel and Ferd.*

Our idea is to take that process—the media process of extending yourself through artificial means—and make it meaningful to the subject. We are into that when we point a camera. Because of video tape, we can roll and roll, and it is relatively cheap.

So we just rap. We are responding to the person, and the experience for them is an enjoyable conversation in which they participate equally. We also do playbacks. We are organically part of it. We take the time and the care to interview in a genuinely human situation.

This is the way it worked in our tape on the International Frisbee Contest in Berkeley, that documentary on a seemingly frivolous subject, which came through as a comment on our culture. First of all, there was no differentiation

between us and the people there. We all throw frisbees, and we enjoy it. Before the interview started we told them who we were and what Video Free America is all about. We explained the technology to them, so they were not bewildered by it. They immediately picked up what we were doing, and they responded.

Then that night we were invited to a party. We went, and shared three hours of the tapes with them. That's the difference from most uses of the media. It's the style. It's the ambience. We don't claim to do accurate reporting. We claim to be human.

Another way that we are trying to change the medium is by plugging video into events—not just recording an event. It's being with it, taking groups who are making

9-112. Scene from *Abraham and Isaac* by John Argue.

9-113B. Video feedback image by Skip Sweeney.

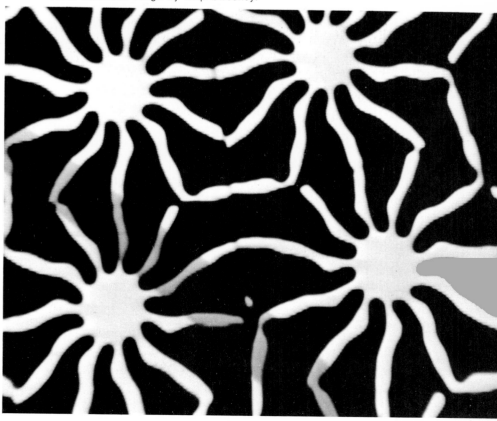

9-113A. Video feedback image created by Skip Sweeney.

9-114A. Scene from *Kaddish*. Video images by Arthur Ginsberg. The video image is live as the actors perform. The audience experiences both live stage performance with live television. (Photograph by Anthony Pepitone.)

9-114B. Scene from *Kaddish*. Note how the facial expression of the actor is reinforced with the large multiple video images. (Photograph by Anthony Pepitone.)

statements or doing their thing and plugging video into it very organically. This requires some thoughtful technology . . . monitors in the environment where they can see them, mikes that move around, rather than a studio situation. We are getting into miking cameras. A mike goes with a camera. It creates a different style of production. Mix the mike and the camera. When you are working spontaneously you don't get a smooth, packaged, programmed event. But that doesn't spoil the content, or all those delightful things that happen because of the chances.

Another thing that we are doing is making visual music. Stereo and hi fi have made most people able to go along with music in a scholarly way. There is no counterpart in visuality: that is still for the most part in museums. So what's going to happen is visual literacy. You will have favorite musicians, and favorite "videoists." With the synthesizer and our other technology, we are trying to find forms. This is Skip Sweeney's specialty—Skip is the most creative person with technology I've met, especially for feedback of sensibility, intricacy, and complexity.

We want to change television by taking the economic albatross off—to achieve the fast movement of information on a low economic scale. This has to be done with craft. Just because it is cheap, and just because it is underground, it does not have to be dull or slipshod. It needs a whole new craft—the shooting style responding to a situation, turning it on and letting it roll.

Perhaps videotape is the precursor of the time machine. People are getting used to seeing themselves displaced in time and space on television. They will get used to seeing themselves displaced without the separation of the film going off to be developed and returned. Play it back. There I am. It's an image. It's electrons—but what are you but just that, electrons?

9-114C. Scene from *Kaddish*. (Photograph by Anthony Pepitone.)

VIDEO
FREE
AMERICA

1948
FELL ST.
SAN
FRANCISCO
CALIF.
94117

(415) 387-5972

9-115. Video Free America brochure.

10 the preservation of the artifacts

It is inevitable that any new movement in the arts would turn to some form of preserving the artifacts of its existence. This seems fundamental to the human condition. There is no indication that the intermedia artist is above this vanity.

The basic problem with intermedia art is the expense of mounting the exhibit. Every aspect is expensive. Even still photography costs are high. Multiprojection systems are high. When the artist integrates film or videotape into the performance, costs mount up. When film is run continuously for an eight-hour day over several months, or even a year, as at Expo '67, great expenses occur in the maintenance of performances after the initial opening.

Many intermedia performances include a number of imaging sources. With all the effort that goes into producing the exhibit, the progenitors want some viable record of the experience.

And so the intermedia artist has gone to the museum to find space for his work, since educational institutions have limited facilities and only a few artists with outstanding credentials are accepted for showings at the great World Fairs. It is logical that the museum would become a focal point for the intermedia exhibition.

Changes in the Traditional Museum

The traditional museum has been a residual depository for our "great natural heritage." This needs no defense. The museum has preserved materials that represent our knowledge of the exploration of man's adventure in civilization. No argument can be mounted that would seriously challenge the importance of the major museum collections for social history.

In the second half of the twentieth century, however, it has become increasingly difficult to disseminate the museums' works of art. The ratio between exhibited art and stored art has become more and more imbalanced— a true challenge to the enlightened museum director.

Henry Geldzahler

Henry Geldzahler, as curator of Contemporary Art at the Metropolitan Museum of Art in New York City, is one of the most influential men in American arts and letters. His career has been remarkable in that he has been largely responsible for recognition of American artists by a Museum that formerly was noted for its conservative stance in terms of living artists. Historically, the Metropolitan Museum of Art featured its distinguished collection embracing the entire history of the arts. If a collection represents man's cultural refinement over a flowering of five thousand years, it is not surprising that curators and administrators for this collection might ignore one or two decades of the most recent art styles.

Largely as a result of his own efforts, Geldzahler began to bring an important change into the Metropolitan Museum scene. He gave strong support to a collection of the best works of contemporary American artists. He was, no doubt, aided in his efforts by the flowering of American painting after World War II. With the advent of Abstract Expressionism as a style in this country, American painting for the first time, began to influence the development of painting in Europe and Asia, rather than the reverse, which had been the case for our first two hundred years.

Geldzahler exerted another influence as well. He began to write and lecture extensively. His books, articles, and papers, coupled with personal appearances at art schools, cultural events, and important social occasions, spread his influence immensely. Coupled with these activities, he took an "activist" stance in relationship to young contemporary artists. He visited their studios, talked with their friends, and even became a subject of their art work. For example, George Segal, interviewed in an earlier chapter of this book, made Geldzahler himself a subject for one of his unique sculptures.

In my interview with Mr. Geldzahler he was frank about his strong reservations concerning the results, so far, from the collaboration between artists, scientists, and engineers. At the same time he has been an early champion of their right to experiment. His comments in this chapter add an important dimension to the concerns of many critics as to the ultimate worth or importance of art wedded to technology.

Allon Schoener

Thomas Hoving, director of The Metropolitan Museum of Art, has made serious efforts to reach a broader segment of the public with the museum's collection. Enormous values prohibit the physical transportation of many works, and the traditional medium of prints and photographs has lost some of its visual impact when compared to the newer medium of television.

In recent years the Metropolitan Museum has begun to reflect the more avant-garde imaging techniques developed by the intermedia artists. It was not without some real trauma that Hoving was able to convince his board of trustees that he saw value in mounting the major multi-media exhibition *Harlem on my Mind,* under the direction of Allon Schoener. In spite of the political and social undercurrents of its opening, it proved to be one of the most popular exhibits ever displayed at the Metropolitan. In this exhibit, and the now-famous one about the Lower East Side of the Jewish Museum, Schoener utilized the full iconography of multimedia. In terms of the preservation of the artifacts, however, it is somewhat sad to realize that both exhibits have been preserved only in print form rather than in some media-based form.

Moma and The Brooklyn Museum E.A.T. shows

It is not surprising that the Museum of Modern Art has been directly involved in a number of special exhibits reflecting the growing interest in environmental art. A recent joint exhibit at the Museum of Modern Art (MOMA) and the Brooklyn Museum was indicative of the readiness in museum circles to provide a stage for the media-based artists.

The exhibit, entitled *The Machine as Seen at the End of the Machine Age,* mounted by the Museum of Modern Art, and the simultaneous presentation of *Experiments in Art and Technology* by The Brooklyn Museum of Art indicate the readiness in museum circles to provide a stage for the media-based artists. Not only did the Museum of Modern Art's exhibit reflect the history of the intermedia movement, but the Brooklyn Museum of Art show brought to the attention of the public several hundred individual works of art created in direct collaboration by engineers and artists. This exhibition was sponsored and mounted by the E.A.T. organization in New York under the direction of Dr. Billy Klüver. It was followed several months later with a series of six environments called *Spaces.*

Peter Poole and Ralph Flynn

Poole and Flynn were part of the original group of modestly-financed hard-working young believers in the early struggling days of E.A.T., discussed in chapter 5. In the interview section of the present chapter they comment on the Moma and Brooklyn Museum shows and the striking advance and acceptance of works resulting from the collaboration of artists and engineers.

Finch College Museum of Art

Elayne Varian

Every movement needs its own David Henry Kahweiler, who opened a gallery in Paris in 1907 where he sponsored the early works of Braque, Picasso, Laurencin, and Gris. Although Elayne Varian, director and curator of the Contemporary Wing at Finch College Museum of Art, would deny this parallel, she richly deserves such recognition. During the sixties, as the new media movement was gathering steam, and now in the seventies, she held one exhibit after another that reflected the preoccupations of this generation of young artists. Her museum is small, understaffed, and underfinanced, but somehow she manages to come up with exciting exhibits. Perhaps her work in the museum field and Howard Wise's in the private gallery domain were the two most important influences in the development of young artists concerned with the media and the message.

The New Museum: The Museum of the Media

Stephen Globus/Ronald Globus/Richard Globus

We have seen a trend that will undoubtedly gather momentum. In terms of the traditional museum, an interesting group of artists has banded together to form the Museum of the Media. The brothers Stephen, Ronald, and Richard Globus, along with several filmmakers and photographers, have been granted a charter by New York State for a publicly and privately supported museum that is essentially media based. The Globus brothers conceive of the museum as a disseminator of public multimedia exhibits in the form of a series of modular projection units. These self-contained modules have an eight-by-eight-foot screen and a motion-picture projector for films prepared by the museum. The units are designed to be transported, and the programming will be updated.

The conception is that any public area could have at least one of the modules and, presumably, for an environmental experience, three as a minimum. The three would then project thematic images reflecting the concerns of the creative personnel of the museum.

Several remarkable conceptions have had a confluence here: first, that the museum should be media based; second, that it should disseminate its information in modular transfer units; third, that it can be used in one or, more desirably, two units. If ten or fifteen modules are employed, however, a multimedia field of 360 degrees can be created to envelop the spectator in the illusion.

A fourth aspect is that this would be a museum without walls, reaching out to the public where it congregates—in a park, a shopping center, a student gathering place in a high school, college, or university, since it is transportable and relatively inexpensive to maintain. A fifth conception is that ultimately the most advanced photographic and image-making techniques will be available to the museum, along with already-promised computer-animation facilities.

The philosophy of the Museum of the Media is humanist in orientation. It attempts to recreate the concept of a world tribal village through an easily transportable museum. Perhaps it is the answer to some of the basic objections to today's museums.

Interviews

Interviews with the personalities discussed in this chapter follow. Photographs illustrate the subject matter of the interview and the theme of the chapter.

HENRY
geldzahler

CURATOR, TWENTIETH-CENTURY ART, THE METROPOLITAN MUSEUM OF ART, NEW YORK CITY

KRANZ. *In the last decade, artists, scientists, and engineers have decided to use contemporary technology to create new works of art. What is your opinion of this movement? Is it a significant development in American art?*

GELDZAHLER. I don't doubt the sincerity of anybody involved in it, but I do doubt the quality of the product, so far anyway. My interest in art is not so much in the process as in the product. The only way that I can judge the significance or effectiveness of a movement is by the work that is produced. I've seen, I think, quite a bit of the art and technology marriage, and, so far, I don't think the progeny is of enormous interest; and I almost doubt whether that's the way art that has lasting value gets produced. Theoretically, the idea is interesting: to get scientists, in touch with technology, together with artists whose minds are open and ready to move; but the association can only work if there's genius involved. It's not a matter of hard work or high intelligence, rather of making a leap, and no one can predict where the next leap is going to come from. The only thing we can do is to hope that we'll be alert enough to recognize it when the leap is made. From all I have seen of the art and technology relationship, the leap hasn't been made yet.

Let me give you a couple of examples of things I've liked, though, now that I've said that it hasn't changed the direction of art. Robert Whitman, with his laser sculpture, has done some interesting pieces at the old Pace Gallery. And I think Bruce Nauman, with his holograph and other advanced visual technology, has done work that comes closer to grabbing my attention than the other things I've seen. People often ask how you decide whether a work of art is worthwhile or not. There's no rule of thumb, but there are a couple of things that help, I think—help me, anyway. One of the key ones is memorability. If I think about it when I'm not in front of it—if it comes up in my imagination from time to time, then it probably interests me enormously. I can say that about Nauman's work but about very little else.

KRANZ. *I would like to explore your point that high intelligence and interest can't guarantee genius . . .*

GELDZAHLER. Anything short of that is craftsmanship, which is interesting but doesn't change anything.

KRANZ. *There have been some serious collaborative ef-*

10-1. Portrait of Henry Geldzahler. (Courtesy The Metropolitan Museum of Art.)

forts—for example, Billy Klüver and Robert Rauschenberg got together and did a thing called Oracle, *which may or may not be called art, but it was the attempt of two very intelligent people to do a collaborative work. Would you give your reactions to it?*

GELDZAHLER. Well, *Oracle* couldn't have been made without Billy Klüver's help. It ended up looking and acting and behaving like a Rauschenberg that had been in touch with advanced technology, but still a Rauschenberg not radically different from the matrix of the work in which it was imbedded.

I'd like to clear up my credentials, for a moment, in the art and technology movement. Between 1967 and 1970, I was program director for Visual Arts in Washington, the National Endowment. While I was there, I shepherded a $50,000 grant through to the art and technology movement, to Billy Klüver, so I'm willing to give it every possible chance, and not to write it off. But I'm still waiting.

KRANZ. *Rubens used quite a strong collaboration to complete some of his monumental paintings. Do you feel that this is a legitimate way for an art form to evolve?*

GELDZAHLER. He was pretty lucky in his helpers—Van Dyck and some of the best painters of the next generation. They were working on the same order of experience as he was. They were turning oil paint into Flemish expression. It's a different thing than expecting people from two such different disciplines to get together. I think the artist is bounded only by his imagination, and not by lack of technology. That's where the real progress is made, in the artist daring to go beyond what he feels comfortable with into something that he learns how to control on his own. And I don't think that it's technical problems that stop him. I think it's being frozen by his own experience, and by society, that clogs the progress. Here's another aspect, too: there are an awful lot of groups now that are producing art together. I find the same thing there—art by committee is not better than art by an individual.

ALLON

schoener

VISUAL ARTS DIRECTOR, NEW YORK STATE COUNCIL ON THE ARTS, NEW YORK CITY

Allon Schoener's interest in art history began in college and progressed through graduate study at Courtauld Institute, University of London, to a master's degree in the subject at Yale University. His views of the role of today's museum are solidly grounded in his training.

In discussing his use of films, slides, and tape recorders in his Lower East Side exhibit at The Jewish Museum (and later in *Harlem on My Mind* at the Metropolitan Museum of Art) Schoener commented:

As an art historian I learned that art is always different in each historical period. The idea of art for art's sake is essentially a late-nineteenth-century development. Different conditions rule today. For art to be a revered and precious commodity in our society does not have the validity that it did seventy-five years ago. I consciously look for art situations that will involve people.

The popular trend is to criticize museums for being out of touch with society. I believe that museums do have social value. It is related to the way that they will adapt to modern communications technology. With their vast resources, museums can become, in a sense, public-communication centers. They have the potential of being converted into something beneficial, which can be updated and practical. If I were asked to evaluate the state of museums in our society, I would say that they are very much out of phase with what is happening.

For a museum curator today, the best kind of training that he could get is working in a television studio. Television is a basic thing in our lives. If you are going to be involved in communication, you must understand the techniques of communication.

In all truth, it should be said that neither the equipment nor the approach was novel. The same kind of equipment has been used in trade shows and sales meetings. This is what was different: I wrote a script that grew out of my training in art history, my experience in television, and in producing exhibitions. My concept involves truth to the subject through the use of historical materials. Nothing that I did was fabricated; I simply edited actual data. For the Lower East Side show, we made a film from letters that appeared in *The Daily Forward,* a Yiddish-language newspaper published in New York City. People loved Zero Mostel reading the letters. The photographs were documentary, the film footage was documentary. Everything that I have ever used has been documentary material.

The exhibit was planned as a forty-minute experience; there was, however, much more information in the galleries than anyone could absorb in that period of time. A lot of the information was detailed and specific. You had the choice of spending forty minutes and getting the essence, or you could spend more time and get more detail. Most of all, I wanted to use the exhibition as a catalytic agent that would stimulate people to think about the subject, once they had come to the museum.

10-2. Allon Schoener seated in front of an 1817 Erie Canal poster in his office at the New York State Council on the Arts.

"This is the age of electronic communication. Like everything else in our lives, museums are being revolutionized by it. Communications—indirect experience—is emerging as their chief function. In the near future, exhibition galleries will be converted into electronic theatres and art museums will operate as electronic communication centers from which verbal and visual information will be transmitted by a variety of media. The museum's concern with communication has increased in relation to the pressure for more information from our rapidly expanding population. During the nineteenth century, museums served primarily as depositories for collections. Recently museum programs have changed. Although there is still stress on building collections, this is not considered to be the museum's sole function. Interpretation—verbal and visual communication—has emerged as a major concern. Exhibitions, publications, and educational programs have achieved equivalence with collections. Nothing will substitute for the direct experience of going through an exhibition in a gallery. Exhibitions are a communications environment in which information is directed toward the gallery visitor. With multimedia exhibitions it is possible to generate a level of supersaturated information content. More information can be directed toward an individual in such an exhibition than is possible with any other technique."
(Taken from *Electronic Museum Theatre* by Allon Schoener.)

Yes, it was a communication-overload situation. People were not supposed to absorb all of it. It would have taken three or four hours to stop and read everything, to look at everything, to get all the details. Every day we travel through information environments; as a result, we collect the data we need and can digest. My exhibitions have been planned to simulate a trip down the street. I created a story line, and people got different things from it, depending on their experience and what they brought to it. I remember one Sunday morning seeing a grandmother, who must have been in her sixties, pointing out a picture that Jacob Riis did of an airshaft with a washtub hanging in it, and saying to her grandson: "That's the kind of a tub I used to take a bath in." Here was a case of a viewer being able to make a connection between her life experience and the exhibit and communicate it to her grandson.

Beyond this, the exhibit became a social center. People who hadn't seen each other in twenty or thirty years were greeting each other, talking to each other, so that the exhibition as a scene in itself became something like a Lower East Side street of that time. It brought out people and their relationships to each other.

10-3. Crowds waiting to enter the Jewish Museum for the *Lower East Side: Portal to American Life* exhibit. (Courtesy Allon Schoener; photographer, Peter Moore.)

10-4. Crowds merge with the photographs and relate to them by discussing them and touching them. (Courtesy Allon Schoener, photographer, Peter Moore.)

10-5. This exhibition at the Jewish Museum, in October 1966, started a whole tradition of new-form exhibitions by traditional museums. The popularity of the exhibit received widespread notice in the media. (Courtesy Allon Schoener; photographer, Peter Moore.)

10-6. *Harlem on My Mind* exhibition at The Metropolitan Museum of Art. The gallery of the 1920's demonstrates mixture of fixed images (photographs) and sound that emanates from the large black structure hanging from the ceiling. (Courtesy Allon Schoener.)

10-7. *Harlem on My Mind* exhibition at The Metropolitan Museum of Art. Gallery for the 1960's consisted of nine slide screens, one screen for each year of the decade through 1968. The audio was a mix of documentary voices and music. The room was designed so that visitors felt themselves merging into the visual atmosphere created by the large screens. (Courtesy, Allon Schoener.)

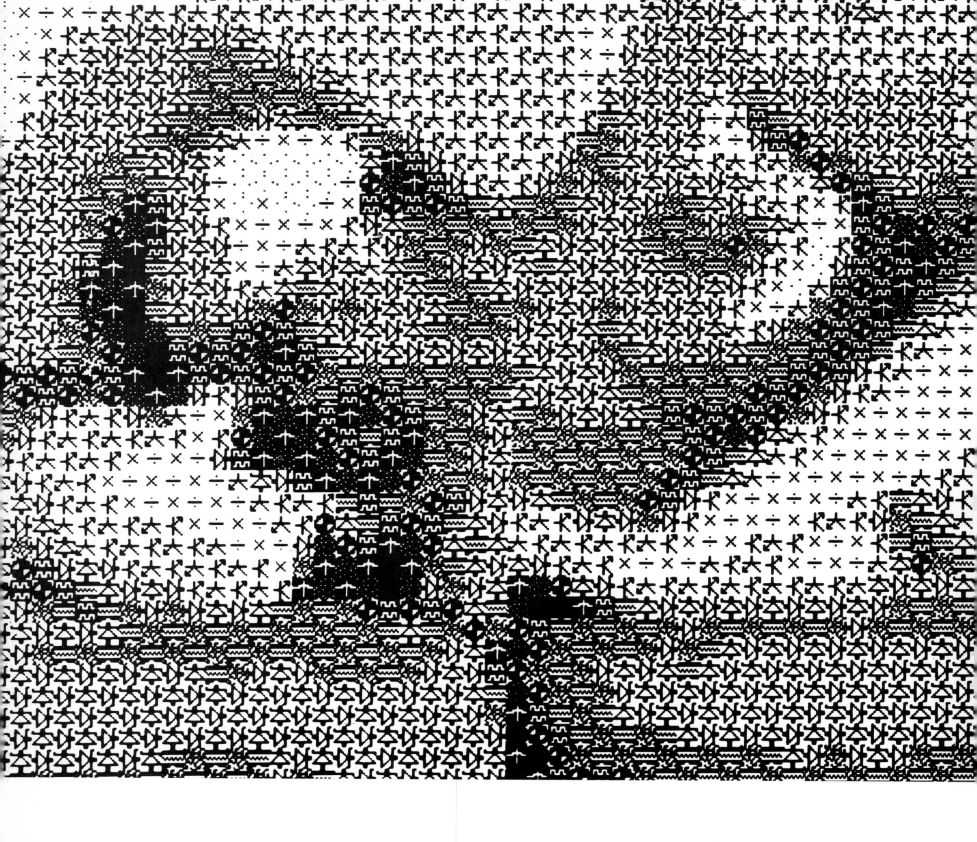

Moma and The Brooklyn Museum E.A.T. Shows

The Machine As Seen At The End Of The Machine Age

Comments by Peter Poole and Ralph Flynn,
E.A.T. staff members.

POOLE. We co-sponsored a competition with the Museum of Modern Art. Our competition was for collaborations only, but the whole competition was open for pieces that involved some kind of modern technology. Out of the total entry of about 180 pieces, ninety were the product of collaboration. MOMA chose nine for their exhibit of the *Machine,* using their usual criteria, mostly aesthetic.

In the E.A.T. competition, the collaborations were judged entirely on their technological merit by scientists and engineers. Most of them just judged the works on their technical merits. The prize went to the engineer, not the artist.

KRANZ. *Don't you think that this is perhaps the basic dichotomy in the attempt to get the artist and the engineer together—you might say that the Museum of Modern Art selecting the aesthetics of the machine, and the engineers selecting the functional aspect of it, implies a schism . . .*

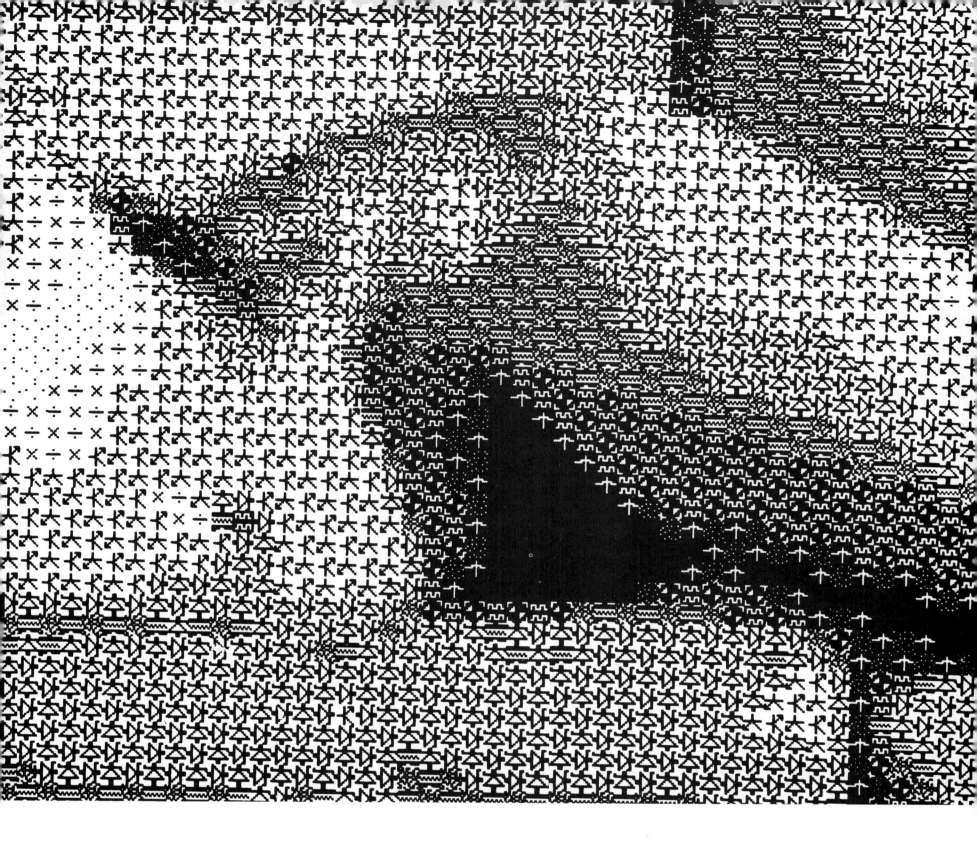

POOLE. It implies that there are two different ways of looking at the same object.

FLYNN. The major success is the fact that the collaboration was done at all, the fact that we have 130 excellent pieces—ninety or so, wouldn't you say, in collaboration. And the pieces we've seen are—well, I can't say they are aesthetically fantastic, but they're exciting and they are technically interesting and a lot of work was involved between the artist and the engineer. Communications went on and a lot of questions and answers took place between the two before they could reach a final piece of work, and I think that that is one of the most important things. Whether we have it at MOMA, The Brooklyn Museum, or whether we have it on the street, the fact that people see it and that this exists and that it does work—the collaboration works. That's the important thing that we are stimulating—this collaboration.

10-8. *Study in Perception 1,* a pointillistic, computer-generated picture created for the cover of The Brooklyn Museum *Experiments in Art and Technology* exhibition catalog by Bell Laboratories scientists Ken Knowlton and Leon Harmon, June 1969. Procedure is described overleaf. (Courtesy Bell Laboratories, Murray Hill, New Jersey.)

10-9. Knowlton and Harmon explain *Study in Perception I.* (Courtesy Bell Laboratories.) (E.A.T. exhibit pieces are shown here and on following pages.)

A 35 mm transparency of a photograph is scanned by a flying-spot scanner, and the resultant electrical signals are converted into numerical representations on magnetic tape.
The first step taken by the computer is to fragment the picture into rows and fragments per row, and the average brightness level of each fragment is computed. The brightness levels are encoded, and the picture is now represented by numbers, each of which represents a small area having one possible brightness value.

Instead of sprinkling black dots randomly in the proportion called for by any given brightness level, the dots are organized into micropatterns (e.g., a cat, an umbrella), which can be seen at close range. For each brightness level, the computer makes a random choice among the predetermined set of micropatterns that fits that level. The picture is produced on frames of microfilm by a microfilm printer and then photographed.

10-10. Tall plastic environment at the *Experiments in Art and Technology* exhibit at The Brooklyn Museum.

10-11. Close-up of the plastic environment.

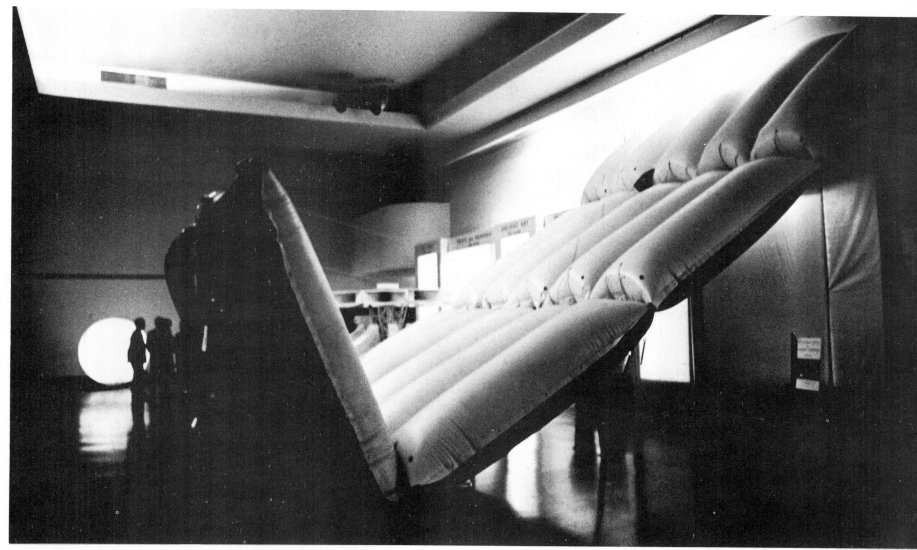

10-12. *Double skin structure—1.* Yukihisa Isobe and Masanori Oe—1968.

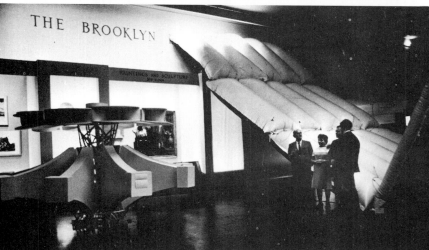

10-13. USCO Loudspeakers—1968. Seven feet high, 13 feet in diameter. Jack Weisberg.

In this two-channel horn-loaded sound system, the bottom group of horns handles all frequencies up to 140 HZ per second and the top group handles all frequencies above that. At 140 HZ each handles equal energy. The brass horns, pointing inward, dynamically load each other, resulting in a horn effectively nine times bigger than each separate horn. Because of the configuration, the radiation angle is 360 degrees. The horn loading creates a very efficient loudspeaker, and this efficiency reduces cone excursion, resulting in low nonlinearity and extremely good transient response.

10-14. *Fakir in ¾-time*—1968. Lucy J. Young and Neils O. Young.

A motor-driven loop of textile tape that remains rigid in motion, like the loop of a lariat, soared like a Brancusi bird, twisted into an amoebic band, and wheeled into an ellipse as it was manipulated by its engineer, Neils O. Young.
The principle is the same as that of the lariat. In the lariat, a loop of cord remains rigid and can even bounce off obstructions, due to the motion of the cord itself. Here, instead of being swung at the end of a tether, the loop is propelled along itself at 100 mph by means of an electric motor and sheave.

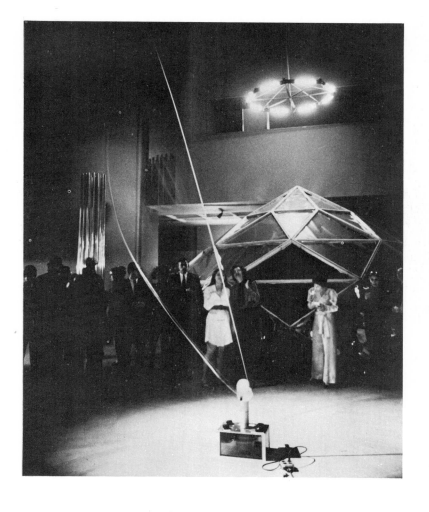

10-15. Ralph K. Morrill's sculpture *YAHWEH 13, 1968,* at the Brooklyn Museum Experiments in Art and Technology show *Some More Beginnings.* It was made in collaboration with Norton Wise.

Aluminum, bicycle wheels, motor, battery, tape-recorders, loudspeaker, amplifier, electric lights—when activated by sound, the sculpture moves in a slow, regular circle. In order to read the words written on the inner drum, the participant is forced to walk backward in the circle. Lights shine in his eyes. Anything said is recorded for three seconds and played back greatly amplified with interjected laughter and comments.

10-16B. View of the environment's interior, with rotating sculptured columns.

10-16C. Environmental participants.

10-16A. Reflective environment at the E.A.T. exhibition opening, The Brooklyn Museum. Couple preparing to cover themselves with reflective foil.

10-17. Two objects of vinyl and vinyl tubing, developed by Sheila Berkley and Graydon Cairl in 1968, change their shape and color while moving on a platform.

One object expands and contracts in various time sequences; the other expands and contracts by means of water circulating in vinyl tubes. The platform, a plexiglass case, contains a revolving device with long magnetic arms that move the objects along the platform.

10-18. Conveyor-belt system by Royce Dendler—1968. This walk moves at twenty-five feet per minute and will hold up to five people at one time.

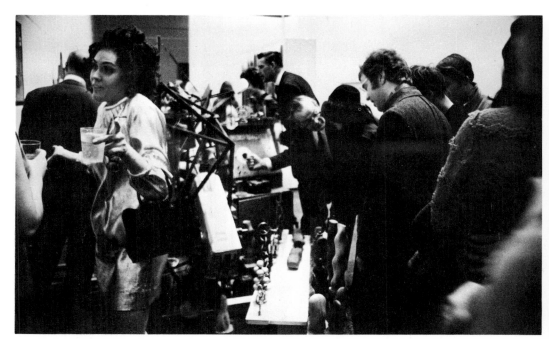

10-19. General view of the spectators at The Brooklyn Museum E.A.T. exhibition.

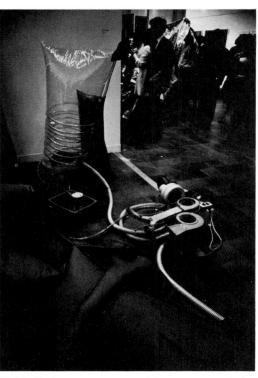

10-20. Environment supported by compressed air.

10-21. *Orbiter*—1968. Metal, wood, styrofoam, modeling paste, and motor. Constructed by Arthur Hoener and Leon Wilde.

A small sphere moves in a number of loops about the center of the sculpture, passing through the tunnel in the large sphere after each loop. A complete cycle of thirteen distinct loops is made in a period of about two minutes, with the loop position continually shifting in increments of approximately 110 degrees. Both the large and small spheres rotate about their own axes. Each time the small sphere emerges from the tunnel, it has rotated approximately twenty degrees. All motions are synchronized, using precision gearing and miniature roller chain drives.

10-22. *First Tighten Up on the Drums*—1968. Device by Norman T. White and Charles J. Grandmaison. Perspex sheeting, neon lights, and electronics.

A perspex panel contains hexagonally arranged neon lights, which flash in a repeating sequence, moving rhythmically across the panel. The rhythm will be imposed on an otherwise uniformly shifting pattern by variations in the shift velocity. The piece, which presents a superficially confusing mosaic of flashing lights, in time is perceived as a set of interacting patterns.

10-21

10-22

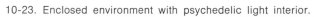

10-23. Enclosed environment with psychedelic light interior.

10-24. Spectator enveloped in projected environment.

10-25. Device by John Harris and Dr. Fred Stern—1968. Observer can activate blower and high-intensity light.

The basic structure consists of two silvered Plexiglas hemispheres, six feet and three feet in diameter. The hemispheres are suspended by thin wires and between them are two eighteen-inch silvered hair-dryer headpieces, which emit a stream of warm or cold air. The control circuitry and blower are enclosed above the device. A tape switch under the foam mat randomly activates the blower and a high-intensity light when an observer stands between the two hemispheres.

THE BROOKLYN MUSEUM E.A.T. SHOW   303

10-26. *Speak That I May See*—1968. Roberta Phillips and Capthorne Mac-Donald. Plaster cast of woman, seated, with cathode ray tube (as face), magnetic tape loop, driver amplifiers.

The face of this plaster and electronic sculpture, in the form of a life-sized seated nude woman, is a cathode ray tube. The time-varying wave forms present in recorded stereophonic music are used to generate patterns that appear simultaneously on this tube. A tape-loop cartridge stores the information, giving a continuous presentation that is repeated every fifteen minutes.

(Photographs of E.A.T. exhibited works courtesy E.A.T. and The Brooklyn Museum.)

ELAYNE

varian

CURATOR, THE FINCH COLLEGE MUSEUM OF ART, CONTEMPORARY WING, NEW YORK CITY

The gallery as platform for artists working with electronic media.

Artists are no longer obliged to observe traditional categories. They are now into everything that has been created —they don't have to use paint, a slab of marble, or any other specific material. There's a whole new world of media available, and anything the artist wants he takes and uses as he likes.

I think it is great. I watch what they are doing. I go to artists' studios, I find out what they are into. I work from that. I found that a number of artists were involved with videotape. They like the immediacy of it; they like the fact that they can make corrections instantly—while they are working. It is also less expensive than film. They find it exciting.

And so, at the end of about a year, I decided to have a Videotape Performance Exhibition. We had ten performances here at the museum. I included in the show the tapes made under a grant of the Boston Philharmonic Orchestra, and tapes from the West Coast, to broaden the scope and not have just an East-Coast show.

My interest in holographic techniques for art grow out of a show, primarily from the standpoint of the scientist, that I saw when I was at Cranbrook Academy to give a

10-27. Elayne Varian at the exhibition *Artists' Videotape Performances,* which she organized at the Finch College Museum of Art. (All photographs courtesy Elayne Varian.)

lecture. I thought that, from the standpoint of the artist, the hologram would have a tremendous use. I asked some artists in Detroit if they were interested. They were. Under the direction of a scientist, who gave them technical advice, they went to work. The artists would go to the studio where the scientist was working and see the method. Then they would think of something that they wanted to portray in this manner.

One of the artists came with fifteen dozen eggs and did two holograms with eggs that went on into infinity. You looked into this, and it went deep, deep, deep—way back of all those eggs. Robert Indiana, being involved for so many years with the word LOVE, did a LOVE hologram. There were many. What I did was to involve the artists in this form. The excitement and creativity were theirs.

I was interested for another reason—holograms as a way to record art history. You could do a whole period of history on one plate. The scientist was going to do this for me for the show, but it was too expensive. Wouldn't it be marvelous to see on one plate all the pictures of a specific era? You could see them by just turning your head slightly. It has endless possibilities that haven't been explored.

Film is also an art form. I can't say that it has always been so, or that Hollywood has always made movies that I would consider an art form, but certainly the artists have used it as an art form. In my show *Projected Art* I had experimental films from the twenties. The artists at that time—Moholy-Nagy and Hans Richter and others—were doing experimental things in surrealism. I was also showing the underground films of the sixties. To see them and find them you had to go to the artists' studios or some little cafe. I spent hours and hours looking at perfectly awful films, which I think could be termed "home movies," in order to find some really great films.

In the *Projected Art* show, we had Stan VanDerBeek's movie mural in the other gallery—twenty or more projectors in that one room. It was exciting, and all of the moment.

Robert Whitman and Andy Warhol were in those early shows. They have expanded their distinguished careers. Both are in our present videotape show. I discovered that Andy Warhol was working in videotape when I went to his studio looking for some of his early films to illustrate two lectures I gave at New York University. I found to my distress that most of Andy's films don't exist. There are no prints of them; parts of the originals are lost. It is a pity, because his films of the sixties were a great epic of the decade.

So, you see, it depends on the artist and how he uses

10-31. Scene from experimental television project produced by station WGBH-TV in Boston with the Boston Symphony Orchestra. Tsai Wen-Ying, Stan VanDerBeek, Constantine Manos, Douglas Davis, Jackie Cassen, Russell Connor, James Seawright, Mimi Garrard, and Nam June Paik developed sequences for this color videotape.

10-28. Peter Campus videotape from his *Dynamic Vision Series, Field #9*, shown at the *Artists' Videotape Performances* exhibit.

10-29. Mrs. Varian with her assistant, Mindy Duitz, at the Dan Graham videotape performance.

10-30. Dan Graham practicing electronic hypnotism at the *Artists' Videotape Performances* exhibition.

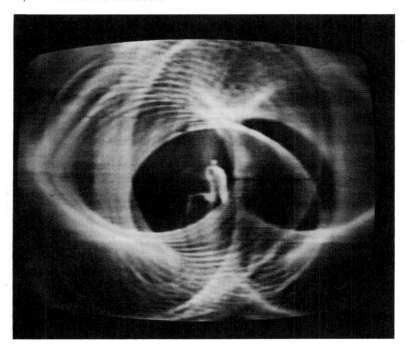

the media. If you let the media use you, it is not creative. But if you are the one who decides what you want and how to use it, then it will be a creative act.

Some critics say that technology can't be art. Critics are not always able to judge what is art, right now. They put down things in the beginning. It takes them a while to get used to it. This has been going on as long as there have been art critics. Remember the Armory Show of 1913, how that was condemned? Nearly all those artists are among the most important artists of today.

10-32. Photographer setting up at the Finch College Museum of Art. (Photograph by Mindy Duitz.)

10-33. One of the weary moments that comes before or after any intermedia performance. (Photograph by Mindy Duitz.)

10-34. Scene at the exhibition. (Photograph by Mindy Duitz.)

10-35A, B. Videotape images from the Dan Graham performance. (Photograph by Mindy Duitz.)

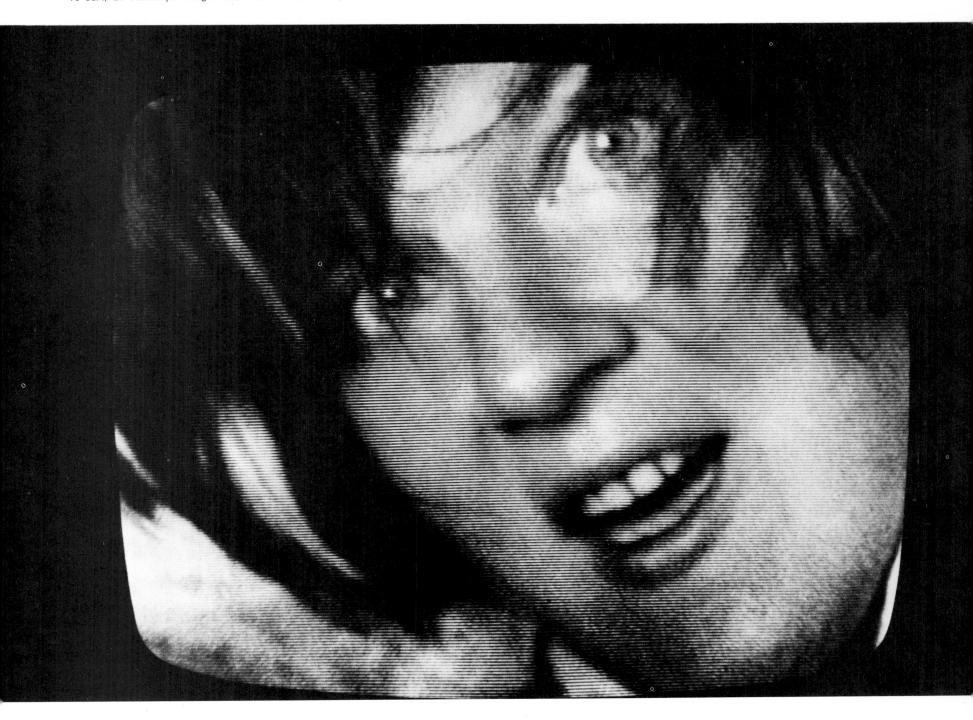

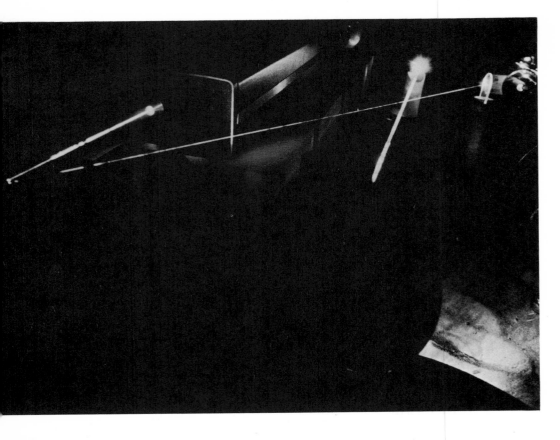

10-36. Holograph set-up used in preparing artists' works for the Finch College Museum of Art, Contemporary Wing exhibition entitled *N Dimensional Space*. This photograph shows the direction and splitting of the lasar beam in the holographic process.

10-37. Physicist Lloyd Gross, standing, and artist Robert Indiana preparing to make a hologram of Indiana's sculpture *Love*. The finished hologram was shown at the *N Dimensional Space* exhibit, Finch College Museum of Art. (Photograph by Tom Rummler.)

THE
globus brothers

CURATORS, MUSEUM OF THE MEDIA, NEW YORK CITY

Author's note: Although this interview was conducted with Stephen Globus, his brothers Ronald and Richard were participants. In a sense, the interview reflects the collective thinking of the Globus brothers on the purposes and function of the unique museum they have created.

KRANZ. *Obviously you want to communicate with a mass audience and you've chosen very sophisticated means to do it.*

GLOBUS. We have three tenets. The first is environmental education. The second is nonverbal education. And the third connects the first two—it is modular construction of the educational facility. Now let's go down each one of them.

Environmental education consists of placing the spectator or participant in the education experience *into* the environment so that he may have an emotional, sensual, stimulative response to this particular environment.

KRANZ. *Yes. Now, what does the environment do for him?*

GLOBUS. Well, instead of the spectator looking at a particular object, he is encased by the object. He's using more of his faculties. We think that while someone is looking at an object and focusing his attention on it, he may be losing some of the other stimuli that are available to him. For example, we are planning to have a show about the Amazon River Basin. Instead of the participant in the educational experience relating to the flora and fauna of the basin and to the spears of the Bushmen, he would be related to a nonselective over-view. Instead of looking at a particular object, he'd be looking at a whole panorama. Someone walking into the Amazon Basin exhibit would be surrounded by the sights, the 360-degree sights, of the Amazon Basin, and he would also be exposed to the sounds that may or may not be heard at that particular place.

An important concept in any exhibit the Museum of the Media will create is the use of experts, the people who are most familiar with that particular subject. If we were going to do a show on Harlem, we would not send our photographers there to interpret Harlem through a non-Harlem resident's eyes. We would get people who eat, sleep, live, and die in Harlem. If we do an exhibit on the Amazon River Basin, we will work in conjunction with

10-38. Group portrait of Richard, Stephen, and Ronald Globus (clockwise). (All photographs courtesy the Globus brothers.)

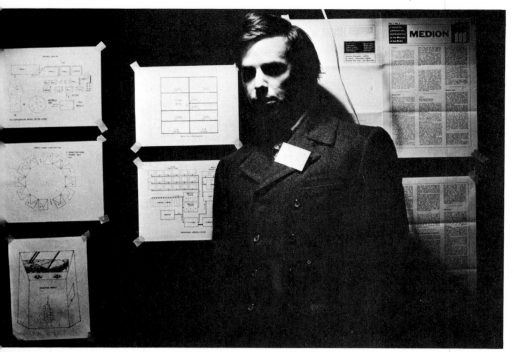

10-39. Ronald Globus, director, against background of graphs, charts, and diagrams of the museum system.

someone familiar with that part of the world. We want to keep the exhibits fairly straight and objective.

KRANZ. *We've covered the first phase of your schema. What about the second?*

GLOBUS. Okay, the second one was nonverbal communication. The spoken word will not be used to explain the content of the exhibit. The first, very obvious, ad-

vantage is that it stops any language problem, or language differences, that the participants might have. A young child, or a foreigner, can relate to the exhibits through the audio-visual stimuli. And, in addition to that, we want the participant to come out with a more intuitive and emotional response, a *feeling* response, than to have a literal interpretive result. Those coming out of our first exhibit, which is on the human head, will have an understanding that they will not be able to express in words, of what the human head is. They will be exposed to hundreds of eyes of different people, of different races. This visual impact cannot be expressed verbally. You cannot express art exhibits verbally. We want to cut out language barriers. We want to have more direct communication with the emotions of other participants.

KRANZ. *The third aspect—the module construction of the exhibits—perhaps that means you have the opportunity to extend the range of the exhibits infinitely . . .*

10-40. Ronald, left, and Richard Globus, standing at central control system at the Museum of the Media.

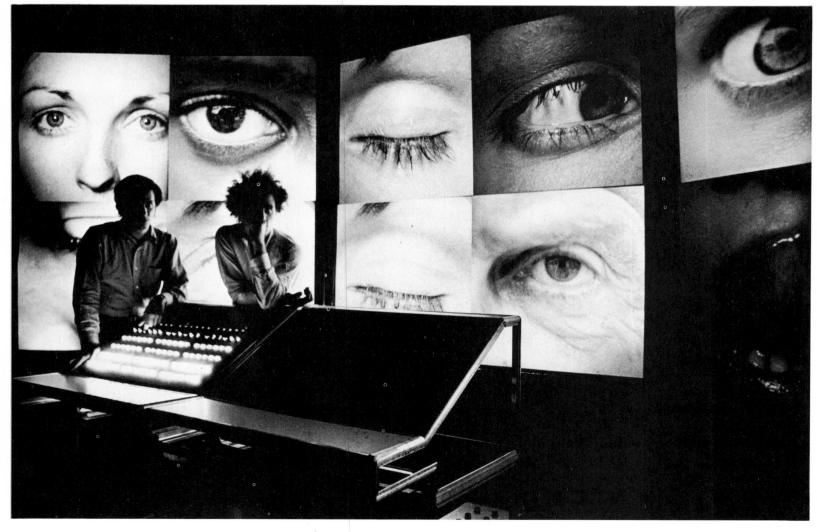

10-41. Richard Globus, script and program coordinator, with source material on light table.

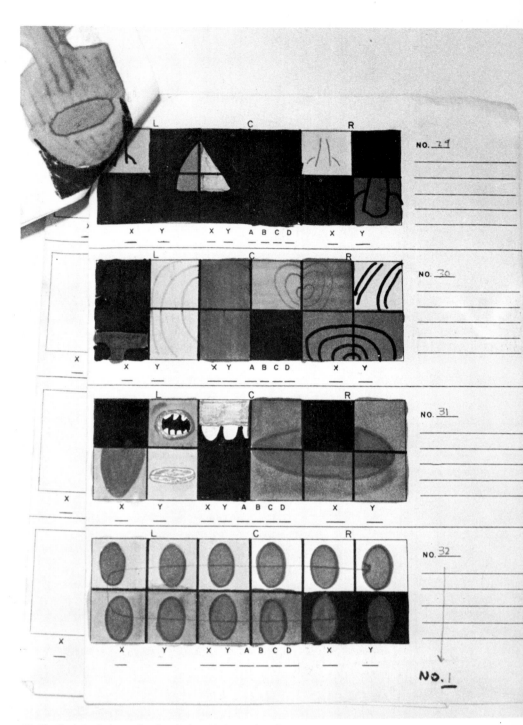

10-42. Script of show. Study of visual information flow.

10-43. Graph showing variation of source photographs. Information was used to set the coordinates of computerized animation stand.

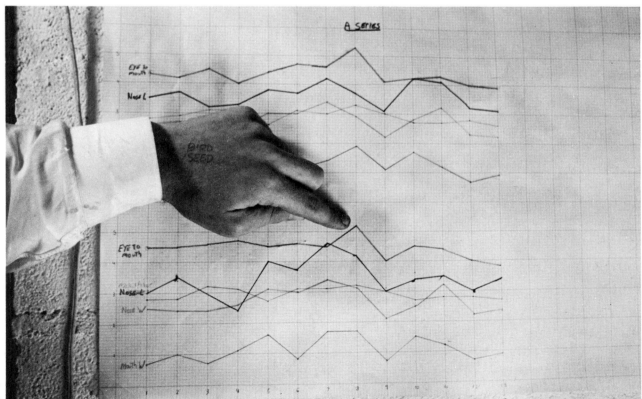

10-44A. Twelve source materials photographs—8 x 10 color transparencies —on a light table. These photographs were later optically modified on a computerized animation stand.

10-44B. Six of the twelve source materials placed on an adjustable projection rack.

10-44C. Sectioning source material into proper coordinates so that each bit of visual material will be on the same registration scale (these coordinates were used on the computerized animation stand).

GLOBUS. We hope that the modules will be purchased by educational institutions, or that other museums of the media will be set up, and that there will be an exchange of software. The module concept means an inexpensive, fairly efficient way of presenting material. Usually cultural objects or artifacts are centralized in major urban areas— New York, Los Angeles, San Francisco. And not only that, once they are in these areas they are even more centralized in the cultural centers of the cities. What we want to do is decentralize museums, bring museums to the people, to the neighborhoods. We think that the Museum of the Media is a practical, inexpensive, efficient way of doing exactly that.

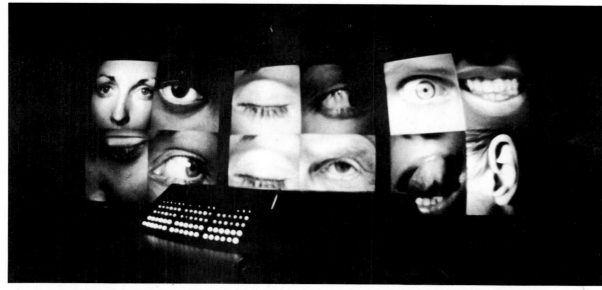

10-45A. Control system silhouette in front of the twelve-screen study of the face.

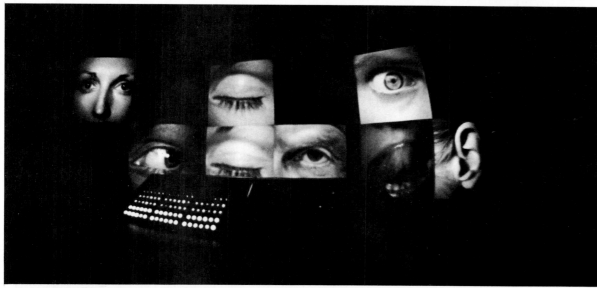

10-45B. Control system silhouette in front of the twelve-screen study of the face.

10-45C. Full-screen projectors cover each screen, instead of four quadrant projectors.

The main rationale is to set up a poor man's museum, a museum that's easily accessible, very easy to set up, inexpensive, and one that is exciting to the general public. This idea connotes a lot of different philosophies. One of the major ones is that by setting up a system of museums, they can communicate through each other. In other words, Milwaukee can set up a show that explores the Milwaukee ghetto, and distribute it to, say, a New York ghetto museum.

10-46. Gordon Douglas discussing the Museum of the Media.

11 epilogue

The tour of the realm has brought us in contact with artists and scientists, media experts, engineers, and interested bystanders. In essence, we cannot avoid the strong impression that the media-based artist will only expand to his full potential and flourish in a society that is constantly creating new goodies for him to exploit and use.

It is appropriate to close with comments from two exceptionally keen minds, Roy Lichtenstein and Theodore R. Conant, who, in their own way, have summarized many of the dichotomies this book has disclosed.

Roy Lichtenstein

The delightful camp artist Roy Lichtenstein talked with me at some length about his reflections on science, art, and technology, with the particular whimsey that his paintings express to the public. It is appropriate for an artist of his stature that he could elevate one of the most banal of artifacts—the graphics of the comic strips—to the level of fine art. His preoccupation with the technically-created aspects of our civilization makes him an ideal spokesman on the implications of the artist's romance with technology.

Lichtenstein generously allowed me and my photographer friend Michael Fredericks, Jr. to visit his studio on two occasions to photograph and interview him. Lichtenstein's loft is located in the Bowery, New York City. Outside, the dreary stretches of Third Avenue hardly prepare one for Lichtenstein's elegant studio-loft and residence.

He is as witty personally as he projects in his droll Pop paintings. I felt, however, that behind his urbane wit stands an artist with deep convictions as to what expression and the need to communicate imposes on the final form of the art product. To this writer, Lichtenstein is a biting social critic who has taken the artifacts of our time —the inane comic books, the insipid dialogue of commercial television, the profoundly vulgar artifacts of popular culture—and simply shot them back like a cannon into the face of the society that made these things in the first place. In my opinion, Lichtenstein's preoccupation with the W.P.A. (Works Progress Administration) aesthetics for part of his drawing style indicates a "subliminal" interest in the meaning of social change through art. It may very well be that the writer is reading more into his visit with the artist than was intended, but it did seem that Lichtenstein has a far deeper committment to a social message than his superficially flippant works would imply.

Theodore R. Conant

Once or twice in a lifetime, you run into a first class intelligence. For me, Theodore Conant was one of those rare experiences. He called himself a filmmaker (which he is) and he admits to the ability to evaluate the aesthetic meaning of the visual image (which he can do, among very few), and he confesses to an interest in educational technology (where he has no peers, in my opinion). Conant has had two or three normal lifetimes: he has been a prominent filmmaker (he was one of the first men to do a visual film record on Marshall McLuhan), he is a world traveller (he has spent more time in the Orient than I have spent in Manhattan), but his long suit has been in his ability to inform influential people on the meaning of the educational experience. For several years he served as Dr. Peter Goldmark's adviser on educational technology at CBS Laboratories, Stamford, Connecticut. More recently, he has advised major international clients on the potential of any given information system for use in the mass market.

His career as a filmmaker, educator, and a protagonist of educational technology makes his summation of this book especially appropriate.

Interviews

Interviews with Lichtenstein and Conant follow.

ROY
lichtenstein

POP ARTIST, NEW YORK CITY

Roy Lichtenstein was born and educated in New York City, studied art at Ohio State University, and, after serving in the army, went back there for a master of fine arts degree. He continued to paint while working in drafting offices, and later taught at the New York State College of Education in Oswego and at the Douglas College division of Rutgers University.

At Rutgers I met people like Kaprow, Bob Watts, and George Segal. I began to be aware of what was being done in New York, particularly in happenings and the areas that Kaprow had a lot to do with. He had ideas about not worrying whether an action or object is art or not. The junk aspect of happenings was not the influential thing in my work. It was the gas-station culture, and the use of American objects, as opposed to European "artistic" subjects. Entire objects, like tires, not things cut up in cubism. It was a combination of things. It didn't flow. Suddenly I started doing cartoons—something in my mind made it okay to do that.

What is a Pop artist? It all depends on what the person saying the words has in mind. From my point of view, a Pop artist is concerned with commercial matter, or commercial methods of portraying the subject matter. I was concerned with both. What I am doing now doesn't fit too well into it, except that there's a residue of style left over from that period of my work.

Artists have been involved all along in doing away with what people think art is about. It's a way of getting to understand art on a deeper level—by stripping it of its outward appearance. People think art is what looks like art. Even artists think that. They have made a revolution; their work may be different from the work preceding them; but when a new generation of artists comes along, they think it's not art. And I might do the same thing.

I used an apparent cartooning technique to do what I think of as traditional art—unifying. Anything can be used. There's no correct way of putting texture or modulations on a canvas, because it all depends on what you start building.

I am interested in the way the cartoon has developed out of the economics of the printing process and out of the idealized notion of what people should look like. The printing process influenced the form and symbolism so that you get heavy black lines hiding the mistakes in the overlay of colors, and the high oversimplification of colors where blond hair is absolutely yellow and everybody's face is made from a 50 per cent red screen. This builds abstract, unrealistic forms, which we take for absolute realism when we read the comic book. We really take that field of dots and black lines and yellow and pink to be somebody's head. By enlarging it, I'm having you look closer at it to see what we've done.

continued on page 318

opposite

C-159. Portrait of Roy Lichtenstein. "We're just using things that are around in exactly the same way that artists have always used things that were around."

C-160. Lichtenstein in his studio.

C-161. An unfinished canvas.

C-162. Lichtenstein working at his drawing board.

C-163. A painting is removed from the studio storage room.

C-164. Paintings by his friends hang in Lichtenstein's handsomely appointed living room.

C-165. A striking sculpture stands on his piano.

C-166. Lichtenstein relaxes.

(Courtesy Roy Lichtenstein; photographer, Michael Fredericks, Jr.)

C-159

C-160

C-161

C-162

C-163

C-164

C-165

C-166

ROY LICHTENSTEIN

11-1. Roy Lichtenstein in conversation with Stewart Kranz in his studio at 190 Bowery, New York City. (Photograph by Michael Fredericks, Jr.)

KRANZ. *Tying in with your own interest in lithography and various technological processes, and your use of specially manufactured perforated paper, would you say that the twentieth-century artist is deeply involved in technology?*

LICHTENSTEIN. I think there is a great influence of technology—it is everywhere, but very few artists are using advanced technology in their work. I don't make a special effort to use advanced technology. I find some uses for technology. It's unavoidable. You begin to think of new and easier ways of making something. However, most of my methods—and I think the methods of most artists—are not that involved in new technology. After all, if I do porcelain enamel on steel, it's been done for centuries—maybe not on steel, but the process has been used for a long time. We're just using things that are around in exactly the same way that artists have always used things that were around. I'm more interested in new concepts than in new technology.

The humor in painting comes, I guess, when situations are contradictory, or when the apparent meaning of the painting is different from its hidden meaning, or when the subject matter is just unusual—things like Warhol's soup cans or Oldenburg's hamburger sculpture. The tradition is to think in heroic terms, and here are these idiotic things. But they really aren't that different. Still-life has been a tradition in painting for a long time. If it were a wine bottle it wouldn't look strange to anybody. I'm sure that soon a Coca Cola bottle will be as acceptable a subject as a wine bottle. These outrages become art very quickly. Well, art has often outraged the public—not that the artist sets out to do this, but if his work has meaning and it's different enough from preceding art (and preceding art is always what we expect to see again), it will outrage the public. But recently some people have learned that art will always be different, and they are alert to new developments and they respond to them.

THEODORE R.

conant

FILMMAKER, FUTURIST; ACTING DIRECTOR, CREATIVE TECHNOLOGY, J. HENRY SCHROEDER BANKING CORPORATION, NEW YORK CITY

Art and technology: It will mean that art will remain a popular means by which a literate (and not necessarily a print-literate) population can express its innermost thoughts and feelings.

KRANZ. *One of the concepts that has come through my research is the interest of the emerging generation in the kinetic image rather than in the more or less traditional art. Would you want to comment on that?*

CONANT. Well, really in some ways, painting is dead. You can go into the gallery and see a nonobjective paint-ing—a Jackson Pollock or a Kline, a Motherwell, a Robert Indiana—and, if you have the talent and wit, you produce the same sort of image very much more quickly with a computer, or more crudely by throwing some chemicals on a piece of celluloid and mucking about, organizing it. One can create abstractions with cathode-ray tubes, tele-vision display, and chemically treated cine film. One can create fantastic images, create them very rapidly, and have precise control. As we get wide-screen televisions and videocassettes, one can have these displays easily accessible, in museum, boardroom, or bedroom. So I think one day painting may very well go the way of the horseless carriage, but of course the skill of the creative imagination, mind, and heart at work will remain. Now, I am not trying to say that there is not, and will not be, a market for, say, Impressionist paintings. Obviously, mu-seums and industrialists want to protect their art invest-ments. But the creative excitement that was around the Impressionist movement in the late nineteenth-century is now in terms of handling moving images and in such areas as mixed-media.

In my generation we were very excited about film, about the possibilities of montage, about Eisenstein and people like Flaherty, Grierson, and Humphrey Jennings—the whole business of the British documentary and the Russian and Nazi propaganda films.

But now, with the possibilities of low-cost film and other kinds of visual presentations, film and closed-circuit tele-vision and tape can be used naturally and easily, as one element in a total visual display. It is possible to do mixed-media in television, on videotape—on film, combining media and film elements; layer upon layer of moving images, very much as one can, in a gramophone or mo-tion-picture sound re-recording session, mix layer on layer of sounds. For example, VanDerBeek is making

patterned environments, making 16 mm film loops of punch-ups and boxing matches, animals copulating, that sort of thing, then putting these loops in film projectors. In television he electronically blends them and mixes them, much as one can mix sound sources in a radio play or an audio collage for *musique concrete*. It is also possible to mix these all together for one image, small or large, or spread them out and cover a sort of planetar-ium area with them, screen on screen on screen, and add or superimpose; light-show techniques as well . . . layer on layer.

KRANZ. *What about the interest that many younger artists have in the multimedia presentation—the attempt to over-load the senses and bombard with multiple images to get to the subliminal in terms of communication?*

11-2. Theodore R. Conant at the J. Henry Schroder Banking Corporation, New York City. Art and Technology poster hangs on the wall.

11-3. Conant in the Schroder conference rooms.

CONANT. A mixture of motives. One, of course, is the great American desire for gadgetry, for coping, and copulating, with machines. It's as much a love story with the machine as it is with the media. This is very American. There's a Henry Ford electric-train-playing sort of thing in almost every American. We want to see how far we can go.

Now that one can buy inexpensive slide and movie projectors, low-cost videotape, and rebate terminals, almost anyone can experiment. It's in the air. It's inevitable that you are going to get more and more image-on-image and sound-on-sound.

Film makers began going into music, and music people began going into film and copying the film techniques of multiple-track mixing and remixing; and then the technology improved and one now has multiple-track audio-recorders, where one can lay eight, sixteen, thirty-two tracks on one piece of tape. One can obviously do this almost ad infinitum.

These techniques, bounced from the amateurs to the professionals, back and forth—the underground film-makers interacting—have created a nonprint vocabulary. Take the whole rise of the sound level of the audio inherent in film displays—if you want to make a real impact, you've got to hit harder.

In a way, that's what media and its relation to basic emotions, to, say, violence and war, is about. Of course, there has always been violence in war, but I am thinking of the peculiar interaction of technology, mass-producing violence . . . on TV, film, and the "theatre of cruelty."

We stage violence with moving images and television images, film images, collages of sound, "live" visuals intermixed with canned impressions. If you want to imprint your paw print on somebody's psyche, you've got to hit him with more . . . or with something awfully good.

This is why you have an escalation of violence and of sex in film, and indeed in all media. Take the ending of *Bonnie and Clyde*—that you remember. A little more violent than you usually see on your home television. There is, there will be, an escalation of body-contact

things, whether they be in praise of love or death, something you don't see in your living room on your idiot box. And something you'll more likely remember.

KRANZ. *Is environmental art, with its attempt to make the spectator a participant—even to change values or point of view in some instances—another way of trying to make a more memorable experience?*

CONANT. We are in a society of increasing technology and increasing alienation, and people do desperately want to be moved, and to move with things. There's no question about this business of trying to involve people. There are a number of theater groups all up and down the East and West Coasts that will take questions from the audience and improvise skits. Tremendously effective. This can be done with film, a little more awkward, but the Czechs, as you know, had a film at Expo where you could choose the ending. It's a little easier, because of the versatility of the human animal, to do it in the theater setting. As computers come in, it will be increasingly possible to have interactive, randomly mixed, multimedia presentations.

There are some experimental educational television transmissions that are using two transmitters, and people like Stan VanDerBeek, to program television transmittal simultaneously—for example, two television transmitters and a stereo FM radio station simultaneously.

So, one way or another, you create multimedia in the parlor or bedroom—in color or black and white, depending on the facility and the ingenuity of the programmer.

continued on page 322

11-4. Conant appraising film at Schroder's.

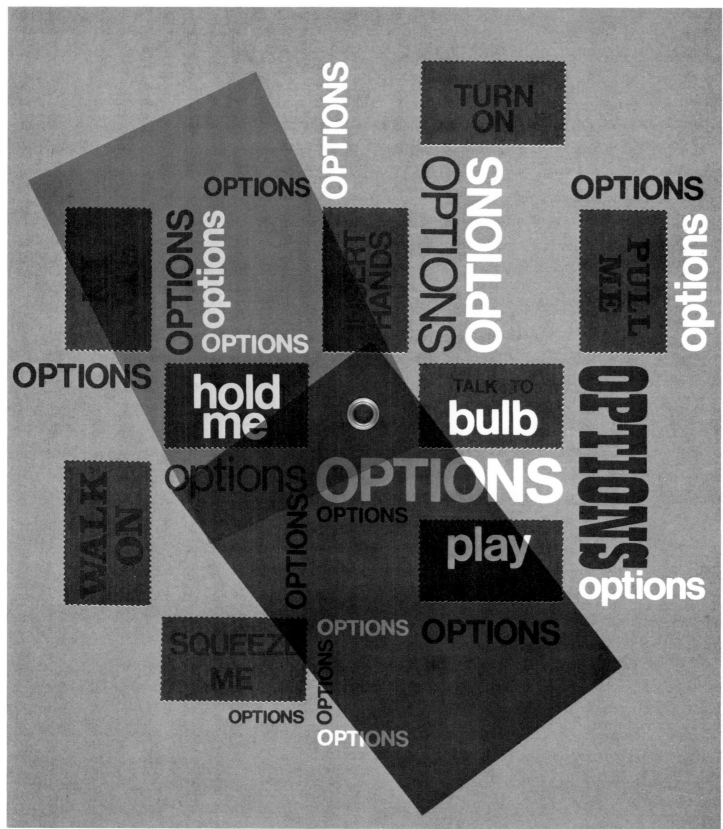

11-5. Cover from the program for a spectator-oriented exhibition entitled *Options*. The exhibition was first held at the Milwaukee Art Center from June 22 to August 18, 1968, and later at the Museum of Contemporary Art in Chicago. All the works in this exhibition were spectator-activated. (Courtesy the Milwaukee Art Center.)

"Options marks the first of what is planned as a new series of exhibitions to be entitled Directions. Organized by the Milwaukee Art Center, the series will be presented on a regularly recurring basis in conjunction with the Friends of Art/Lakefront Festival of the Arts. Each exhibition in the series will, as the general title indicates, explore a recent development or trend in contemporary art. While the emphasis will be on very current phenomena, as is appropriate for an art museum which has become so importantly concerned with recent art, the various exhibitions in the series will likely take quite different forms. This is to say that the series will be flexible, varied, and entirely open to modification as time progresses. The present exhibition, Options, points up a development which has become quite widespread on the art scene in the last few years, but which has had neither sufficient recognition as an esthetic trend nor been the subject of a major museum show. Many works of art are being created today which deny one of the prime tenets of tradition—that art should be fixed, set, and unchangeable, the established and final statement of the artist. All kinds of things are being created today which are deliberately subject to change and modification after they have left the hand of the artist. There are paintings with movable parts, sculpture which can be rolled, punched, pinched, sat upon, gotten into, walked on, felt, turned on, and played like an instrument. Colors change, forms move and assume new relationships. Objects light up, jump, glow, inflate, or make sounds, sometimes talking back to you. One pushes buttons, sets things going, dodges, caresses, walks right into, or avoids things in turn.

In most cases some kind of manipulation is indeed required of the viewer, who thereby becomes more than a mere "looker." He is a participant who actively determines the nature of the work of art he experiences. It was thus that we at first considered use of the term participation in the title of the exhibition, and while this indeed remains a most important aspect of its theme, it soon became apparent that a broader, more basic term was called for. After all, as is pointed out elsewhere here, all art involves a certain amount of participation in order to be effective at all, even though previously this had seldom involved actual physical activity. Furthermore, there is an exceptionally broad range of kinds of participation involved, varying not only in method of manipulation but in the extent to which the artist permits variations and whom he lets undertake them. Finally, many of the works in the exhibition stand alone as visual objects without the option of participation, merely assuming an additional dimension thereby. Thus the more accurate and basic term 'Options' was arrived at as pointing to the common quality held by all such works—that they offer choices and alternatives." (Taken from Directions 1: *Options 1968*, Milwaukee Art Center exhibit.)

KRANZ. *Is the artist's embracing of technology, which is a distortion of everything he should stand for, a sort of Wagnerian suicide, as some of the critics have said?*

CONANT. I think that artists, like engineers and scientists, go where the action is. Scientists do research in many areas of marginal intellectual respectability, which are dignified by the fact that there is money there. They go with action, money, and respectability. Scientists are just as avaricious, just as frail and mortal as businessmen, politicians . . . or artists.

What does the patron want? Well, we are not in the world of the Borgias—we have Borgias but perhaps they are not so rich as they used to be, also not so cultured, but at any rate they are not helping the artist in quite the same way as they used to in the days of the Italian city-state. So you go where the action is. And painting is somewhat a dead end. Just as theater is. Just as literature is. What do you do after Becket? Given the transcendent role of technology in our society, artists are attracted to this. It is also inevitable that they go this way because this is where it's all at—action, power, money, and adulation.

We are creating a new class. We do not have a quasi hereditry or quasi aristocracy with certain values and tastes, as was the case in much of old Europe. Today, people who are buying art, collecting art, subsidizing art —many of them have come up rather quickly from rather obscure and uncouth origins. As a result, and perhaps also because of the nature of the times, there is a good deal of anti-intellectualism in the art market. Many perhaps relate more to Warhol's Campbell's Soup cans than they do to abstractions, which require real intellectual

vigor. There's no question that the growth of Art Nouveau type things, and Pop and Op type things, is because of accessibility. Everyone knows comic strips, everyone knows consumables, and so on. For people who are a bit insecure, who are coming into a new area, the aura of anti-intellectualism means that they are absolutely on equal terms. They can make the same kind of inane noises, buy the same kind of paintings that everyone else buys. I don't mean that all Op and Pop are in this category. A few very good people are in this field. Some transcend the limitations of the style.

KRANZ. *Is there a deleterious result on the artist or the scientist in working directly with technology, with collaborative projects? What do you see as the strength and weaknesses of this movement?*

CONANT. I would not think so. An artist, if he is going to produce anything worthwhile, has to produce organisms of some sort with paint or plaster or clay or celluloid or electro-optics—realizations, manifestations that somehow "speak to his condition." The real artist paints for himself, first of all. He paints to express things that he must express.

Increasing numbers of people in our culture want to express themselves. The use of the English language is not something that is being greatly encouraged either by our schools or by our culture. The downgrading of the pen and typewriter and the upgrading of the image will mean that art remains a popular means by which a literate, and not necessarily a print-literate, population can express with images and sounds its innermost thoughts and feelings.

list of illustrations

bibliography

Chapter 1

Aldridge, Larry, "New Talent USA," *Art in America.* New York: July–August 1966, pp. 22 ff.

Arnason, H. H., *History of Modern Art.* New York: Harry N. Abrams, Inc., 1968.

"The Avant-Garde: Subtle, Cerebral, Elusive," New York: *Time,* November 22, 1968, pp. 70 ff.

Cardinal Wiseman, *Points of Contact between Science and Art.* London: Hurst and Blackett, Publishers 1863.

Erikson, Erik N., ed., *The Challenges of Youth.* New York: Anchor Books, 1963.

Esterow, Milton, "Broad Side of a Barn Is One Artist's Canvas." New York: *The New York Times,* April 7, 1967, p. 39.

Fuller, R. Buckminster, *Intuition.* New York: Doubleday, 1972

———. *Operating Manual for Spaceship Earth.* Carbondale: Southern Illinois University Press 1969.

Goodman, Paul. *Growing Up Absurd.* New York: Random House, 1960.

———. *Like a Conquered Province: the moral ambiguity of America.* New York: Random House, 1967.

Kanfer, Stefan. "The Shock of Freedom in Films." New York: *Time,* December 8, 1967, pp. 66 ff.

Kaprow, Allan. "An Artist's Story of a Happening." *The New York Times,* October 6, 1963.

———. *Assemblages, Environments and Happenings.* New York: Harry N. Abrams, Inc., 1966.

———. "The Happenings Are Dead, Long Live the Happenings." New York: *Art Forum,* March, 1966.

Kauffmann, Stanley. "Mind Over Matter." New York: *The New Republic,* April 29, 1967, pp. 18 ff.

Kostelanetz, Richard. *The Theatre of Mixed Means.* New York: The Dial Press, Inc., 1968.

Kramer, Hilton. "The Sixties in Retrospect." *The New York Times,* July 2, 1967, p. 19D.

Leider, Philip. "Gallery '68: High art and low art." New York: *Look Magazine,* January 9, 1968, pp. 12 ff.

Leonard, John. "The Return of Andy Warhol." *The New York Times Magazine,* November 10, 1968, pp. 32 ff.

"Luddites." London: *Encyclopedia Britannica,* Volume 14, p. 402.

Lukas, J. Anthony. *Don't Shoot—We Are Your Children* New York: Random House, 1971.

Mailer, Norman. *Of a Fire on the Moon.* Boston-Toronto: Little, Brown and Company, 1969.

Marks, Robert W. "The Dymaxion World of Buckminster Fuller." New York: Reprinted from *American Fabrics,* Spring, 1953, and *Gentry,* Spring, 1953.

Mead, Margaret. *Continuities in Cultural Evolution.* New Haven: Yale University Press, 1965.

Mekas, Jonas, ed., "Expanded Arts." New York: *Film Culture,* Winter, 1966–67.

"Message of History's Biggest Happening: Woodstock Music and Art Fair." New York: *Time,* August 29, 1969, pp. 32–33.

Morris, Desmond. *The Naked Ape: a zoologist's study of the human animal.* New York: McGraw-Hill, 1967.

Mumford, Lewis. *The Myth of the Machine, Technics and Human Development.* New York: Harcourt, Brace & World, 1967.

"The Playmate as Fine Art." *Playboy,* January, 1967, pp. 141–149.

Read, Herbert, *Art and Society.* New York: Schocken Books, 1967.

Reich, Charles A. *The Greening of America.* New York: Random House, 1970.

Reinhold, Robert. "Rise of History of Science Is a Reply to Technology." *The New York Times,* February 18, 1970, pp. 49 ff.

Rusher, W. A. "Mass infantilism, anyone? Woodstock Music and Art Fair." New York: *National Review,* October 7, 1969, p. 1012.

Russell, John. "Why Aubrey Beardsley Is Back." *The New York Times Magazine,* February 5, 1967, pp. 14 ff.

Skinner, B. F. *Walden Two.* New York: Macmillan Company, 1948.

———. *Beyond Freedom and Dignity.* New York: Alfred A. Knopf, Inc., 1971.

"Social Realism in Blue: An Interview with James Rosenquist." New York: *Studio,* February, 1968, pp. 76–83.

Toffler, Alvin. *Future Shock.* New York: Random House, 1970.

Wind, Edgar. "The Long Battle Between Art and the Machine." New York: *Harper's Magazine,* February, 1964, pp. 65 ff.

"Whole New Minority Group: the Aquarians at Woodstock." New York: *Newsweek,* September 1, 1969, pp. 20 ff.

"Woodstock Festival." New York: *The New Yorker* (Notes and Comment), August 30, 1969, pp. 17–21.

Young, Edgar; Silocck, Bryan; and Dunn, Peter. *Journey to Tranquility: the history of man's assault on the moon.* London: Jonathon Cape, Ltd., 1969.

Chapter 2

Bryant, Gloria. "What's Happening! Bell Labs engineers go arty." Murray Hill: New Jersey: *WE* (Western Electric), January, 1967, pp. 14–21.

Canaday, John. "Light Brigade Charges-Up at the Wise." New York: *The New York Times,* February 4, 1967, p. 23.

Clurman, Harold. "Alwin Nikolais Dance Theatre." New York: *The Nation,* December 22, 1969, p. 703.

"Conversations with Gyorgy Kepes, Billy Klüver, and James Rosenquist." New York: *Art in America,* January–February, 1968, pp. 38 ff.

Dance Theatre of Alwin Nikolais, The brochure: New York: Alwin Nikolais Dance Company, December, 1968.

Drysdale, Susan. "Kepes and Rainer, artists hailed on three continents." Boston: *The Christian Science Monitor,* May 26, 1972, p. 7.

Geldzahler, Henry; Cage, John; and Kosloff, Max. *Robert Rauschenberg: Paintings, Drawings and Combines, 1949–1964.* London: Whitechapel Gallery, 1964 exhibition catalogue.

Goldberg, Herman. "Do-it-yourself Kinetic Art." *Color,* 1968, pp. 128 ff.

Glueck, Grace. "For Better Vision, Optacles." New York: *The New York Times,* February 13, 1966.

Hering, Doris. "Alwin Nikolais Dance Company, Henry Street Settlement Playhouse." New York: *Dance Magazine,* February, 1968, p. 86.

Kepes, Gyorgy. *The Language of Vision.* Chicago: Paul Theobald and Company, 1944.

———. "Light and Design." *Design Quarterly.* Minneapolis: Walker Art Center, 1967.

Kepes, Gyorgy, ed. *The Visual Arts Today.* Middletown: Wesleyan University Press, 1960.

———. *Vision and Value.* New York: Braziller, 1966.

Klüver, Billy. "Theater and Engineering, An Experiment: Notes by an Engineer." New York: *Art Forum,* February, 1967, pp. 31 ff.

———. "Interface: Artist/Engineer." Typescript of talk given at Massachusetts Institute of Technology, April 21.

———. "Laser Amplifier Noise at 3.5 Microns in Helium-Xenon." *Journal of Applied Physics,* July, 1966, pp. 2887–2999.

Kostelanetz, Richard. "The Artist as Playwright and Engineer." New York: *The New York Times Magazine,* October 9, 1966, pp. 32 ff.

Kramer, Hilton. "Remedy for the Disengaged Spectator." New York: *The New York Times,* March 25, 1967, p. 19.

KunstLichtKunst. Stedelijk van Abbemuseum Eindhoven. Amsterdam: 25 september tm 4 december 1966 (Lumia Exhibition Catalogue).

Light in Orbit. New York: The Howard Wise Gallery, February 4–March 4, 1967 exhibition catalogue.

"Luminal Music." New York: *Time,* April 28, 1967, pp. 78 ff.

"Magic and the Globolinks." New York: *Time,* January 3, 1969, p. 50.

"Malina: Artist-Scientist of the Space Age." New York: *Unesco Courier,* September, 1964, pp. 18–21.

Moran, Nancy. "Art and Technology Merge at Exhibit." New York: *The New York Times,* March 3, 1970.

"Most Happy Fella." New York: *Time,* September 18, 1964, pp. 84 ff.

9 Evenings: theatre & engineering: New York: Program of 25th Street Armory Show, New York City, October 13–23, 1966 (Experiments in Art and Technology).

"Palatnik Experiments." *Americas,* August, 1965, p. 46.

Reinhold, Robert. "M.I.T. Center Seeks to Wed Esthetics and Technology." New York: *The New York Times,* December 26, 1969, p. 31.

Robinson, L. J. and Paxton, Steve. "Art and Technology: A Dialogue." *IKON,* February, 1968, 1967, pp. 16 ff.

Solomon, Alan R. *Robert Rauschenberg,* New York: The Jewish Museum, 1963 exhibition catalogue.

Stein, Donna M. *Thomas Wilfred: Lumia, A Retrospective Exhibition.* Washington, D.C.: The Corcoran Gallery of Art, April 16–May 30, 1971 exhibition catalogue.

"A Wacky Collaboration of Science and Art." New York: *Fortune,* January, 1967, pp. 16 ff.

Whitman, Simone. "Theatre and Engineering: An Experiment—Notes by a Participant." New York: *Art Forum,* February, 1967, pp. 26–30.

Wilfred, Thomas. *Light Display Apparatus—4 claims.* Washington, D.C.: United States Patent Office. (Filed May 13, 1931, Serial No. 537, 052. Patented September 11, 1934, No. 1, 973, 454.)

———. "Light and the Artist." *The Journal of Aesthetics and Art Criticism,* June, 1947.

———. "Letter to the Editor." *The Journal of Aesthetics and Art Criticism,* March, 1948.

Chapter 3

Brockway, Merrill. "The Walls Come Tumbling Down," typescript. New York: *WCBSTV Eye on Art,* July 2, 1967.

Culkin, John M., S.J. "A Schoolman's Guide to Marshall McLuhan." New York: *Saturday Review,*

March 18, 1967.

"Debut of a Metal Giant." New York: *Time,* April 11, 1969, pp. 51–52.

"Digital remote control captures the conventions: CBS nominates a convention hopeful." New York: *Electronics,* August 19, 1968, pp. 74–83.

Donner, Stanley T., ed. *The Meaning of Commercial Television.* Austin: University of Texas Press, 1967.

Friendly, Fred W. *Due to Circumstances Beyond Our Control.* New York: Random House, 1967.

Gans, Herbert J. "The Mass Media as an Educational Institution." New York: *The Urban Review,* February, 1967, pp. 5 ff.

———. "Some Changes in American Taste and their Implications for the Future of Television." In *The Future of Commercial Television, 1965–1975.* Palo Alto: Stanford University Department of Communications, 1965.

Howard, Jane, "Oracle of the Electric Age." New York: *Life Magazine,* February 25, 1966, pp. 5 ff.

McLuhan, Marshall. *Culture Is Our Business.* New York–Toronto: McGraw-Hill Book Company, Inc., 1970.

———. *The Gutenberg Galaxy.* Toronto: University of Toronto Press, 1970.

McLuhan, Marshall and Fiore, Quenton. *The Medium is the Message.* New York: Random House, 1967.

McLuhan, Marshall. *Understanding Media.* New York: McGraw-Hill Book Company, Inc., 1964.

McLuhan, Marshall and Leonard, George B. "The Future of Education." New York: *Look Magazine,* February 21, 1967.

Melvin, Kenneth. "McLuhan the Medium." *Phi Delta Kappan,* June, 1967, pp. 488–91.

Mosher, R. S. and Listen, R. A. *A Versatile Walking Truck.* Booklet prepared for 1968 Transportation Engineering Conference, ASME-NYAS, October 28–30, 1968, General Electric.

Stevens, William B. "Robot Multiplies Man's Strength." New York: *The New York Times,* April 3, 1969, pp. 1, 25.

Visual Communication: Esthetic and Educational Dimensions. Washington, D.C.: NAEA, 1968, Eastern Regional Convention Program, National Art Education Association.

Welles, Chris. "How it feels to live in TOTAL DESIGN." New York: *Life Magazine,* April 29, 1966, pp. 59 ff.

Zinsser, William. "A Grant to Beauty." New York: *Look Magazine.*

Chapter 4

Anderson, R. Wayne. "Thermal Mapping in Color Using the Evaporograph." *PMI* (Photo Methods for Industry), October, 1963.

Arena, A. and Umlas, M. "A New Panoramic Camera Development." *Photogrammetric Engineering,* February, 1968, pp. 169–178.

Arnheim, Rudlof. *Art and Visual Perception.* Berkeley and Los Angeles: University of California Press, 1960.

Behrens, Roy. "Perception in the Visual Arts." *Art Education,* March, 1969, pp. 13 ff.

Betagraphy. McMinnville, Oregon: Technical Bulletin, Field Emission Corporation, July, 1968.

Birren, Faber. *Color Psychology and Color Therapy.* New York: McGraw-Hill Book Company, Inc., 1950. Reprint, Hyde Park: University Books, 1961.

———. *History of Color in Painting.* New York: Van Nostrand Reinhold Company, 1965.

———. *Light, Color and Environment.* New York: Van Nostrand Reinhold Company, 1969.

———. "Psychological Implications of Color and Illumination." New York: *Illuminating Engineering,* May, 1969, pp. 1–6.

Bridgman, Charles F. "Radiography in Art and Science." *Chemistry,* December, 1966, pp. 19–27.

Brown, David A. "Aerial Camera With Rotary Lens Designed To Give Improved Resolution." New York: *AVIATION WEEK & Space Technology,* April 26, 1965.

Bruce, Robert. "AERIAL PHOTOGRAPHY today and tomorrow." New York: *Signal,* January, 1967, pp. 28–32.

Chevreul, M. E. *The Principles of Harmony and Contrast of Colors,* 1854. Edited and with commentary notes by Faber Birren. New York: Van Nostrand Reinhold Company, 1967.

Denes, P. B. "The Elusive Process of Speech." Murray Hill, New Jersey: *RECORD,* Bell Laboratories, September, 1966, pp. 254 ff.

Edson, Lee. "Hottest Thing Since Color TV—EVR." New York: *The New York Times Magazine,* December 17, 1967, pp. 1 ff.

Elam, Frank B. "Infrared Photography by the Evaporograph Method." *Convention Report,* 70th Exposition of Professional Photography, pp. 134–136.

"Emigré Nobelists." New York: *Newsweek,* November 15, 1971.

Fender, Derek, and Julesz, Dr. Bela, "Extension of Panum's Fusional Area in Binocularly Stabilized Vision." *Journal of the Optical Society of America,* June, 1967, pp. 819–830.

"First Film of Cancer Cells in Action." *Look Magazine,* November 16, 1967, pp. 57–58.

Fritz, Norman L. "Optimum Methods for Using Infrared-Sensitive Color Film." *Photogrammetric Engineering,* October, 1967.

Gabor, Dr. Dennis. "Character Recognition by Holography." New York: *Nature,* 1965, pp. 422, 433.

———. *Inventing the Future.* New York: Alfred A. Knopf, Inc., 1964.

———. "Summary of CBS Laboratories Seminar on 'Imaging with Coherent Light.'" Stamford, Connecticut: CBS Laboratories, April 8, 1965.

Gabor, Dr. Dennis and Stroke, George W. "Holography and its Applications." *Endeavor,* January, 1969, pp. 40 ff.

Gazzaniga, Michael S. "The Split Brain in Man." New York: *Scientific American,* August, 1967, pp. 24 ff.

"The Genius at CBS." New York: *Time,* December 20, 1968.

"Giant 'eye' on space maps Venus, Mercury." Boston: *The Christian Science Monitor,* June 9, 1972, p. 9.

"Gifted Refugees." New York: *Time,* November 15, 1971.

Goldmark, Dr. Peter Carl. "Deadline for Survival." New York: Paper given before New York Academy of Science, January 8, 1969.

Gregory, R. L. *Eye and Brain.* New York: McGraw-Hill Book Company, Inc., 1966.

Harlow, Dr. William M. Patterns of Life, *The Unseen World of Plants.* New York: Harper & Row, 1966.

Julesz, Dr. Bela. "Computers, Patterns and Depth Perception." Murray Hill, New Jersey: *Bell Laboratories RECORD,* September, 1966, pp. 260–266.

———. "Experiment in Perception," New York: *Psychology Today,* July, 1968, pp. 16–23.

———. "Texture and Visual Perception." New York: *Scientific American,* February, 1965, pp. 38–48.

Kepes, Gyorgy. *Sign, Image, Symbol.* New York: George Braziller, Inc., 1965.

Kersta, Dr. L. G. *Voiceprint Identification,* Typescript. Somerville, New Jersey: Voiceprint Laboratories.

Kersta, L. G.; Schwartz, M. L.; and Heinz, Alfred. "Heartprints and Other Body Sounds," Typescript. Somerville, New Jersey: Voiceprint Laboratories.

Klein, Frederick C. "The Innovators—Inventions by Goldmark of CBS have Sweeping Social, Economic Force." New York: *The Wall Street Journal,* May 17, 1968, p. 1.

Kock, W. E. "Nobel Prizes for Physics: Gabor and Holography." New York: *Science,* November 12, 1971.

Lieth, Emmett N. and Upatnicks, Juris. "Photography by Laser." New York: *Scientific American,* June, 1965, pp. 24–28.

———. "Wavefront Reconstruction with Diffused Illumination and Three-Dimensional Objects." *Journal of the Optical Society of America,* November, 1964, pp. 1295 ff.

"Making 3-D Pictures With Sound." New York: *Time,* November 10, 1967, pp. 64–67.

Medical Radiography and Photography. Rochester, New York: Eastman Kodak Company, November 3, 1958.

"Only Artist on the Moon." New York: *The New Yorker,* May 20, 1972, pp. 29–30.

Ostwald, Wilhelm. *The Color Primer,* edited and with special chapters by Faber Birren. New York: Van Nostrand Reinhold Company, 1969.

Pennington, Keith S. "Advances in Holography." New York: *Scientific American,* February, 1968, pp. 40–48.

Presti, A. J. "High-Speed Sound Spectrograph." *The Journal of the Acoustical Society of America,* September, 1966, pp. 628 ff.

"Pure Light for Practical Pictures." New York: *Time,* March 10, 1966, p. 60.

Savage, Major J. C. *Night Skywriting.*

Schawlaw, Arthur and Benrey, Ronald. "PS Builds a Laser." New York: *Popular Science,* November, 1964, pp. 62–64.

Schwuttke, G. H. "New X-Ray Diffraction Microscopy Technique for the Study of Imperfections in Semiconductor Crystals." *Journal of Applied Physics,* September, 1965, pp. 2712 ff.

"Sound Judgment." New York: *Time,* June 23, 1967, p. 66.

Stroke, George W. "Recent Advances in Holography." *Technology Review,* May, 1967, pp. 16–22.

Strong, C. L. "How to Make Holograms and Experiment with Ready-Made Holograms." New York: *Scientific American,* February, 1967.

Sullivan, Walter. "New Photo Technique Projects A World of 3-Dimension Views." New York: *The New York Times,* March 19, 1967, p. 1 and p. 60.

"Technical Aspects of Visible Speech." *Journal of the Acoustical Society of America,* July, 1946, pp. 1–89.

Thomas, Frank P. "Skywriting Up to Date." Baltimore: *American Mercury Magazine, Inc.,* March, 1960.

White, Harvey E. and Levatin, Paul. "'Floaters' in

the Eye." New York: *Scientific American,* June, 1962, pp. 119 ff.

Wright, Ward, "Rotating Prism Panoramic Camera Adds New Dimension to Photo-Recon Technique." New York: *AVIATION WEEK & Space Technology,* February 25, 1963.

Yost, E. F. "Forward Oblique Panoramic Photography." *Technical Memorandum No. SME-AG-8, Fairchild Space and Defense Systems,* January 15, 1963.

Yost, Prof. Edward F. and Wendereth, Sondra. "Multispectral Color Aerial Photography." *Photogrammetric Engineering,* September, 1967, pp. 1020–1033.

Chapter 5

Apfelbaum, Henry. "I Remember MOMA." Murray Hill, New Jersey: *Reporter,* Bell Telephone Laboratories, March/April, 1968, pp. 15–18.

"Big Machines on Campus." New York: *Time,* May 19, 1967, p. 98.

Blake, Peter. "Downtown in 3-D." New York: *Architectural Forum,* September, 1966, pp. 31–49.

Blake, Peter. "Vincent Ponte: A New Kind of Urban Designer." New York: *Art in America,* September, 1969.

Canaday, John. "Art that Pulses, Quivers and Fascinates." New York: *The New York Times Magazine,* February 21, 1965.

"The Computer Age—Book Publisher Salvation?" New York: *Saturday Review,* July 23, 1966, p. 32.

"Computer Art Contest." *Computers and automation,* August, 1965.

"Cybernetic Serendipity." New York: *Science & Mechanics,* May, 1969, pp. 60–61.

"Cycle of Evolution: The Work of R. Buckminster Fuller." New York: *Architectural Record,* June, 1955, pp. 155–162.

"Design and the Computer" Minneapolis: Design Quarterly 66/67, Walker Art Center.

Dibner, Bern. *Leonardo Da Vinci, Military Engineer.* New York: Publications of Burndy Library, 1946.

E.A.T. News, Vol. 1, No. 1—Vol. 1, No. 2. New York: Experiments in Art and Technology, Inc. 1967.

Friedlander, Gordon D. "Automation Comes to the Printing and Publishing Industry." New York: *IEEE Spectrum,* April, May, 1968.

———. "Birth of the New City—An Exciting Creation." New York: *IEEE Spectrum,* April, 1967.

———. "The Burndy Library: window on the history of science." New York: *IEEE Spectrum,* March, 1970.

———. "At the Crossroads in Air-traffic Control." New York: *IEEE Spectrum,* June, July, August, 1970.

Fuller, R. Buckminster. "Architecture Out of the Laboratory." Ann Arbor, Michigan: *Student Publication.* University of Michigan, Spring, 1955, pp. 9-34.

Harmon, Leon D., and Knowlton, Kenneth C. "Picture Processing by Computer." *American Association for the Advancement of Science,* April 4, 1969, pp. 19–29.

Human Use of Computing Machines, The: Proceedings of a symposium concerned with diverse ways of enhancing perception and intuition. Murray Hill, New Jersey: Bell Telephone Laboratories, June 20–21, 1966.

IDIION. Information Displays, Inc., brochure. Mt. Kisco, New York.

Loftis, John. "The Plastic Arts in the Sixties—What is it that has got lost?" New York: *Art Journal,* Spring, 1967, pp. 240–244.

Lourie, Janice R. "The Textile Designer of the Future." New York: *Handweaver and Craftsman,* Winter, 1966, p. 8.

"Love, Hate & the Machine." New York: *Time,* December 6, 1968, pp. 86–89.

Machover, Dr. Carl. *CRT Graphic Terminals,* Typescript. Ann Arbor, Michigan: University of Michigan Engineering Summer Conference talk, June 17–28, 1968.

———. *The Intelligent Terminal,* Typescript. Urbana: University of Illinois. Conference talk, March 30–April 2, 1969.

Mathews, M. V., and Miller, Jean R. *Computer editing, typesetting and image generation.* Murray Hill, New Jersey: Bell Telephone System Technical Publication, Monograph 5109, February, 1966.

———. "Computer Composers: Comments and Case Histories." *TECHNE, A Projects and Process Paper,* November 6, 1970, pp. 10–11.

McCarthy, John. "Information—an introduction to an issue on information and its processing by computer." New York: *Scientific American,* September, 1966.

Morrill, Milly, and Freeman, Margaret. "Post-Industrial Society—Good-bye to the Melting Pot." Northhampton, Massachusetts: Smith Alumnae Quarterly, November, 1968, pp. 27–29.

"Nelson's the name and what he proposes to do could outdo Engelbart." New York: *Electronics,* November 24, 1967, p. 17.

Noll, Dr. A. Michael. "Art Ex Machina." New York: *IEEE Student Journal,* September, 1970.

———. "Choreography and Computers." New York: *Dance Magazine,* January, 1967.

———. "Computer animation and the fourth dimension." Murray Hill, New Jersey: Reprinted from Fall Joint Computer Conference, 1968, Bell Telephone Laboratories.

———. "Computer-Generated Three-Dimensional Movies." *Computers and Automation,* May, 1965, pp. 32–34.

———. "Computer Graphics in Acoustics Research." New York: *IEEE Transactions on Audio and Electroacoustics,* June, 1968, pp. 213–220.

Oster, Dr. Gerald, "Optical Art," *Applied Optics,* November, 1965, pp. 1359–1369.

———. *The Science of Moiré Patterns.* Harrington, New Jersey: Edmund Scientific Company, 1964.

"Plug-in Instruction—Computer Influence on Education." New York: *Saturday Review,* July 23, 1966, p. 25.

"QUIKTRAN Music Man." New York: *Data Processor,* International Business Machines Corporation, March, 1967, pp. 17 ff.

Raben, Dr. Joseph. "Computers and Literary Studies." New York: *Data Processor,* International Business Machines Corporation, March, 1967, pp. 11 ff.

Seitz, W. C. *The Responsive Eye.* New York: Museum of Modern Art, 1965, Exhibition Catalogue.

Sinden, Frank W. *Synthetic Cinematography.* Murray Hill, New Jersey: Bell Telephone System Technical Publication, Monograph 5159, April, 1966.

Techne, A Projects and Process Paper. New York: Experiments in Art and Technology (E.A.T.)

Vol. 1, No. 1, April 14, 1969, Vol. 1, No. 2, November 6, 1970.

"Textile Graphics." New York: *Handweaver & Craftsman,* Winter, 1967.

"Weaving by Computer." New York: *Handweaver & Craftsman,* Summer, 1968.

"Yesterday's Visions of Tomorrow." Architects of 18th Century France conjured up designs that exploit and forecast the modern. New York: *Life Magazine,* February 9, 1968, pp. 42 ff.

Chapter 6

CBS IN OUTER SPACE. Brochure. Stamford, Connecticut: CBS Laboratories, A division of Columbia Broadcasting System, Inc., 1968.

Chajet, George. "Part-Task Learning of Pilot Skills: Three Experimental Investigations." *Navexos P.* 1300–30, pp. 18 ff. Orlando, Florida: Naval Training Device Center.

"A Chance to Be First." New York: *Time,* October 11, 1968, pp. 68 ff.

Kress, Robert W., and Fogel, Gerald D. "LM Program Real Time Simulation." New York: IBM CORP. Reprinted from *Proceedings of the IBM Scientific Computing Symposium on Digital Simulation of Continuous Systems,* June 20–22, 1966.

LaRussa, Joseph. "A New Infinity Image System." Orlando, Florida: *Proceedings of the Second Naval Training Device Center and Industry Conference,* pp. 128 ff. November 28–30, 1967.

Sachleben, J. H., and Solan, M. J. "Hardware's Role." New York: *Engineering Control,* February, 1967, pp. 53–59.

Shepard, Alan B., Jr. *"Training by Simulation."* Washington, D.C.: Lecture delivered at the Smithsonian Institution, February 19, 1964. Edwin A. Link Publication 4597, January, 1965.

Stoodley, Dr. Gerald R. "An IBM 7094 Program for Making Perspective Drawings." Bethpage, L.I.: Grumman Research Department, September, 1964.

Stoodley, Dr. Gerald R. and Miller, J. S. "Digital Computer Generated Stereoscopic Pontille (Marked by Dots) Surfaces." Bethpage, L.I.: Grumman Research Department, April, 1965.

Systems Simulation. Bethpage, L.I.: Grumman Laboratory Facilities, November, 1967.

Virtual Image Out-the-Window Display Systems Study. New York: Farrand Optical Company, Inc., January, 1966.

Chapter 7

Alloway, Lawrence. *Systemic Painting.* New York: The Solomon R. Guggenheim Museum, September–November, 1966 (Exhibition Catalogue).

———. "Frankenthaler as Pastoral." New York: *Art News,* November, 1971, pp. 67–68.

Arnason, H. H. *American Abstract Expressionists and Imagists.* New York: The Solomon R. Guggenheim Museum, October–December, 1961.

Ashton, Dore. " 'Protest and Hope at the New School." New York: *Studio,* December, 1967, p. 278.

Baro, Gene. "The Achievement of Helen Frankenthaler." New York: *Art International,* September, 1967, pp. 33–38.

Bourdon, David. "A New Cut in Art; Oddly shaped canvases by Frank Stella challenge viewers."

New York: *Life Magazine,* January 16, 1968.

Dine, Oldenburg, Segal. Toronto: Art Gallery of Toronto, 1967 exhibition catalogue.

Friedman, Martin. *Adolph Gottlieb.* Minneapolis: Walker Art Center, Colwell Press, 1965 exhibition catalogue.

Haftmann, Werner. "The Contemporary Scene—Art since 1945." In *Painting in the Twentieth Century, Volume I.* New York, Washington: Frederick A. Praeger, Publishers, 1966.

Kaprow, Allan. "Segal's Vital Mummies." New York: *Art News,* February, 1964, pp. 30–33, 65.

Kosloff, Max. "Art and the New York Avant Garde." *Partisan Review,* Fall, 1964, pp. 535–554.

Kramer, Hilton. "No Great Master but a Great Influence." New York: *The New York Times Magazine,* December 18, 1966, pp. 28 ff.

Mulas, Ugo. Segal in *New York: The New Art Scene.* New York: Holt, Rinehart and Winston, 1967.

Perreault, John. "Plaster Caste." New York: *Art News,* November, 1968, pp. 54 ff.

Pincus-Witten, Robert. "George Segal as Realist." New York: *Art Forum,* Summer, 1967, pp. 84–88.

"Presences in Plaster." New York: *Time,* December 13, 1968, p. 84.

Rose, Barbara. *Frankenthaler.* New York: Harry N. Abrams, Inc., 1972.

Rosenberg, Harold. "Exhibits at the Guggenheim and the Whitney." New York: *The New Yorker,* March 23, 1968, pp. 107–110 ff.

Rosenstein, Harris. "Gottlieb at the Summit." New York: *Art News,* April, 1966, pp. 42 ff.

Seckler, D. G. "Artist in America: victim of the culture boom?" New York: *Art in America,* December, 1963, p. 35.

"Sense of 'why not?'—George Segal on his art." New York: *Studio,* October, 1967, pp. 146–149.

"Super Micro-Macro World of Wonderama, The." New York: *Time,* December 17, 1965, pp. 68 ff.

Waldman, Diane, "Gottlieb: Signs and Suns." New York: *Art News,* February, 1968, pp. 26–29 ff.

Chapter 8

Bann, Stephen; Gadney, Reg; Pepper, Frank; and Steadman, Philip. *Four Essays on Kinetic Art.* London: Motion Books, 1966.

Cage, John. *A Year from Monday.* Middletown: Wesleyan University Press, 1967.

Dunn, Peter. "New York's Musical Avant-garde." London: *London Times,* December 29, 1967.

Fisher, Robert, and Kranz, Stewart. *The Design Continuum, An Approach To Understanding Visual Forms.* New York: Van Nostrand Reinhold Company, 1966.

Gilbert, Dr. John. *Rotation* (An opera in one act for five players and two dancers). New York: Columbia University Teachers' College dissertation, 1969.

Hiemenz, J. "Moog at the Museum." New York: *Hi Fi Musical America,* November, 1969.

Jordan, William E. "Norman McLaren: His Career and Technique." Montreal: National Film Board of Canada.

Kostelanetz, Richard. "New Sound for a Plugged-in Age." *Look Magazine,* January 9, 1968, p. 45.

———. "The Two Extremes of Avant-Garde Music." New York: *The New York Times Magazine,* January 15, 1967.

Land, Edwin H. "Stereoscopic Motion Pictures." A special report to the Board of Directors of the Polaroid Corporation, February 5, 1953.

McLaren, Norman. "Cameraless Animation." Montreal: National Film Board of Canada, 1958.

Morrow, Stephen. "Nagrin's Thucydides." Buffalo, New York: *The Spectrum,* October 24, 1968.

"New Magic in Animation." New York: *Time,* December 27, 1968, pp. 42–43.

Nordell, Roderick. "Moog Quartet in 'Live' Concert." Boston: *The Christian Science Monitor,* February 24, 1971, p. 4.

Oka, Takashi. "Art: That Controversial Grand Palais Exposition." Boston: *The Christian Science Monitor.* July 10, 1972, p. 10.

Osborne, Robert C. "Art Is Anything You Can Get Away With." New York: *Art Education,* May, 1968, p. 20.

Photons: Group of twelve by Les Levine. New York: *Studio,* December, 1968, p. 245.

Popular Photography: New York: 30th Anniversary Edition, May, 1967.

Reid, Alistair. *To Be Alive!* From the film produced by Francis Thompson, Inc., for Johnson Wax. New York: Macmillan Company, 1966.

Rosenberg, Harold. *The Anxious Object: Art Today and its Audience.* New York: Horizon Press, 1964.

Rosten, Lee. "They Made our World . . . Edison." New York: *Look Magazine,* February 25, 1967, pp. 100–102.

Salzman, Eric. "Avant-garde is What's Happening." New York: *Opera News,* November 2, 1968, pp. 9–13.

———. *20th Century Music: An Introduction.* New York: Prentice-Hall, 1967.

Starr, Cecile. "Ideas on Film—Animation: Abstract and Concrete." New York: *The Saturday Review,* December 13, 1952.

"Texts of the *Groupe Recherché d'art Visuel,*The. Paris: 1960–1965." New York: *Image,* Winter, 1966, pp. 13–30.

"Theatre of Light." New York: *Sunday New York News Coloroto Magazine,* November 19, 1967.

"3-D." New York: *Look Magazine,* February 25, 1964, p. 105.

Vestal, David. "30 Years of Books That Shaped Photography." New York: *Popular Photography,* May, 1967, pp. 104 ff.

Wasserman, Burton. "When the Current Turns On," New York: *Art Education,* May, 1968, pp. 16–19.

Weaver, Mike. "Film as Kinetic Art." New York: *Image,* October, 1966, pp. 10 ff.

Youngblood, Gene. *Expanded Cinema.* New York: E. P. Dutton & Company, Inc. Paperback.

Chapter 9

Barnes, Clive. "The Cold War in Modern-Dance." New York: *The New York Times Magazine,* July 28, 1968, pp. 14 ff.

Bell, Don. *Film At Expo '67.* Typescript. Montreal: The National Film Board of Canada, 1967.

Bourdon, D. "Disposable Art—Plastic Man." New York: *Life Magazine,* August 22, 1969, pp. 62–67.

"DANCE: The Great Leap Forward." New York: *Time,* March 15, 1968, pp. 44–48.

Davis, Douglas. "Television's Avant-Garde." New York: *Newsweek,* February 9, 1970, pp. 60–63.

Epstein, Rudolph R.; Douglas, J. Creighton; and Mundie, Peter. "The *Labyrinthe* Pavilion at

Expo '67." New York: *Journal of the Society of Motion Picture and Television Engineers,* March, 1968, pp. 186–191.

"A Film Revolution to Blitz Man's Mind." New York: *Life Magazine,* July 14, 1967.

Gentleman, Wally and Douglas, J. Creighton. "A Cruciform System for Expo '67." New York: *Journal of the Society of Motion Picture and Television Engineers,* March, 1968, pp. 191–193.

Glueck, Grace. "The Far Out is Way In." New York: *The New York Times,* April 14, 1968, p. D30.

———. "Merges on the Rue Madison." *The New York Times,* October 16, 1966, p. D23.

———. "Multi-Media: massaging the sense for the message." *The New York Times,* September 16, 1967.

H'Doubler, Margaret N. *Dance: A Creative Art Experience.* Madison: University of Wisconsin Press, 1957.

Hendrick, Kimmis. "Like a whirlwind off some desert." Boston: *The Christian Science Monitor,* June 10, 1972, p. 12.

Hughes, Allen. "Judson Dance Theater Seeks New Paths." New York: *The New York Times,* June 26, 1968, p. 34.

———. "Theater: A Musical Spectacle from Czechoslovakia." New York: *The New York Times,* August 4, 1964.

Johnston, Jill. "Summers Gardens." New York: The VILLAGE VOICE, March 12, 1964.

Kappler, Frank. "The mixed-media communication that puzzles, excites and involves." New York: *Life Magazine,* July 14, 1967, p. 280.

Kranz, Stewart. "Some Reflections on Mixed Media." New York: *MEDION,* Museum of the Media, Vol. 1, No. 2, 1969, p. 3.

Kutik, William M. "Global Village." Cambridge, Massachusetts: *The Harvard Crimson,* January 28, 1970.

Labyrinthe Technical Bulletin Number 8. Montreal: The National Film Board of Canada Technical Operations Branch, March, 1968.

Lester, Elenore. "Intermedia: Tune In, Turn On—And Walk Out?" New York: *The New York Times Magazine,* May 12, 1968, pp. 30 ff.

Lewin, Frank. "Man and His Sound—Expo '67." New York: *Journal of the Society of Motion Picture and Television Engineers,* March, 1968, pp. 194–209.

Litwin, Dr. George H. *A Theory of Achievement Motivation.* Edited by John W. Atkinson and Norman T. Feather. New York: John Wiley and Sons Inc., 1966.

Low, Colin. "Multi-Screens and Expo '67." New York: *Journal of the Society of Motion Picture and Television Engineers,* March, 1968, pp. 185–186.

"LSD ART—New Experience that Bombards the Senses." New York: *Life Magazine,* September 9, 1966, pp. 64 ff.

"Magic in Montreal—The Films of EXPO '67." New York: *Time,* July 7, 1967, pp. 80–82.

"Man & His World." New York: *Time,* May 5, 1967, pp. 48 ff.

Maskey, Jacqueline. "Fantastic Gardens." New York: *Dance Magazine,* April, 1964.

Mekas, Jonas. "Interview with Gerd Stern." New York: *Film Culture,* Winter, 1966–1967.

———. "Movie Journal on the Global Village." New York: The VILLAGE VOICE, November 20, 1969.

Mundie, P. "Audio Facilities for the Labyrinthe Pavilion." Expo '67. New York: *Journal of the Audio Engineering Society,* January, 1968.

"National Film Board of Canada." New York: *Industrial Photography,* May, 1963.

National Film Board of Canada 67/68 film catalogue. Montreal: National Film Board of Canada.

Newman, T. R., ed. "Artist Speaks: Interview with Les Levine." New York: *Art in America,* November, 1969, pp. 56–59.

"On All Sides." New York: *Time,* May 3, 1968, pp. 56–59.

Perreault, John. "Plastic Man Strikes." New York: *Art News,* March, 1968.

Reilly, John, and Stern, Rudi. "Free Media." New York: *New Times,* April 20, 1970.

———. *Global Village—the electronics of shared experience.* New York: Global Village pamplet.

"Robert Whitman." *The Theatre of Mixed Means,* chapter 9. New York: The Dial Press, Inc., 1968.

Shirey, D. L. "In the Worst of Taste." New York: *Newsweek,* November 10, 1968, p. 125.

USCO. *The Theatre of Mixed Means,* chapter 10. New York: The Dial Press, Inc., 1968.

"USCO, Our Time Base Is Real." New Orleans: *Tulane Drama Review,* Fall, 1966.

VanDerBeek, Stan. "Culture: Intercom and Expanded Cinema." New Orleans: *Tulane Drama Review,* Fall, 1966, pp. 38–48.

———. "Re: Vision." New York: *The American Scholar,* Spring, 1966, pp. 335–340.

"Vers un art multi-sensorial." Ontario '67. Toronto: Gouvernement de l'Ontario, Canada.

Wagner, Richard. *On Music and Drama.* Albert Goldman and Evert Springhorn, editors. New York: Dutton, 1964.

Woods, Albert M. and Ramirez, Carlos. "Multi-Media or Plain Talk?" New York: *Audio-Visual Communications,* June, 1968, pp. 12 ff.

Chapter 10

"All Package." New York: *Time,* February 7, 1969, p. 60.

Alloway, Lawrence. *Directions 1: Options 1968.* Milwaukee: Milwaukee Art Center, June 22–August 18, 1968, & Museum of Contemporary Art Chicago, September 14–October 20, 1968, exhibition catalogue.

"Art Outgrows the Museum." New York: *Time* cover story, October 13, 1967, pp. 80 ff.

Berenson, Ruth. "Door Count: American Museums Are Crowded To The Rafters." New York: *National Review,* March 26, 1968, pp. 304–305.

Canaday, John. "Scratches on Paintings Caused Minor Damage." New York: *The New York Times,* January 17, 1969.

"Challenge to Apollo." New York: *Time,* October 14, 1966, p. 90.

Geldzahler, Henry. *American Painting in the Twentieth Century.* New York: The Metropolitan Museum of Art, 1965.

Genauer, Emily. "Art and the Artist." New York: *New York Post Magazine,* January 25, 1969, p. 14.

Glueck, Grace. "Art: 'Harlem on My Mind' in Slides, Tapes and Photos." New York: *The New York Times,* January 17, 1969.

———. "Modules for the Millions." *The New York Times,* June 22, 1969.

"Harlem Experiment." New York: *Time,* January 24, 1969, p. 44.

"Home in a Barrel Vault." New York: *Time,* February 23, 1968, p. 67.

Horovitz, Israel. "Feel It: Museum of Contemporary Crafts Explores Anti-visual Experience." New York: *Craft Horizons,* March, 1969, pp. 14–15 ff.

"Hoving of the Metropolitan; Role of Museums in a Changing Society." New York: *Newsweek,* April 1, 1968, pp. 54–62.

"It Takes a Lot of Space To Make a Museum a Home." New York: *Time,* September 13, 1968, pp. 72–76.

Katz, Karl. *Ingathering: Ceremony and Tradition in New York Public Collections.* New York: The Jewish Museum, 1968.

"The Manse That Mocked a Monarch." New York: *Time,* August 9, 1968, pp. 60–63.

Medion. A newsletter published and distributed free by the *Museum of the Media.* New York: Vol. 1, No. 1, February, 1969—Vol. 1, No. 2, 1969.

———. Vol. II, No. 1, First Quarter. New York: *Museum of the Media,* 1970.

Museum of the Media, brochure. New York: Museum of the Media, 1968.

"New Look for Old Tradition." New York: *Time,* February 7, 1969, p. 68.

"Objects: Museum of Contemporary Crafts." New York: *The New Yorker,* July 6, 1968, pp. 18–19.

Rose, Barbara. "Gallery without Walls." New York: *Art in America,* March, 1968, pp. 60–71.

Schickel, Richard. *The Museum* brochure. New York: The Museum of Modern Art, 1970.

"Sprouting a New Wing." New York: *Time,* February 28, 1969, p. 68.

"Stirring Men to Leap Moats." New York: *Time,* November 1, 1968, pp. 76–83.

Tallmer, Jerry. "The Show on Everyone's Mind." New York: *New York Post Magazine,* January 25, 1969, pp. 4, 5.

"The Ultimate Cube." New York: *Time,* September 20, 1968, p. 74.

Varian, Elayne H. *N Dimensional Space.* New York: Finch College Museum of Art, Contemporary Wing, 1970 exhibition catalogue.

———. *Projected Art.* New York: Contemporary Study Wing, Finch College Museum of Art, December 8, 1966—January 8, 1967 exhibition catalogue.

Chapter 11

Baro, Gene. "Roy Lichtenstein: Technique as Style." New York: *Art International,* March, 1966, pp. 96–97.

Calas, Nicolas. "Roy Lichtenstein: Insight through Irony, the Guggenheim Retrospective." New York: *Arts Magazine,* September, 1969, pp. 29–33.

Caplans, John. "Talking with Roy Lichtenstein." New York: *Art Forum,* May, 1967, pp. 34–40.

Geldzahler, Henry. *New York Painting and Sculpture.* 1940–1970, New York: E. P. Dutton & Co., Inc., 1969.

Glaser, Bruce. "Lichtenstein-Oldenburg-Warhol: A Discussion." New York: *Art Forum,* February, 1966, pp. 20–24.

"Kidding Everybody." New York: *Time,* June 21, 1967, p. 72.

Mulas, Ugo. "Lichtenstein," in *The New Art Scene.* New York: Holt, Rinehart and Winston, 1967, pp. 166–179.

"Rosenquist and Lichtenstein are alive." New York: *Time,* January 26, 1968.

Roy Lichtenstein. London: The Tate Gallery, 1968 exhibition catalogue.

Sandberg. "Some Traditional Aspects of Pop Art." New York: *Art Journal,* Spring, 1967, pp. 228–233.

Siegfried, J. C. "Spirit of the Comics." *Arts and Artists,* December, 1969, pp. 18–21.

"Studies in Iconography: the Master of the Crying Girl." New York: *Art in America,* March, 1966, pp. 96–97.

index

(Page numbers in italics indicate illustrations)